MILESTONES
IN
MATHEMATICAL DISCOVERY

The great mathematicians whose works are
presented in this Signet Sci........ ....book
are each rest.......... ....h
into new ....ve
made ....
propelled.
scope. Co...... .....ve
of the ....mathematics.

Here, in the original words of the masters, the
reader can learn about geometry, both
Euclidean and non-Euclidean; arithmetic;
algebra; analytic geometry; the theory
of irrational numbers; set-theory; calculus of
probability; mathematical logic; and a
new branch of mathematics—topology. He can
witness the brilliant progress of Euclid,
Archimedes, Descartes, Euler, Russell, as they
expound their investigations into
the science of mathematics.

The extracts presented range from the elementary
to the abstract, from those readily
understandable to the reader with a limited
mathematical background to those that
will challenge the mental powers of the more
advanced. Immediately following each
extract the editor has provided a commentary
in which he clarifies what has been
set forth and indicates why these men are
some of the greatest creative thinkers of the ages.

breakthroughs
in
mathematics

PETER WOLFF

A SIGNET SCIENCE LIBRARY BOOK

Published by
THE NEW AMERICAN LIBRARY

FIRST PRINTING, NOVEMBER, 1963

SIGNET TRADEMARK REG. U. S. PAT. OFF. AND FOREIGN COUNTRIES
REGISTERED TRADEMARK—MARCA REGISTRADA
HECHO EN CHICAGO, U.S.A.

SIGNET SCIENCE LIBRARY BOOKS are published by The New American Library of World Literature, Inc. 501 Madison Avenue, New York, New York 10022

PRINTED IN THE UNITED STATES OF AMERICA

TO MY WIFE,

Patricia

CONTENTS

III ADVANCED TOPICS

INTRODUCTION

The nine mathematicians whose works are represented in the following pages are among the most famous in the whole history of mathematics. Each of them made a significant contribution to the science—a contribution which changed the succeeding course of the development of mathematics. That is why we have called this book *Breakthroughs in Mathematics*. Just as surely as there are technological breakthroughs which change our way of living, so are there breakthroughs in the pure sciences which have such an impact that they affect all succeeding thought.

The mathematicians whose works we examine bridge a span of more than 2200 years, from Euclid, who lived and worked in Alexandria around 300 B.C., to Bertrand Russell, whose major mathematical work was accomplished in the first years of the twentieth century. These nine chapters survey the major parts of mathematics; a great many of its branches are touched on. We shall have occasion to deal with geometry, both Euclidean and non-Euclidean, with arithmetic, algebra, analytic geometry, the theory of irrationals, set-theory, calculus of probability, and mathematical logic. Also, though this is a matter of accident, the authors whose works we study come from almost every important country in the West: from ancient Greece and Hellenistic Rome, Egypt, France, Germany, Great Britain, and Russia.

No collection of nine names could possibly include all the great mathematicians. Let us just name some of the most famous ones whom we had to ignore here: Apollonius of Perga, Pierre de Fermat, Blaise Pascal, Sir Isaac Newton, Gottfried Wilhelm Leibniz, Karl Friedrich Gauss, Georg Cantor, and many, many others. There are a number of reasons why we chose the particular authors and books represented. In part, a choice such as this is, of course, based on subjective and personal preferences. On objective grounds, however, we were mainly interested in presenting treatises or parts of treatises that would exemplify the major branches of mathematics, that would be complete and understandable in themselves, and that would not require a great deal of prior mathematical knowledge. There is one major omission which we regret: none of the works here deals with the calculus. The reason is that neither Newton nor Leibniz (who simultaneously developed modern calculus) has left us a short and simple treatise on the subject. Newton, to be sure, devotes the beginning of his *Principia* to the calculus, but unfortunately his treatment of the matter is not easy to understand.

What is the purpose in presenting these excerpts and the commentaries on them? Very simply, we want to afford the reader who is interested in mathematics and in the history of its development an opportunity to see great mathematical minds at work. Most readers of this book will probably already have read some mathematical books—in school if nowhere else. But here we give the reader a view of mathematics as it is being developed; he can follow the thought of the greatest mathematicians as they themselves set it down. Most great mathematicians are also great teachers of mathematics; certainly these nine writers make every possible effort to make their discoveries understandable to the lay reader. (The one exception may be Descartes, who practices occasional deliberate obscurity in order to show off his own brilliance.) Each of these selections can be read independently of the others, as an example of mathematical genius at work. Each selection will make the reader acquainted with an important advance in mathematics; and he will learn about it from the one person best qualified to teach him—its discoverer.

Breakthroughs in Mathematics is not a textbook. It does not aim at the kind of completeness that a textbook possesses. Rather it aims to supplement what a textbook does by presenting to the reader something he cannot easily obtain elsewhere: excerpts from the words of mathematical pioneers themselves. Most people with any pretense to an education have heard the names of Euclid, Descartes, and Russell, but few have read their works. With this little book we hope to close that gap and enable a reader not merely to read *about* these men and to be told that they are famous, but also to read their works and to judge for himself why and whether they are justly famous.

Ideally, these nine selections can and should be read without need of further explanation from anyone else. If there are any readers who would like to attempt reading only the nine selections (Part I of each chapter) without the commentaries (Part II of each chapter), they should certainly try to do so. The task is by no means impossible; and what may be lost in time is probably more than outweighed by the added pleasure as well as the deeper understanding that such a reader will carry away with him.

However, the majority of readers will probably not want to undertake the somewhat arduous task of proceeding without any help. For them, we have provided the commentaries in Part II of each chapter. These commentaries are meant to supplement but not to replace the reader's own thought about what he has read. In these portions of each chapter, we point out what are the highlights of the preceding selection, what are some of the difficulties, and what additional steps should be taken in order to understand what the author is driving at. We also provide some very brief biographical remarks about the authors and, where necessary, supply the historical background for the book under discussion. Furthermore, we occasionally go beyond what the author tells us in his work, and indicate the significance of the work for other fields and future developments.

Just as the nine selections give us merely a sampling of mathematical thought during more than 2000 years, so the commentaries do not by any means exhaust what can be said about the various selections. Each commentary is supposed to help the reader understand the preceding selection; it is not supposed to replace it. Sometimes, we have concentrated on explaining the difficult parts of the work being considered; sometimes, we have emphasized something the author has neglected; at still other times, we extend the author's thought beyond its immediate application. But no attempt is or could be made at examining all of the selections in complete detail and pointing out everything important about them. Such a task would be impossible and unending. Different commentaries do different things; in almost every chapter, the author's selection contains more than we could discuss in the commentary.

In short, our aim is to help the reader overcome the more obvious difficulties so that he can get into the original work itself. We do this in the hope that the reader will understand what these mathematicians have to say and that he will *enjoy* himself in doing so. Nothing is more fatal to the progress of a learner in a science than an initial unnecessary discouragement. We have tried to save the reader such discouragement and to stay by his side long enough and sympathetically enough so that he can learn directly from these great teachers.

Peter Wolff

I

geometry

CHAPTER ONE

Euclid—The Beginnings of Geometry

PART I

The following selection consists of the first 26 propositions in Book I of Euclid's *Elements of Geometry*. This is just a little more than half of the first book, which altogether contains 48 propositions. Book I itself, however, is only part of the *Elements*; there are thirteen books in this work.

Book I presents the major propositions of plane geometry, except those involving circles. Book II deals with the transformation of areas. Books III and IV add propositions about circles. Book V takes up the subject of ratios and proportions in general; Book VI applies it to geometry. Books VII, VIII, and IX are not geometrical in character at all, but arithmetical; that is, they treat of numbers. Book X takes up a rather special subject, namely incommensurable lines and areas. This is the longest of the thirteen books. Books XI and XII deal with solid geometry. Book XIII also has to do with solid geometry, but with a rather special part of it: the five regular solids. These are the solids that have as their surfaces regular polygons (polygons all of whose angles and sides are equal). The last proposition in the entire work proves that there can only be these five solids and no more. The five are these: the tetrahedron, consisting of four equilateral triangles; the hexahedron (or cube), consisting of six squares; the octahedron, consisting of eight equilateral triangles; the icosahedron, consisting of twenty equilateral triangles; and finally the dodecahedron, consisting of twelve regular pentagons.

Euclid:
*Elements of Geometry**

BOOK I

DEFINITIONS

1. A **point** is that which has no part.
2. A **line** is breadthless length.
3. The extremities of a line are points.
4. A **straight line** is a line which lies evenly with the points on itself.
5. A **surface** is that which has length and breadth only.
6. The extremities of a surface are lines.
7. A **plane surface** is a surface which lies evenly with the straight lines on itself.
8. A **plane angle** is the inclination to one another of two lines in a plane which meet one another and do not lie in a straight line.
9. And when the lines containing the angle are straight, the angle is called **rectilineal**.
10. When a straight line set up on a straight line makes the adjacent angles equal to one another, each of the equal angles is **right**, and the straight line standing on the other is called a **perpendicular** to that on which it stands.
11. An **obtuse angle** is an angle greater than a right angle.
12. An **acute angle** is an angle less than a right angle.
13. A **boundary** is that which is an extremity of anything.
14. A **figure** is that which is contained by any boundary or boundaries.
15. A **circle** is a plane figure contained by one line such that all the straight lines falling upon it from one point among those lying within the figure are equal to one another.
16. And the point is called the **centre** of the circle.
17. A **diameter** of the circle is any straight line drawn through the centre and terminated in both directions by the

* From *The Thirteen Books of Euclid's Elements,* trans. by Sir Thomas L. Heath (2nd ed.; London: Cambridge University Press, 1926). Reprinted by permission.

circumference of the circle, and such a straight line also bisects the circle.

18. A **semicircle** is the figure contained by the diameter and the circumference cut off by it. And the centre of the semicircle is the same as that of the circle.

19. **Rectilineal figures** are those which are contained by straight lines, **trilateral** figures being those contained by three, **quadrilateral** those contained by four, and **multilateral** those contained by more than four straight lines.

20. Of trilateral figures, an **equilateral triangle** is that which has its three sides equal, an **isosceles triangle** that which has two of its sides alone equal, and a **scalene triangle** that which has its three sides unequal.

21. Further, of trilateral figures, a **right-angled triangle** is that which has a right angle, an **obtuse-angled triangle** that which has an obtuse angle, and an **acute-angled triangle** that which has its three angles acute.

22. Of quadrilateral figures, a **square** is that which is both equilateral and right-angled; an **oblong** that which is right-angled but not equilateral; a **rhombus** that which is equilateral but not right-angled; and a **rhomboid** that which has its opposite sides and angles equal to one another but is neither equilateral nor right-angled. And let quadrilaterals other than these be called **trapezia**.

23. **Parallel** straight lines are straight lines which, being in the same plane and being produced indefinitely in both directions, do not meet one another in either direction.

POSTULATES

Let the following be postulated:

1. To draw a straight line from any point to any point.

2. To produce a finite straight line continuously in a straight line.

3. To describe a circle with any centre and distance.

4. That all right angles are equal to one another.

5. That, if a straight line falling on two straight lines make the interior angles on the same side less than two right angles, the two straight lines, if produced indefinitely, meet on that side on which are the angles less than two right angles.

COMMON NOTIONS

1. Things which are equal to the same thing are also equal to one another.

2. If equals be added to equals, the wholes are equal.

3. If equals be subtracted from equals, the remainders are equal.

4. Things which coincide with one another are equal to one another.

5. The whole is greater than the part.

PROPOSITIONS

PROPOSITION 1

On a given finite straight line to construct an equilateral triangle.

Let *AB* be the given finite straight line.

Thus it is required to construct an equilateral triangle on the straight line *AB*.

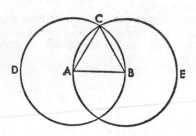

With centre *A* and distance *AB* let the circle *BCD* be described;   [Post. 3]
again, with centre *B* and distance *BA* let the circle *ACE* be described;   [Post. 3]
and from the point *C*, in which the circles cut one another, to the points *A*, *B* let the straight lines *CA*, *CB* be joined.   [Post. 1]

Now, since the point *A* is the centre of the circle *CDB*, *AC* is equal to *AB*.   [Def. 15]

Again, since the point *B* is the centre of the circle *CAE*, *BC* is equal to *BA*.   [Def. 15]

But *CA* was also proved equal to *AB;* therefore each of the straight lines *CA, CB* is equal to *AB.*

And things which are equal to the same thing are also equal to one another;   [C.N. 1]
therefore *CA* is also equal to *CB.*

Therefore the three straight lines *CA, AB, BC* are equal to one another.

Therefore the triangle *ABC* is equilateral; and it has been constructed on the given finite straight line *AB.* (Being) what was required to do.

PROPOSITION 2

To place at a given point (as an extremity) a straight line equal to a given straight line.

Let *A* be the given point, and *BC* the given straight line. Thus it is required to place at the point *A* (as an extremity) a straight line equal to the given straight line *BC.*

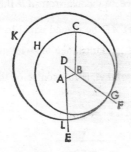

From the point *A* to the point *B* let the straight line *AB* be joined;   [Post. 1]
and on it let the equilateral triangle *DAB* be constructed. [I. 1]

Let the straight lines *AE, BF* be produced in a straight line with *DA, DB*;   [Post. 2]
with centre *B* and distance *BC* let the circle *CGH* be described;
                                                          [Post. 3]
and again, with centre *D* and distance *DG* let the circle *GKL* be described.   [Post. 3]

Then, since the point *B* is the centre of the circle *CGH*, *BC* is equal to *BG.*

Again, since the point D is the centre of the circle GKL, DL is equal to DG.

And in these DA is equal to DB; therefore the remainder AL is equal to the remainder BG. [C.N. 3]

But BC was also proved equal to BG; therefore each of the straight lines AL, BC is equal to BG.

And things which are equal to the same thing are also equal to one another; [C.N. 1]
therefore AL is also equal to BC.

Therefore at the given point A the straight line AL is placed equal to the given straight line BC. (Being) what it was required to do.

PROPOSITION 3

Given two unequal straight lines, to cut off from the greater a straight line equal to the less.

Let AB, C be the two given unequal straight lines, and let AB be the greater of them.

Thus it is required to cut off from AB the greater a straight line equal to C the less.

At the point A let AD be placed equal to the straight line C; [I. 2]
and with centre A and distance AD let the circle DEF be described. [Post. 3]

Now, since the point A is the centre of the circle DEF, AE is equal to AD. [Def. 15]

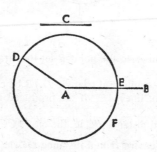

But C is also equal to AD.

Therefore each of the straight lines AE, C is equal to AD; so that AE is also equal to C.   [C.N. 1]

Therefore, given the two straight lines AB, C, from AB the greater AE has been cut off equal to C the less. (Being) what it was required to do.

PROPOSITION 4

If two triangles have the two sides equal to two sides respectively, and have the angles contained by the equal straight lines equal, they will also have the base equal to the base, the triangle will be equal to the triangle, and the remaining angles will be equal to the remaining angles respectively, namely those which the equal sides subtend.

Let ABC, DEF be two triangles having the two sides AB, AC equal to the two sides DE, DF respectively, namely AB to DE and AC to DF, and the angle BAC equal to the angle EDF.

I say that the base BC is also equal to the base EF, the triangle ABC will be equal to the triangle DEF, and the remaining angles will be equal to the remaining angles respectively, namely those which the equal sides subtend, that is, the angle ABC to the angle DEF, and the angle ACB to the angle DFE.

For, if the triangle ABC be applied to the triangle DEF, and if the point A be placed on the point D and the straight line AB on DE, then the point B will also coincide with E, because AB is equal to DE.

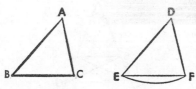

Again, AB coinciding with DE, the straight line AC will also coincide with DF, because the angle BAC is equal to the angle EDF; hence the point C will also coincide with the point F, because AC is again equal to DF.

But B also coincided with E; hence the base BC will coincide with the base EF.

[For if, when B coincides with E and C with F, the base BC does not coincide with the base EF, two straight lines will enclose a space: which is impossible. Therefore the base *BC* will coincide with *EF*] and will be equal to it.   [*C.N.* 4]

Thus the whole triangle *ABC* will coincide with the whole triangle *DEF*, and will be equal to it.

And the remaining angles will also coincide with the remaining angles and will be equal to them, the angle *ABC* to the angle *DEF*, and the angle *ACB* to the angle *DFE*.

Therefore etc. (Being) what it was required to prove.

PROPOSITION 5

In isosceles triangles the angles at the base are equal to one another, and, if the equal straight lines be produced further, the angles under the base will be equal to one another.

Let *ABC* be an isosceles triangle having the side *AB* equal to the side *AC*; and let the straight lines *BD*, *CE* be produced further in a straight line with *AB*, *AC*.   [Post. 2]

I say that the angle *ABC* is equal to the angle *ACB*, and the angle *CBD* to the angle *BCE*.

Let a point *F* be taken at random on *BD*; from *AE* the greater let *AG* be cut off equal to *AF* the less;   [I. 3] and let the straight lines *FC*, *GB* be joined.   [Post. 1]

Then, since *AF* is equal to *AG* and *AB* to *AC*, the two sides *FA*, *AC* are equal to the two sides *GA*, *AB*, respectively; and they contain a common angle, the angle *FAG*.

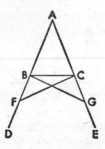

Therefore the base *FC* is equal to the base *GB*, and the triangle *AFC* is equal to the triangle *AGB*, and the remaining angles will be equal to the remaining angles respectively, namely those which the equal sides subtend, that is, the angle *ACF* to the angle *ABG*, and the angle *AFC* to the angle *AGB*.
                [I. 4]

And, since the whole *AF* is equal to the whole *AG*, and in these *AB* is equal to *AC*, the remainder *BF* is equal to the remainder *CG*.

But *FC* was also proved equal to *GB*; therefore the two sides *BF*, *FC* are equal to the two sides *CG*, *GB* respectively; and the angle *BFC* is equal to the angle *CGB*, while the base *BC* is common to them; therefore the triangle *BFC* is also equal to the triangle *CGB*, and the remaining angles will be equal to the remaining angles respectively, namely those which the equal sides subtend; therefore the angle *FBC* is equal to the angle *GCB*, and the angle *BCF* to the angle *CBG*.

Accordingly, since the whole angle *ABG* was proved equal to the angle *ACF*, and in these the angle *CBG* is equal to the angle *BCF*, the remaining angle *ABC* is equal to the remaining angle *ACB;* and they are at the base of the triangle *ABC*.

But the angle *FBC* was also proved equal to the angle *GCB*; and they are under the base.

Therefore etc.

Q.E.D.

PROPOSITION 6

If in a triangle two angles be equal to one another, the sides which subtend the equal angles will also be equal to one another.

Let *ABC* be a triangle having the angle *ABC* equal to the angle *ACB*.

I say that the side *AB* is also equal to the side *AC*.

For, if *AB* is unequal to *AC*, one of them is greater.

Let *AB* be greater; and from *AB* the greater let *DB* be cut off equal to *AC* the less; let *DC* be joined.

Then, since *DB* is equal to *AC*, and *BC* is common, the two sides *DB*, *BC* are equal to the two sides *AC*, *CB* respectively;

and the angle *DBC* is equal to the angle *ACB*; therefore the base *DC* is equal to the base *AB*, and the triangle *DBC* will be equal to the triangle *ACB*, the less to the greater: which is absurd.

Therefore *AB* is not unequal to *AC*; it is therefore equal to it.

Therefore etc.   Q.E.D.

PROPOSITION 7

Given two straight lines constructed on a straight line (from its extremities) and meeting in a point, there cannot be constructed on the same straight line (from its extremities), and on the same side of it, two other straight lines meeting in another point and equal to the former two respectively, namely each to that which has the same extremity with it.

For, if possible, given two straight lines *AC, CB* constructed on the straight line *AB* and meeting at the point *C*, let two other straight lines *AD, DB* be constructed on the same straight line *AB*, on the same side of it, meeting in another point *D* and equal to the former two respectively, namely each to that which has the same extremity with it, so that *CA* is equal to *DA* which has the same extremity *A* with it, and *CB* to *DB* which has the same extremity *B* with it; and let *CD* be joined.

Then, since *AC* is equal to *AD*, the angle *ACD* is also equal to the angle *ADC*;   [I. 5]

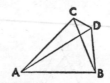

therefore the angle *ADC* is greater than the angle *DCB*; therefore the angle *CDB* is much greater than the angle *DCB*.

Again, since *CB* is equal to *DB*, the angle *CDB* is also equal to the angle *DCB*. But it was also proved much greater than it: which is impossible.

Therefore etc.   Q.E.D.

PROPOSITION 8

If two triangles have the two sides equal to two sides respectively, and have also the base equal to the base, they will also have the angles equal which are contained by the equal straight lines.

Let *ABC*, *DEF* be two triangles having the two sides *AB*, *AC* equal to the two sides *DE*, *DF* respectively, namely *AB* to *DE*, and *AC* to *DF*; and let them have the base *BC* equal to the base *EF*; I say that the angle *BAC* is also equal to the angle *EDF*.

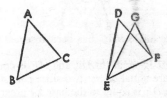

For, if the triangle *ABC* be applied to the triangle *DEF*, and if the point *B* be placed on the point *E* and the straight line *BC* on *EF*, the point *C* will also coincide with *F*, because *BC* is equal to *EF*.

Then, *BC* coinciding with *EF*, *BA*, *AC* will also coincide with *ED*, *DF*; for, if the base *BC* coincides with the base *EF*, and the sides *BA*, *AC* do not coincide with *ED*, *DF* but fall beside them as *EG*, *GF*, then, given two straight lines constructed on a straight line (from its extremities) and meeting in a point, there will have been constructed on the same straight line (from its extremities), and on the same side of it, two other straight lines meeting in another point and equal to the former two respectively, namely each to that which has the same extremity with it. But they cannot be so constructed.

[I. 7]

Therefore it is not possible that, if the base *BC* be applied to the base *EF*, the sides *BA*, *AC* should not coincide with *ED*, *DF*; they will therefore coincide, so that the angle *BAC* will also coincide with angle *EDF*, and will be equal to it.

Therefore etc.   Q.E.D.

PROPOSITION 9

To bisect a given rectilineal angle.

Let the angle *BAC* be the given rectilineal angle.

Thus it is required to bisect it.

Let a point *D* be taken at random on *AB*; let *AE* be cut off from *AC* equal to *AD*;   [I. 3]

let *DE* be joined, and on *DE* let the equilateral triangle *DEF* be constructed; let *AF* be joined.

I say that the angle *BAC* has been bisected by the straight line *AF*.

For, since *AD* is equal to *AE*, and *AF* is common, the two sides *DA*, *AF* are equal to the two sides *EA*, *AF* respectively.

And the base *DF* is equal to the base *EF*; therefore the angle *DAF* is equal to the angle *EAF*.   [I. 8]

Therefore the given rectilineal angle *BAC* has been bisected by the straight line *AF*.   Q.E.F.

PROPOSITION 10

To bisect a given finite straight line.

Let *AB* be the given finite straight line.

Thus it is required to bisect the finite straight line *AB*.

Let the equilateral triangle *ABC* be constructed on it, [I. 1] and let the angle *ACB* be bisected by the straight line *CD*; [I. 9]

I say that the straight line *AB* has been bisected at the point *D*.

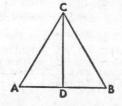

For, since *AC* is equal to *CB*, and *CD* is common, the two sides *AC*, *CD* are equal to the two sides *BC*, *CD* respectively; and the angle *ACD* is equal to the angle *BCD*; therefore the base *AD* is equal to the base *BD*.   [I. 4]

Therefore the given finite straight line *AB* has been bisected at *D*.   Q.E.F.

PROPOSITION 11

To draw a straight line at right angles to a given straight line from a given point on it.

Let *AB* be the given straight line, and *C* the given point on it.

Thus it is required to draw from the point *C* a straight line at right angles to the straight line *AB*.

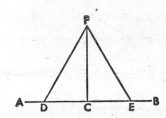

Let a point *D* be taken at random on *AC*; let *CE* be made equal to *CD*;   [I. 3]
on *DE* let the equilateral triangle *FDE* be constructed,   [I. 1]
and let *FC* be joined; I say that the straight line *FC* has been drawn at right angles to the given straight line *AB* from *C* the given point on it.

For, since *DC* is equal to *CE*, and *CF* is common, the two sides *DC*, *CF* are equal to the two sides *EC*, *CF* respectively; and the base *DF* is equal to the base *FE*; therefore the angle *DCF* is equal to the angle *ECF*;   [I. 8]
and they are adjacent angles.

But, when a straight line set up on a straight line makes the adjacent angles equal to one another, each of the equal angles is right;   [Def. 10]
therefore each of the angles *DCF*, *FCE* is right.

Therefore the straight line *CF* has been drawn at right angles to the given straight line *AB* from the given point *C* on it.

                    Q.E.F.

PROPOSITION 12

*To a given infinite straight line, from a given point which is
not on it, to draw a perpendicular straight line.*

Let *AB* be the given infinite straight line, and *C* the given
point which is not on it; thus it is required to draw to the given
infinite straight line *AB*, from the given point *C* which is not
on it, a perpendicular straight line.

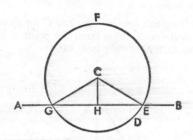

For let a point *D* be taken at random on the other side of
the straight line *AB*, and with centre *C* and distance *CD* let
the circle *EFG* be described;   [Post. 3]
let the straight line *EG* be bisected at *H*,   [I. 10]
and let the straight lines *CG*, *CH*, *CE* be joined.   [Post. 1]

I say that *CH* has been drawn perpendicular to the given
infinite straight line *AB* from the given point *C* which is not
on it.

For, since *GH* is equal to *HE*, and *HC* is common, the two
sides *GH*, *HC* are equal to the two sides *EH*, *HC* respectively;
and the base *CG* is equal to the base *CE*; therefore the angle
CHG is equal to the angle *EHC*.   [I. 8]

And they are adjacent angles.

But, when a straight line set up on a straight line makes the
adjacent angles equal to one another, each of the equal angles
is right, and the straight line standing on the other is called
a perpendicular to that on which it stands.   [Def. 10]

Therefore *CH* has been drawn perpendicular to the given
infinite straight line *AB* from the given point *C* which is not
on it.   Q.E.F.

Proposition 13

If a straight line set up on a straight line makes angles, it will make either two right angles or angles equal to two right angles.

For let any straight line *AB* set up on the straight line *CD* make the angles *CBA, ABD*; I say that the angles *CBA, ABD* are either two right angles or equal to two right angles.

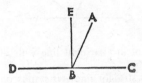

Now, if the angle *CBA* is equal to the angle *ABD*, they are two right angles.   [Def. 10]

But, if not, let *BE* be drawn from the point *B* at right angles to *CD*;   [I. 11]
therefore the angles *CBE, EBD* are two right angles.

Then, since the angle *CBE* is equal to the two angles *CBA, ABE*, let the angle *EBD* be added to each; therefore the angles *CBE, EBD* are equal to the three angles *CBA, ABE, EBD*.
                                                         [C.N. 2]
Again, since the angle *DBA* is equal to the two angles *DBE, EBA*, let the angle *ABC* be added to each; therefore the angles *DBA, ABC* are equal to the three angles *DBE, EBA, ABC*.
                                                         [C.N. 2]
But the angles *CBE, EBD* were also proved equal to the same three angles; and things which are equal to the same thing are also equal to one another;   [C.N. 1]
therefore the angles *CBE, EBD* are also equal to the angles *DBA, ABC*. But the angles *CBE, EBD* are two right angles; therefore the angles *DBA, ABC* are also equal to two right angles.

Therefore etc.   Q.E.D.

Proposition 14

If with any straight line, and at a point on it, two straight lines not lying on the same side make the adjacent angles equal to two right angles, the two straight lines will be in a straight line with one another.

For with any straight line *AB*, and at the point *B* on it, let the two straight lines *BC*, *BD* not lying on the same side make the adjacent angles *ABC*, *ABD* equal to two right angles; I say that *BD* is in a straight line with *CB*.

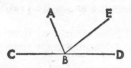

For, if *BD* is not in a straight line with *BC*, let *BE* be in a straight line with *CB*.

Then, since the straight line *AB* stands on the straight line *CBE*, the angles *ABC*, *ABE* are equal to two right angles.

[I. 13]

But the angles *ABC*, *ABD* are also equal to two right angles; therefore the angles *CBA*, *ABE* are equal to the angles *CBA*, *ABD*.

[Post. 4 and *C.N.* 1]

Let the angle *CBA* be subtracted from each; therefore the remaining angle *ABE* is equal to the remaining angle *ABD*,

[*C.N.* 3]

the less to the greater: which is impossible. Therefore *BE* is not in a straight line with *CB*.

Similarly we can prove that neither is any other straight line except *BD*. Therefore *CB* is in a straight line with *BD*.

Therefore etc.

Q.E.D.

Proposition 15

If two straight lines cut one another, they make the vertical angles equal to one another.

For let the straight lines *AB*, *CD* cut one another at the point *E*; I say that the angle *AEC* is equal to the angle *DEB*, and the angle *CEB* to the angle *AED*.

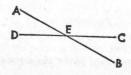

For, since the straight line *AE* stands on the straight line *CD*, making the angles *CEA*, *AED*, the angles *CEA*, *AED* are equal to two right angles.   [I. 13]

Again, since the straight line *DE* stands on the straight line *AB*, making the angles *AED*, *DEB*, the angles *AED*, *DEB* are equal to two right angles.   [I. 13]

But the angles *CEA*, *AED* were also proved equal to two right angles; therefore the angles *CEA*, *AED* are equal to the angles *AED*, *DEB*.   [Post. 4 and *C.N.* 1]

Let the angle *AED* be subtracted from each; therefore the remaining angle *CEA* is equal to the remaining angle *BED*.
                                                                      [*C.N.* 3]

Similarly it can be proved that the angles *CEB*, *DEA* are also equal.

Therefore etc.   Q.E.D.

[PORISM. From this it is manifest that, if two straight lines cut one another, they will make the angles at the point of section equal to four right angles.]

PROPOSITION 16

In any triangle, if one of the sides be produced, the exterior angle is greater than either of the interior and opposite angles.

Let *ABC* be a triangle, and let one side of it *BC* be produced to *D*; I say that the exterior angle *ACD* is greater than either of the interior and opposite angles *CBA*, *BAC*.

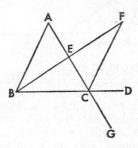

Let *AC* be bisected at *E* [I. 10] , and let *BE* be joined and produced in a straight line to *F*; let *EF* be made equal to *BE* [I. 3], let *FC* be joined [Post. 1], and let *AC* be drawn through to G.
                                                                [Post. 2].

Then, since *AE* is equal to *EC*, and *BE* to *EF*, the two sides

AE, EB are equal to the two sides *CE, EF* respectively; and the angle *AEB* is equal to the angle *FEC*, for they are vertical angles.   [I. 15]

Therefore the base *AB* is equal to the base *FC*, and the triangle *ABE* is equal to the triangle *CFE*, and the remaining angles are equal to the remaining angles respectively, namely those which the equal sides subtend;   [I. 4]
therefore the angle *BAE* is equal to the angle *ECF*.

But the angle *ECD* is greater than the angle *ECF*;   [C.N. 5]
therefore the angle *ACD* is greater than the angle *BAE*.

Similarly also, if *BC* be bisected, the angle *BCG*, that is, the angle *ACD* [I. 15], can be proved greater than the angle *ABC* as well.

Therefore etc.   Q.E.D.

Proposition 17

In any triangle two angles taken together in any manner are less than two right angles.

Let *ABC* be a triangle; I say that two angles of the triangle *ABC* taken together in any manner are less than two right angles.

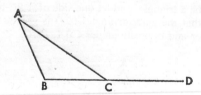

For let *BC* be produced to *D*.   [Post. 2]

Then, since the angle *ACD* is an exterior angle of the triangle *ABC*, it is greater than the interior and opposite angle *ABC*. Let the angle *ACB* be added to each; therefore the angles *ACD, ACB* are greater than the angles *ABC, BCA*. But the angles *ACD, ACB* are equal to two right angles.   [I. 13]

Therefore the angles *ABC, BCA* are less than two right angles.

Similarly we can prove that the angles *BAC, ACB* are also less than two right angles, and so are the angles *CAB, ABC* as well.

Therefore etc.   Q.E.D.

PROPOSITION 18

In any triangle the greater side subtends the greater angle.

For let *ABC* be a triangle having the side *AC* greater than
AB; I say that the angle *ABC* is also greater than the angle
BCA.

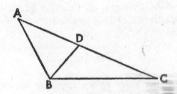

For, since *AC* is greater than *AB*, let *AD* be made equal to
AB [I. 3], and let *BD* be joined.

Then, since the angle *ADB* is an exterior angle of the triangle *BCD*, it is greater than the interior and opposite angle
DCB.   [I. 16]

But the angle *ADB* is equal to the angle *ABD*, since the side
AB is equal to *AD*; therefore the angle *ABD* is also greater
than the angle *ACB*; therefore the angle *ABC* is much greater
than the angle *ACB*.

Therefore etc.   Q.E.D.

PROPOSITION 19

*In any triangle the greater angle is subtended by the greater
side.*

Let *ABC* be a triangle having the angle *ABC* greater than the
angle *BCA*; I say that the side *AC* is also greater than the side
AB.

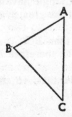

For, if not, *AC* is either equal to *AB* or less.

Now *AC* is not equal to *AB*; for then the angle *ABC* would also have been equal to the angle *ACB*;   [I. 5]
but it is not; therefore *AC* is not equal to *AB*.

Neither is *AC* less than *AB*, for then the angle *ABC* would also have been less than the angle *ACB*;   [I. 18]
but it is not; therefore *AC* is not less than *AB*.

And it was proved that it is not equal either. Therefore *AC* is greater than *AB*.

Therefore etc.   Q.E.D.

PROPOSITION 20

In any triangle two sides taken together in any manner are greater than the remaining one.

For let *ABC* be a triangle; I say that in the triangle *ABC* two sides taken together in any manner are greater than the remaining one, namely *BA*, *AC* greater than *BC*; *AB*, *BC* greater than *AC*; *BC*, *CA* greater than *AB*.

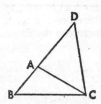

For let *BA* be drawn through to the point *D*, let *DA* be made equal to *CA*, and let *DC* be joined.

Then, since *DA* is equal to *AC*, the angle *ADC* is also equal to the angle *ACD*;   [I. 5]
therefore the angle *BCD* is greater than the angle *ADC*.
    [C.N. 5]

And, since *DCB* is a triangle having the angle *BCD* greater than the angle *BDC*, and the greater angle is subtended by the greater side,   [I. 19]
therefore *DB* is greater than *BC*.

But *DA* is equal to *AC*; therefore *BA*, *AC* are greater than *BC*.

Similarly we can prove that *AB*, *BC* are also greater than *CA*, and *BC*, *CA* than *AB*.

Therefore etc.   Q.E.D.

PROPOSITION 21

If on one of the sides of a triangle, from its extremities, there be constructed two straight lines meeting within the triangle, the straight lines so constructed will be less than the remaining two sides of the triangle, but will contain a greater angle.

On *BC*, one of the sides of the triangle *ABC*, from its extremities *B*, *C*, let the two straight lines *BD*, *DC* be constructed meeting within the triangle; I say that *BD*, *DC* are less than the remaining two sides of the triangle *BA*, *AC*, but contain an angle *BDC* greater than the angle *BAC*.

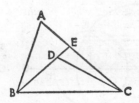

For let *BD* be drawn through to *E*.

Then, since in any triangle two sides are greater than the remaining one,   [I. 20]
therefore, in the triangle *ABE*, the two sides *AB*, *AE* are greater than *BE*.

Let *EC* be added to each; therefore *BA*, *AC* are greater than *BE*, *EC*.

Again, since, in the triangle *CED*, the two sides *CE*, *ED* are greater than *CD*, let *DB* be added to each; therefore *CE*, *EB* are greater than *CD*, *DB*.

But *BA*, *AC* were proved greater than *BE*, *EC*; therefore *BA*, *AC* are much greater than *BD*, *DC*.

Again, since in any triangle the exterior angle is greater than the interior and opposite angle,   [I. 16]
therefore, in the triangle *CDE*, the exterior angle *BDC* is greater than the angle *CED*.

For the same reason, moreover, in the triangle *ABE* also, the exterior angle *CEB* is greater than the angle *BAC*. But the angle *BDC* was proved greater than the angle *CEB*; therefore the angle *BDC* is much greater than the angle *BAC*.

Therefore etc.   Q.E.D.

PROPOSITION 22

*Out of three straight lines, which are equal to three given
straight lines, to construct a triangle: thus it is necessary that
two of the straight lines taken together in any manner should
be greater than the remaining one.*

Let the three given straight lines be *A*, *B*, *C*, and of these let
two taken together in any manner be greater than the remaining one, namely *A*, *B* greater than *C*; *A*, *C* greater than *B*; and
B, *C* greater than *A*; thus it is required to construct a triangle
out of straight lines equal to *A*, *B*, *C*.

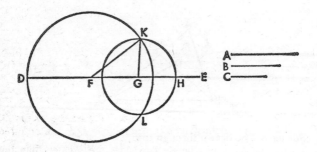

Let there be set out a straight line *DE*, terminated at *D* but
of infinite length in the direction of *E*, and let *DF* be made
equal to *A*, *FG* equal to *B*, and *GH* equal to *C*.   [I. 3]

With centre *F* and distance *FD* let the circle *DKL* be described; again, with centre *G* and distance *GH* let the circle
KLH be described; and let *KF*, *KG* be joined; I say that the
triangle *KFG* has been constructed out of three straight lines
equal to *A*, *B*, *C*.

For, since the point *F* is the centre of the circle *DKL*, *FD*
is equal to *FK*.

But *FD* is equal to *A*; therefore *KF* is also equal to *A*.

Again, since the point *G* is the centre of the circle *LKH*, *GH*
is equal to *GK*.

But *GH* is equal to *C*; therefore *KG* is also equal to *C*. And
FG is also equal to *B*; therefore the three straight lines *KF*,
FG, *GK* are equal to the three straight lines *A*, *B*, *C*.

Therefore out of the three straight lines *KF*, *FG*, *GK*, which
are equal to the three given straight lines *A*, *B*, *C*, the triangle
KFG has been constructed.   Q.E.F.

PROPOSITION 23

On a given straight line and at a point on it to construct a rectilineal angle equal to a given rectilineal angle.

Let *AB* be the given straight line, *A* the point on it, and the angle *DCE* the given rectilineal angle; thus it is required to construct on the given straight line *AB*, and at the point *A* on it, a rectilineal angle equal to the given rectilineal angle *DCE*.

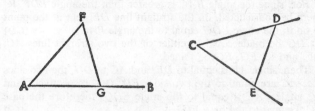

On the straight lines *CD*, *CE* respectively let the points *D*, *E* be taken at random; let *DE* be joined, and out of three straight lines which are equal to the three straight lines *CD*, *DE*, *CE* let the triangle *AFG* be constructed in such a way that *CD* is equal to *AF*, *CE* to *AG*, and further *DE* to *FG*.

[I. 22]

Then, since the two sides *DC*, *CE* are equal to the two sides *FA*, *AG* respectively, and the base *DE* is equal to the base *FG*, the angle *DCE* is equal to the angle *FAG*.   [I. 8]

Therefore on the given straight line *AB*, and at the point *A* on it, the rectilineal angle *FAG* has been constructed equal to the given rectilineal angle *DCE*.   Q.E.F.

PROPOSITION 24

If two triangles have the two sides equal to two sides respectively, but have the one of the angles contained by the equal straight lines greater than the other, they will also have the base greater than the base.

Let *ABC*, *DEF* be two triangles having the two sides *AB*, *AC* equal to the two sides *DE*, *DF* respectively, namely *AB* to *DE*, and *AC* to *DF*, and let the angle at *A* be greater than the angle

at D; I say that the base BC is also greater than the base EF.

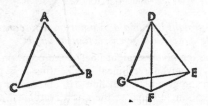

For, since the angle BAC is greater than the angle EDF, let there be constructed, on the straight line DE, and at the point D on it, the angle EDG equal to the angle BAC;   [I. 23] let DG be made equal to either of the two straight lines AC, DF, and let EG, FG be joined.

Then, since AB is equal to DE, and AC to DG, the two sides BA, AC are equal to the two sides ED, DG, respectively; and the angle BAC is equal to the angle EDG; therefore the base BC is equal to the base EG.   [I. 4]

Again, since DF is equal to DG, the angle DGF is also equal to the angle DFG;   [I. 5] therefore the angle DFG is greater than the angle EGF.

Therefore the angle EFG is much greater than the angle EGF.

And, since EFG is a triangle having the angle EFG greater than the angle EGF, and the greater angle is subtended by the greater side,   [I. 19] the side EG is also greater than EF. But EG is equal to BC.

Therefore BC is also greater than EF.

Therefore etc.   Q.E.D.

Proposition 25

If two triangles have the two sides equal to two sides respectively, but have the base greater than the base, they will also have the one of the angles contained by the equal straight lines greater than the other.

Let ABC, DEF be two triangles having the two sides AB, AC equal to the two sides DE, DF respectively, namely AB to DE, and AC to DF; and let the base BC be greater than the base EF; I say that the angle BAC is also greater than the angle EDF.

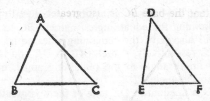

For, if not, it is neither equal to it or less.

Now the angle *BAC* is not equal to the angle *EDF*; for then the base *BC* would also have been equal to the base *EF*, [I. 4] but it is not; therefore the angle *BAC* is not equal to the angle *EDF*.

Neither again is the angle *BAC* less than the angle *EDF*; for then the base *BC* would also have been less than the base *EF*, [I. 24] but it is not; therefore the angle *BAC* is not less than the angle *EDF*.

But it was proved that it is not equal either; therefore the angle *BAC* is greater than the angle *EDF*.

Therefore etc. Q.E.D.

PROPOSITION 26

If two triangles have the two angles equal to two angles respectively, and one side equal to one side, namely, either the side adjoining the equal angles, or that subtending one of the equal angles, they will also have the remaining sides equal to the remaining sides and the remaining angle to the remaining angle.

Let *ABC*, *DEF* be two triangles having the two angles *ABC*, *BCA* equal to the two angles *DEF*, *EFD* respectively, namely the angle *ABC* to the angle *DEF*, and the angle *BCA* to the angle *EFD*; and let them also have one side equal to one side, first that adjoining the equal angles, namely *BC* to *EF*; I say that they will also have the remaining sides equal to the remaining sides respectively, namely *AB* to *DE* and *AC* to *DF*, and the remaining angle to the remaining angle, namely the angle *BAC* to the angle *EDF*.

For, if *AB* is unequal to *DE*, one of them is greater.

Let *AB* be greater, and let *BG* be made equal to *DE*; and let *GC* be joined.

Then, since *BG* is equal to *DE*, and *BC* to *EF*, the two sides *GB*, *BC* are equal to the two sides *DE*, *EF* respectively; and the angle *GBC* is equal to the angle *DEF*; therefore the base *GC* is equal to the base *DF*, and the triangle *GBC* is equal to the triangle *DEF*, and the remaining angles will be equal to the remaining angles, namely those which the equal sides subtend;   [I. 4]

therefore the angle *GCB* is equal to the angle *DFE*. But the angle *DFE* is by hypothesis equal to the angle *BCA*; therefore the angle *BCG* is equal to the angle *BCA*, the less to the greater: which is impossible. Therefore *AB* is not unequal to *DE*, and is therefore equal to it.

But *BC* is also equal to *EF*; therefore the two sides *AB*, *BC* are equal to the two sides *DE*, *EF* respectively, and the angle *ABC* is equal to the angle *DEF*; therefore the base *AC* is equal to the base *DF*, and the remaining angle *BAC* is equal to the remaining angle *EDF*.   [I. 4]

Again, let sides subtending equal angles be equal, as *AB* to *DE*; I say again that the remaining sides will be equal to the remaining sides, namely *AC* to *DF* and *BC* to *EF*, and further the remaining angle *BAC* is equal to the remaining angle *EDF*.

For, if *BC* is unequal to *EF*, one of them is greater.

Let *BC* be greater, if possible, and let *BH* be made equal to *EF*; let *AH* be joined.

Then, since *BH* is equal to *EF*, and *AB* to *DE*, the two sides *AB*, *BH* are equal to the two sides *DE*, *EF* respectively, and they contain equal angles; therefore the base *AH* is equal to the base *DF*, and the triangle *ABH* is equal to the triangle *DEF*, and the remaining angles will be equal to the remaining angles, namely those which the equal sides subtend;   [I. 4]

therefore the angle *BHA* is equal to the angle *EFD*.

But the angle *EFD* is equal to the angle *BCA*; therefore, in the triangle *AHC*, the exterior angle *BHA* is equal to the interior and opposite angle *BCA*: which is impossible.   [I. 16]

Therefore *BC* is not unequal to *EF*, and is therefore equal to it.

But *AB* is also equal to *DE*; therefore the two sides *AB*, *BC* are equal to the two sides *DE*, *EF* respectively, and they contain equal angles; therefore the base *AC* is equal to the base *DF*, the triangle *ABC* equal to the triangle *DEF*, and the remaining angle *BAC* equal to the remaining angle *EDF*.   [I. 4]

Therefore etc.   Q.E.D.

PART II

Geometry is a pursuit which suffers from the fact that initially it is—or seems to be—almost too easy. The word "algebra" calls to mind unintelligible scribbles and fearsome formulas; geometry, on the other hand, seems like an easygoing and useful discipline. The worst thing about geometry seems to be its name, but apprehension concerning it quickly vanishes when we learn—as no book on geometry fails to tell us—that "geometry" means "measurement of the earth" and that the ancient Egyptians practiced geometry because they found it necessary to resurvey their lands each year after the floods of the Nile had inundated their country.

This view of geometry is, no doubt, in very large part correct. Of all the various branches of mathematics, geometry is the one that is most easily apprehended by the student new to the subject. Yet there is also something dangerous in the very ease with which geometrical matters can be comprehended: we may think that we understand more than we really do.

An example of the kind of misunderstanding that many people have concerning geometry but of which they are unaware lies in the matter of terminology. For instance, many people will call the figure here drawn a "square." (See Figure 1–1) Now this is wrong; yet if it were called to their attention, such people would perhaps be annoyed at the pettiness which did not realize that they meant the figure was "sort of squarish" and so might as well be called a square. In one sense, they would be right; words, after all, are a matter of convention, and furthermore the figure here depicted (a rectangle) *is* sort of squarish.

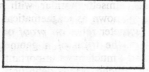

Figure 1–1

But the matter is not to be dismissed as simply as all that. It is precisely the task of geometry to make exact what we mean when we say that a rectangle is not a square and yet is "sort of squarish." If we proceed with this task and succeed in making clear the similarities and the differences between a rectangle and a square, we shall then have defined both "square" and "rectangle." And this is the first—though by no means the only or the most important—task of geometry.

There are many other areas where familiarity with geometrical subject matter may interfere with our ability—at least initially—to think *scientifically* about geometry. Ask a layman to look at Figure 1–2. It is drawn so that the two sides of the

Figure 1–2

triangle issuing from the peak are equal. (Such a triangle is called isosceles.) Suppose I now assert that the two angles at the bottom of the triangle are also equal. Chances are very good that a layman would accept that statement and perhaps even add the exclamation "of course!" There is nothing wrong here on the surface. The two angles at the base *are* in fact equal. What is not so clear, however, is that this is a matter of course. Intuition may tell us that the angles are equal. But geometry, when conducted as a science, does not rely on intuition. A geometer would refuse to believe a statement of the kind made above until it had been proved. Nor should such refusal be considered perverse; there are many known instances where the "obvious truth" turned out to be false. (The reader is probably himself familiar with some such cases; many are popularly known as mathematical puzzles.) Instead of intuition, the geometer relies on *proof* or *demonstration* to convince himself of the truth of a geometrical proposition. This is a second, and a much more important, task of geometry.

In his *Elements,* Euclid brings definition and proof, order and precision, to the entire geometrical area. Euclid is neither the first nor the greatest geometer who ever lived. However, he is probably the greatest known compiler and organizer of geometrical material. Although before Euclid there were geometers and geometrical knowledge, not much of geometry hung together in a systematic fashion. Euclid arranged what he found (and added some things of his own), and the result is a systematic body of knowledge which has ever since been known as Euclidean geometry.

Some of the geometers whose achievements are preserved in Euclid's *Elements* are known to us. For example, it is thought that Book V, which deals with ratios and proportions, is due to Eudoxus, while Book X, which is the longest of the thirteen books and deals with a very specialized subject—geometrical magnitudes incommensurable with one another—is ascribed to Theaetetus. Aristotle mentions Eudoxus as a geometer and astronomer; Theaetetus is one of the speaker's in Plato's dialogue *Theaetetus.* Book XIII of the Elements, which discusses the five regular solids (tetrahedron or triangular pyramid, hexahedron or cube, octahedron, icosahedron, and dodecahedron) is thought to be the special contribution of Euclid himself.

Very little is known about Euclid's life. He lived and worked around 300 B.C. in Alexandria, though he was probably trained in Athens. He wrote several works besides the *Elements,* but his fame rests on this book.

Book I of the *Elements* covers the major portions of plane geometry. Omissions arise from the fact that almost nothing is said about circles (this subject is reserved for Books III and IV) and that there is no measurement of lines and areas in Book I.

Book I begins with what we may call a "preliminary part," followed by a much longer "main part." The preliminary part has three sections: Definitions, Postulates, and Common Notions. The main part consists of 48 propositions. The Definitions list and describe the things Euclid talks about (such as points, lines, and triangles); the Postulates contain a number of statements which Euclid asks us to accept for the sake of what is to follow; the Common Notions (or Axioms) contain statements which Euclid feels are self-evident or obvious and therefore are or should be commonly known. The 48 propositions then follow; each of these either shows how a certain geometrical construction is to be done or proves some geometrical truth.

Although Euclid provides no internal divisions in the "proposition" section of Book I, we can nevertheless divide it into three quite distinct parts. The first part goes from Proposition 1 to Proposition 26. Of the three parts this is the most diversified, but its main subject matter is triangles. The second part goes from Proposition 27 to Proposition 32. This part deals almost exclusively with parallel lines. The third part goes from Proposition 33 to the end of the book—Proposition 48. Its subject matter is parallelograms. There is a definite progression in these three parts. The "triangle" part of the book culminates in certain propositions about the equality (or congruency) of triangles. The congruency propositions are needed in the "parallel lines" part of the book. And the last part of the book, in turn, is dependent on the middle part.

Each of these three large parts in Book I can again be subdivided into groups of propositions. We shall briefly indicate how this might be done in the first part (Propositions 1–26); this will also help the reader gain some notion of the content of Book I. Propositions 1–3 constitute a group whose purpose is to show how to cut off from a straight line a segment equal to another straight line. Proposition 4 stands by itself; it is a congruency proposition, showing that two triangles are congruent if two sides and the included angle of one triangle are equal to the corresponding two sides and included angle of the other triangle. Propositions 5–8 are another "congruency" group culminating in Proposition 8, which states that two triangles are congruent if the three sides of one triangle are equal to the corresponding three sides of the other triangle. Proposition 9–12 form what we may call a "construction group" of propositions; four very important constructions, showing how to bisect straight lines and angles and how to drop and erect perpendiculars, are demonstrated here. Propositions 13–15 are a group dealing with angles. Propositions 20–22 deal with the size relationships existing among the sides of a triangle. Proposition 23 stands by itself, because it is needed at this point: it shows how to construct an angle equal to a given angle. Propositions 24–26 constitute a group that combines what has been learned in Propositions 16–19 and in Propositions 20–22. The culmination of this group is Proposition 26, another congruency proposition which shows that two triangles are congruent if one side and two angles of one triangle are equal to the corresponding side and angles of the other triangle.

Now it is time to look at Euclid's work in some detail. We begin with the Definitions. It is quite easy to understand what definitions are and why they must precede the remainder of Euclid's work. Before Euclid can talk intelligently about triangles, rectangles, etc., he must tell us what these things are; otherwise we should know neither what he is talking about nor whether he is correct in his assertions. Thus it is entirely appropriate that Euclid define "point," "line," "triangle," "circle," "straight line," etc.

Are Euclid's definitions good ones? For example, a point is defined as "that which has no part." A line is defined as "breadthless length," and a straight line is said to lie "evenly with the points on itself." Are these definitions really helpful in understanding the things under consideration? If we did not already know what a point is, would the definition help us? Or would it tend to confuse us? For instance, it might seem that according to Euclid a point is nothing at all; for if it were anything, it would have to have parts. And, in the definition of a straight line, how helpful is it to say that it lies evenly with the points on itself? We may also wonder if Euclid has defined a sufficient number of terms. Why, for instance, did he not define the term "part"? Or, the term "evenly"? This latter term would seem to be crucially important, since straightness is defined by means of it. Here we see a fundamental fact of definitions: Not everything can be defined. This fact is so important that we must investigate it a little more.

Defining something means giving its meaning with the help of other terms. But these other terms may themselves be in need of definition. And, indeed, if we are faced with someone who takes nothing for granted and wants to be sure of everything, we will be forced to go on defining. It is easy to see that this is a losing game: if the original term being defined is A and if we define A in terms of B, C, and D, then we can be asked to define B, C, and D. In doing so, new terms must be used. We obviously cannot use the term A to define B, since it is A's meaning that is at stake. But the new terms, say E, F, and G, must themselves be defined, and so on. This clearly cannot go on forever, for there is no end to it. How do we stop it? By saying, as we did above, that not everything can, or need be, defined.

This solution, easy and neat as it appears, has its own difficulties. We may claim that to define "point" as "that which has no part" is perfectly sound, because the term "part" needs no definition. Furthermore, we may say or assume that the other words in the sentence, such as "that" and "has" are even less in need of a definition, because their meaning is self-evident and clear. It would be hard to maintain that the meaning of "part" is not well known. However, is it better known than the meaning of the term "point"? Why, in other words, define "point" in terms of other words which are claimed to be well known and unambiguous? Why not just claim that the meaning of the word "point" is well known and unambiguous and be done with it? Similar arguments could be construed against the need or even helpfulness of trying to define "line" or "straight line." It is not helpful, we may feel, to speak of "breadthless length"; these two terms are, if anything, more obscure than the term "line." As for the definition of "straight line," that seems worse than no definition at all: surely no one would know what I am talking about if I said, "Here is a line that lies evenly with the points on itself"; whereas just as surely, almost everybody would know what I meant were I to speak of a "straight line."

This matter cannot be resolved in an absolute fashion. Since not every term can be defined, it becomes a matter of prudence which terms should be defined and which should be left undefined. Euclid apparently followed the rule that he would try to define all specifically geometrical terms that he needed, using nongeometrical language to do it. Thus, he defines "point," "line," "straight line," etc., because these are the elements with which he has to deal. He apparently feels he cannot or should not assume familiarity with them, whereas he can assume some working knowledge of terms like "part," "breadth," etc., because they are part of everyday speech.

After the initial few definitions, the difficulties of defining become less and less, because the terms defined earlier can be used in the later definitions. We need say very little more about the definitions; they should present no problems. Two other definitions are worth noting, however.

Definition 10 defines a right angle. Whenever two lines intersect, four angles are formed; and of these four, two are adjacent to each other. A right angle, Euclid states, is formed when two lines intersect in such a fashion that two adjacent angles are equal to each other. (See Figure 1–3.) Each of the two equal adjacent angles is then a right angle.

If angle A = angle B, then A, B are both right angles.

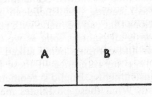

Figure 1–3

The definition is perhaps more remarkable for what it does not say than for anything else. It does not say that a right angle is equal to 90°. This is an instance of Euclid's carefulness in his defining process. The term "degree" has not been defined by him (and in fact is nowhere defined in the *Elements*); hence he does not employ it in his definition of a right angle. More than prudence is involved here: the term "degree," if it were defined, would be seen to be dependent on "right angle"; that is, the definition of "angle of 1°" would have to be "an angle which is the 90th part of a right angle."

The other definition to which we want to call attention is the last one. It defines parallel lines as those straight lines which never meet, no matter how far they are extended in either direction, provided that the two lines are in the same plane. (If they are not in the same plane, they could fail to meet and yet not be parallel. Such non-meeting, but not-parallel lines in three dimensions are called "skew.")

This brings us to the postulates, which are five in number. Of these, the most famous and the most interesting is the fifth postulate, the so-called "parallel postulate." This postulate is thought to be Euclid's own contribution to plane geometry, and if he had done nothing else in geometry, he would be famous for it. We shall discuss this postulate in great detail in the next chapter, in connection with the selection from Lobachevsky.

Of the remaining four postulates, the first three are very much alike; they "postulate" that certain geometrical constructions can be done. The root meaning of the word "postulate" is "to demand"; in fact, Euclid demands of us that we agree that the following things can be done: that any two points can be joined by a straight line; that any straight line may be extended in either direction indefinitely; that given a point and a distance, a circle can be drawn with that point as center and that distance as radius. Sometimes these postulates are paraphrased as meaning that Euclidean geometry restricts itself to constructions that can be made with ruler and compass. This interpretation is all right as long as we do not take it too literally. The ruler and compass being talked about are mental instruments. There is no reference in these postulates to any actual drawing instruments; Euclid's geometry is not that of the drawing board. What these postulates mean is that Euclid asks us to grant that he may connect any two points with a line, in his mind. It takes only a moment's reflection to see that Euclid cannot be talking about pencil lines drawn with a ruler. A line, according to his definition, is length without breadth, and no pencil can ever draw a line that has no breadth. It may be a thin line, but it will have breadth.

In other words, Euclid is talking about ideal figures, and the constructions which he here asks us to believe can be made are ideal constructions. Why is there any need for constructions at all? The simplest answer is that constructions enable us to *do* something. Without constructions, we would have to confine geometry to those things which are described in the Definitions; we could never admit any new entities into geometry. By means of constructions, on the other hand, we construct or make new things out of old; we can combine the various things defined—such as lines and triangles and circles —into new figures and make propositions about them.

These postulates are in a way completely arbitrary. It is possible to have geometries in which some of these postulates are omitted, or in which other postulates are substituted for them. We can easily imagine a geometry which would not contain Postulate 1. This geometry might substitute another postulate such as this: Between any two points there is a unique shortest possible line which can be drawn. Postulate 2 might also be abandoned and the following substituted: No line can be indefinitely extended; all lines are finite.

Strange as these postulates may seem, they would serve (with certain exceptions) for the geometry that can be studied on the surface of a sphere. Here the shortest distance between any two points on the surface is always a "great circle." Any two points on a sphere (except end points of a diameter) can be joined by a unique great circle (a great circle is one whose center is at the center of the sphere); but all great circles are finite in length and all are equally long. Figure 1–4 shows two points *A* and *B* on the surface of a sphere which are joined by a "great circle." Another great circle, in the position of an

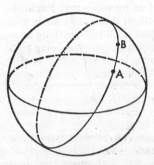

Figure 1–4

"equator," has been drawn to illustrate how all great circles are equal. Among other things, then, the postulates indicate what kind of geometry Euclid is talking about. He is *not* talking about spherical geometry, for in such a geometry his postulates would obviously not apply.

Though the particular postulates that Euclid chooses are arbitrary, they are obviously chosen with a good deal of prudence. They are those postulates which are needed in order to prove the important propositions of ordinary plane geometry. Here, as elsewhere, Euclid follows common sense. He departs from it only where it is absolutely necessary. Euclid could have chosen other postulates; for instance, he might have postulated that around any two points an ellipse of a given eccentricity can be drawn. Such a postulate would be just as permissible as the one about the circle which he uses. A great many propositions could be proved with the help of this postulate which cannot be proved with Euclid's (and vice versa). As it happens, however, the propositions which the ellipse-postulate permits us to prove are rather recondite, whereas the propositions which Euclid's circle-postulate allows us to prove (and which would be lost if the other one were adopted) are all very well known and very useful. By "lost" we mean that these propositions could no longer be derived from the postulates of the system; but neither could the opposites of these propositions be derived.

The fourth postulate is not an operational postulate. It simply states that all right angles are equal to one another. This postulate is worthy of note, because at first sight it seems superfluous. It seems obvious that all right angles are the same.

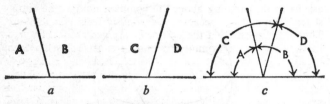

Figure 1–5

But again what seems so obvious is not necessarily so. To show this, look at Figure 1–5a and b. If $A = B$, then A and B are both right angles. If $C = D$, then C and D are both right angles also. But is it clear that $A = C$, or $B = D$? Not necessarily. In the diagrams as drawn, we have in fact tried to make A not equal to C, and B not equal to D. The reader may object that the diagrams also look as though A and B were not equal, and as though C and D were not really equal. This is granted as far as looks are concerned; but geometry does not go by looks. If it is maintained that the diagrams as we have drawn them represent impossible situations—that is, that A and C must be equal, because otherwise A and B cannot be equal—then that is merely a restatement of Euclid's fourth postulate. Like the postulate, it is an assertion of certain relations of equality, without proof. Euclid's postulate makes explicit what we feel must be true: if the postulate did not hold, the situation depicted in Figure 1–5c might prevail (if the two figures 1–5a and b were superimposed on one another). This situation cannot exist, however, if all right angles are equal to one another.

Finally we come to the common notions, or axioms. Euclid sets down five statements which, he feels, are self-evident. That is to say, they are true and known to be true by everyone who understands the meaning of the terms in the statements. The common notions do seem rather obvious; the first one, for instance, states: "Things which are equal to the same thing are also equal to one another." Their very obviousness and simplicity may inspire contempt; and a less careful geometer than

Euclid might not bother to put them down at all. But here again Euclid follows the rule to put down everything that he needs as a tool for the propositions that are to come.

Is there any difference between the postulates and the common notions? In Euclid's mind, there clearly is. He is apologetic about the postulates (as the name indicates). He asks us to grant him the truth of the postulates. But Euclid does not ask us to do anything about the common notions; he simply states them as true, because he obviously feels that they are. Thus we may say that the postulates are geometrical assumptions, whereas the common notions are general self-evident truths. This statement points to another difference between postulates and axioms: the former are geometrical in nature, while the axioms are generally true. Presumably another science, such as arithmetic, would have postulates different from those of geometry. But the axioms used in arithmetic would be the same as those used in geometry.

This, at least, seems to be Euclid's way of looking at things. Other views are possible. For instance, some mathematicians maintain that postulates and common notions are not really different. The postulates can be (and perhaps even should be) stated in nongeometrical language; and the common notions, according to these mathematicians, are not more self-evident than the postulates. Both common notions and postulates should be recognized for what they are: assumptions. We will not, at the moment, pursue this view any further. Again we recognize, however, that Euclid is on the side of common sense. It *seems* as though the common notions are a lot more evident than the postulates, and it certainly *seems* as though they have a wider applicability than the postulates do.

Now it is time to turn to some of the actual propositions in Book I. We have earlier noted that the propositions fall into three main parts and that each of these parts can again be divided into a number of groups. We have also already pointed out that the various parts and groups are organically related— that is, that the earlier parts lead naturally to later ones. Is it the case, then, that the order of the propositions in Book I is completely prescribed? Or to restate the question: Is it the case that the order of the propositions cannot be different from what it is? The answer to this question is a qualified "yes." It is not true that the order of the propositions as given by Euclid is absolutely the only one that could have been chosen. A look at other geometry textbooks will show that this is so. But, starting with Euclid's definitions, postulates, and axioms, there are not many other orders that could have been taken, and certainly not many that would be as good as the one Euclid has chosen. Thus, while we cannot say that the order of the propositions in Book I is absolutely and necessarily determined by their content, it is correct to say that the order is more than arbitrary, that there is a natural progression from earlier to later propositions, and that Euclid is very much aware of the progressive character of the book. He never loses sight of the fact that later propositions must depend only on earlier ones, and very frequently we find that a proposition is clearly introduced for no other purpose than to make the proof of the next one possible.

"Proof" is, of course, the all-important term in geometry. In a moment we shall see what a geometrical proof looks like. But first we are bound to notice one thing: the first proposition in Book I—that is, the first proposition in the entire *Elements*—is not a proof at all. Instead of proving that something is the case, it sets out to construct something. "On a given finite straight line," the proposition says, "to construct an equilateral triangle."

We encountered constructions earlier, when we noted that the first three postulates were construction postulates. Indeed, the statement of Proposition 1 is such that grammatically it could be turned into a postulate; Euclid might have said: Let it be postulated, on a given finite straight line, to construct an equilateral triangle.

Why did Euclid not do this? The answer is quite simple: he did not have to. A postulate, after all, is a sign of a sort of weakness. It constitutes a demand on the part of the geometer that something be granted him—either that something is true (as in Postulate 4) or that something can be done (as in Postulates 1–3). If we do not grant the geometer's postulates, he cannot force us to do so; on the other hand, we cannot then expect him to prove his geometrical propositions, either.

The more postulates a geometer makes, the less surprising it becomes that he can prove many and complicated propositions. Just to go to the absurd extreme, a geometer could postulate as true all geometrical propositions. Such procedure would not be wrong, but it would of course be useless and uninteresting. At the other extreme, and just as absurd in his way, would be the geometer who wanted to make no postulates whatsoever. Such a geometer, too, could not be gainsaid. But his method would be as valueless as the other: he could prove no propositions whatever. In the middle is the kind of geometry in which postulates are made: enough postulates so that all the propositions of geometry can be proved, but no more than necessary. This is the kind of geometry which Euclid aims to present to us here. To have made Proposition 1 a postulate would have offended, therefore, against the (implied) principle of using as few postulates as possible.

Now let us look at how the construction is accomplished. From each of the end points A and B of the given line a circle is described, with the given line as its radius. (See Figure 1–6.)

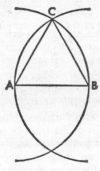

Figure 1–6

These two circles meet (actually, they meet twice: once above and once below the given line), in a point C. Euclid then connects this newly found point C with each of the end points A and B of the given line. Thus a triangle ABC is formed. The construction is now over; all that remains to be done is to show that ABC is an equilateral triangle. This is easy enough: AB and AC are equal, because they are radii of the same circle; BA and BC are equal because *they* are radii of the same circle. Finally, AC and BC are equal because they are equal to the same thing, namely AB. Thus Euclid concludes that "that which it was required to do" has been done. The last phrase in Latin is *quod erat faciendum*; that is why the letters "Q.E.F." are often placed at the end of construction propositions.

What permits Euclid to draw a circle around A (and around B)? Postulate 3, of course. Similarly, Postulate 1 justifies Euclid's joining the point C with A and B. Thus, the construction of Proposition 1 is executed by means of the constructions that are permitted through the postulates. At the end of Proposition 1, Euclid has a new construction available, namely, that of an equilateral triangle. In the next proposition, therefore, Euclid could make use of any one of four constructions: to join two points by a straight line, to extend a straight line, to draw a circle with any given radius and center, to construct an equilateral triangle with a given side.

How valid is Euclid's proof that the figure constructed is actually the one called for? Euclid makes no attempt to prove that the figure ABC is in fact a triangle; presumably this is clear and obvious from the diagram. (It may not be so obvious as Euclid thinks; remember that the lines and figures with which Euclid is concerned are not those on paper but ideal lines and figures in the geometer's mind. There might be some difficulty in inferring something about the shape of a figure that is ideal and invisible from a visible and material diagram.) The proof that the three sides of the triangle are all equal depends on the definition of a circle. Euclid reminds us (as the bracketed figure indicates) that in Definition 15 a circle is defined as the kind of figure in which all radii are equal. This, together with Common Notion 1, is sufficient to show that all three sides of the triangle are of the same length.

A purist could raise some objections to Euclid's procedure. For instance, how do we know that the two circles, one with the center at A, and the other with the center at B, meet at all? And if they do meet, is Euclid correct in assuming, as he obviously does, that they meet in a point? This latter fact could probably be proved from the definition of "line" as "breadthless length"; but Euclid certainly does not do it.

Proposition 2 deserves a close look. As in Proposition 1, a construction is called for. We are given a point, and we are given a finite straight line. The point is not on the line. The problem is to place the given line (or more correctly, another

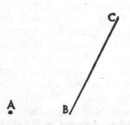

Figure 1–7

line equal to it in length) in such a way that the given point is one of the end points of the line. (See Figure 1–7.) The whole language of the proposition is very physical; it speaks of placing lines, of touching lines, etc. Accordingly, the answer to the problem also seems physically simple: just pick up the given line and put it over where the point is. If lines and points were in fact physical entities, this solution would be excellent. Since, however, they are ideal things, the solution cannot depend on any physical picking up or motion through space. What must be done can involve only those constructions or operations which are possible because of the postulates or the one additional tool which Euclid now has—Proposition 1. There is nothing in these postulates or Proposition 1 about "picking up" a line or about its geometrical equivalent, which would be the permission to move a line through space. In fact, if we look at what Proposition 2 tries to accomplish, we can see that—provided the construction can be shown to be possible—it will give the geometer the permission to move lines through space. Proposition 2 is the substitute for a postulate "To move a line anywhere in space without changing its length."

To accomplish the construction, the given point and one end of the given line are first connected. (It can be either end;

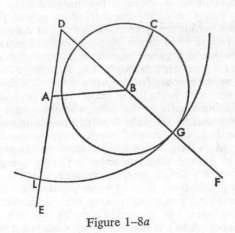

Figure 1–8a

Figure 1–8a indicates how it is done in one case, and Figure 1–8b shows the other case.) On this line an equilateral triangle is built, according to Proposition 1. Then the two "arms"

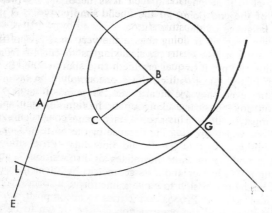

Figure 1–8*b*

of this triangle, *DA* and *DB*, are extended indefinitely, according to Postulate 2. Now comes the real trick of the proposition. A circle is described, with *B* as center and the given line *BC* as radius. This circle intersects the extended line *DB* in the point *G*. This gives us the line *DG*, which is longer than the line we are looking for by the amount *DB*. But if we now draw a circle around *D* as center with the line *DG* as radius, we obtain the line *DL* (where the circle intersects the extension of *DA*). *DL*, therefore, is longer than the line we are looking for also by the amount *DB* (or what is the same thing, *DA*). But that leaves *AL* as the line of the desired length and, furthermore, starting exactly at the point where we want it to, *A*.

This proposition certainly displays Euclid's ingenuity as a geometer. But, we may ask ourselves with some dismay, is this not an awfully complicated amount of construction to have to go through simply in order to place a line at a given point? If such a simple operation requires so many steps and so many justifications, think of how complicated a truly difficult geometrical construction must be! Fortunately we can allay these fears. The manner of showing how this construction is accomplished is indeed complicated, but it will never be needed again. From now on when it is necessary to move a line from where it is to some other location, Euclid simply says, "Let it be done," and refers to Proposition 2 as his justification for the fact that it *can* be done. This is exactly how

Euclid uses the postulates; when it is necessary to draw a straight line between two points, Euclid simply says, "Let it be done," and refers to Postulate 1.

We can see Euclid doing this in the very next proposition. This is yet a third construction, asking us to cut off from a longer line a segment equal in length to a shorter line. Euclid calls the longer line *AB*, the shorter one simply *C*. And he begins his construction by saying "At the point *A* let *AD* be placed equal to the straight line *C*," and he refers us to Proposition 2 at this point. This illustrates a general procedure of geometry: once something has been shown to be true, or once a construction has been shown to be possible, it is not necessary to repeat its proof again and again. If it has once been done, it is enough; the reference to the proposition in which the proof or construction was first made is merely a mnemonic device in case we have forgotten where to look.

So far there has been a perfect progression of the propositions: Proposition 1 depends only on the definitions, postulates, and axioms; Proposition 2 depends on Proposition 1 and on the definitions, postulates, and axioms; Proposition 3 depends on Proposition 2 (which in turn depends on Proposition 1) and on the definitions, postulates, and axioms. This perfect progression is interrupted with Proposition 4, which does not depend on Proposition 3. In fact, it does not depend on any prior proposition, or even on any of the postulates. The only reference to prior material that is made in the body of the proposition is to Common Notion 4. This "independence" of Proposition 4 is somewhat strange; it indicates something special about the manner of proof.

What Euclid tries to prove is that two triangles are equal (congruent) if two sides and the included angle of one are equal to two sides and the included angle of the other one. His method of proof is nothing at all like what he did in the previous three propositions. Euclid "picks up" one triangle and superimposes it (places it) on the second one. Then he notes that if this is done so that point *A* and point *D* coincide (we are referring to Euclid's figure) and so that line *AB* is in the direction of line *DE*, then *B* and *E* must also coincide because of the equal length of *AB* and *DE*. Similarly, because of the equality of the angles at *A* and *D*, the direction of *AC* and *DF* coincide, and because of the equality of *AC* and *DF* the points *C* and *F* coincide. And thus, if *B* and *E* coincide while *C* and *F* also coincide, the connecting straight lines, *BC* and *EF*, must also coincide. (Euclid makes a tacit assumption here: between two points only one straight line can be drawn.) Since the two triangles coincide in all respects, Euclid concludes that they are congruent.

There can be no quarreling with the result. We may wonder, however, about the legitimacy of Euclid's method of proof. How valid is the method of superimposition as geometrical proof? The reader may recall that in connection with Proposition 2 we pointed out that geometrical entities like points and lines are not physical things and that they cannot simply be picked up and moved about in space. Here, however, Euclid does this very thing. If it is legitimate here, why wasn't it legitimate in Proposition 2? If Euclid had allowed himself that method earlier, the whole cumbersome method of construction in Proposition 2 could have been eliminated.

The best answer we can give is that just as "picking up" lines was not legitimate in Proposition 2, so it is really not legitimate here. In other words, it may well be that the proof of Proposition 4 is very faulty indeed, or to put it more bluntly, that it is no proof at all. Does this mean that what Proposition 4 states is not true? Not at all; it merely means that Euclid's way of proving it is unsatisfactory. Are there other ways of proving this proposition? There may be, especially if we supplement Euclid's postulates with some additional ones (such as one about the movability of geometrical figures without distortion). But if additional postulates are needed in order to prove Proposition 4, could we not simply solve the problem by making Proposition 4 itself a postulate? The answer is that we certainly could. The only question is whether it is preferable to have Proposition 4 itself as a postulate or to have a different postulate about the movability of geometrical figures. The second postulate would be more general in character; that may or may not be an advantage. Whichever solution is adopted, it is clear that the proof of Proposition 4 cannot be accepted unless at least one additional assumption is made. That additional assumption may be the truth of Proposition 4 itself, or it may be some other assumption from which the truth of Proposition 4 can be demonstrated.

No matter how we resolve the difficulty concerning Proposition 4, it still remains true that it in no way depends on any of the preceding propositions. Hence, could not Proposition 4 have come before the first three propositions? Or to put the same question in a slightly different way: Is there any reason why Proposition 1 rather than Proposition 4 should be put first in the book?

There *is* a reason for beginning with Proposition 1, and it derives from the fact that Proposition 1 is a construction, whereas Proposition 4 is not. Construction propositions (and postulates) perform a very important function in geometry. Suppose that there were no construction postulates and that no proposition had as yet been proved in Book I. The only purely geometrical knowledge we would have then would reside in the definitions. These define certain ideal entities, such as straight lines, triangles, and circles. Do we know, as the result of these definitions, that these things actually exist? Lest it seem that we have raised a foolish question, because anything which has been defined *must* exist, we point to the fact that there are many things that can be defined but which do not exist. A favorite example, of course, is mermaids. There is nothing self-contradictory about the definition of a mermaid; yet such beings do not exist. Many other things can be defined and yet no guarantee given that they exist. We are not talking about obviously self-contradictory definitions (such as that of a round square), but of definitions of things that could, but as a matter of fact do not, exist.

How do we know, then, that straight lines exist? From Postulate 1, because that postulate states that a straight line can be drawn between any two points; a line that can be drawn obviously exists. Similarly, Postulate 3 assures us of the real existence of circles. But how do we know that triangles exist? There is no postulate to assure us that triangles can be drawn. Instead of a postulate, however, there is a proposition that assures that triangles exist. Proposition 1 shows us how an equilateral triangle can be drawn; and if it can be drawn, it exists.

Construction propositions, therefore, not only show us how to perform certain geometrical constructions, but they also assure us that the geometrical entity being constructed is a really existing one. This in turn indicates why it is preferable to have Proposition 1 precede Proposition 4, even though the two propositions are independent of each other. If Euclid began Book I with Proposition 4, his readers might wonder whether he is stating something and proving something about a figure that does not have any reality.

We need say very little about Proposition 5 except to point out that it is a typical proposition. It is a demonstration, not a construction; it does not employ any strange methods of proof like Proposition 4, and in general it is an example of what most people have in mind when they think of a geometri cal theorem. The proposition is also a good instance of Euclid's careful progressive method. It could not come any earlier in Book I, because it depends on both Propositions 3 and 4. Another respect in which this proposition is typical is that it involves a subsidiary construction; that is, a construction is made in the proof for no other purpose than to make the demonstration possible.

Proposition 6 is in one way much less important than Proposition 5, but it is of more interest to us because of the way in which it is proved. The method of proof is called "reduction to the absurd." It is one of the most frequently used methods in all of mathematics.

Proposition 6 is the converse of Proposition 5. The latter showed that in isosceles triangles the base angles are equal; the former proves that if in a triangle the base angles are equal, then the triangle is isosceles. We are given, therefore, that the angle at B and the angle at C are equal. (See Figure 1–9a.) We

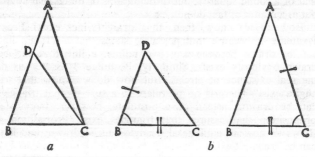

Figure 1–9

are to prove that $AB = AC$. Let us assume, Euclid says, the opposite of what we want to prove. We will then go on to show that this (the opposite) cannot possibly be true. The opposite of AB's being equal to AC is that AB is not equal to AC. If AB is not equal to AC, then one side has to be greater than the other. It does not matter for the purposes of the proof which side it is; let us say that it is AB that is greater. Since AB is greater, cut off from AB the segment DB equal to AC. Then join DC. Euclid shows, by using Proposition 4, that the two triangles DBC and ACB are equal. (To show which two triangles Euclid is talking about, we have separated them in Figure 1–9b. The corresponding parts have been marked.)

But it is clearly impossible that these two triangles are equal, Euclid continues, because one triangle is wholly contained within the other. Hence we have been led to an impossible or absurd conclusion. Since all the steps in the proof were, however, logically impeccable, what can be the source of the impossible conclusion? It can be only one thing: the initial assumption that *AB* is greater than *AC*. Since true premises never lead to false conclusions (as long as no logical fallacies are committed), it must be that the premise "*AB* is greater than *AC*" is false. If that premise is false, its contradictory must be true; that is, it must be true that *AB* is not greater than *AC*. This still leaves the possibility that *AB* is smaller than *AC*, but that premise can be shown to lead to an absurdity just as quickly as the previous one. Thus, the only premise which does not lead to any absurdity is that *AB* is equal to *AC*.

The power of this method lies in the fact that it is not restricted to geometry. It can be used anywhere. Simply assume the truth of the opposite (contradictory) of what you want to prove. Then see if this assumption leads to any absurdities or impossibilities. If it does, the original assumption must be false, and so its contradictory (which is what you wanted to prove in the first place) is true.

The method depends on two logical principles: First, a false conclusion is a sign of a false premise somewhere in a logical process (assuming that the various steps of the process are carried out according to the ordinary laws of logic). Second, if a proposition is false, then its contradictory is true; and again, if a proposition is true, then its contradictory is false. This is not surprising, because two contradictory propositions are defined as a pair of propositions such that only one can be true at a time, and only one can be false at a time. For example, the contradictory of the proposition "this board is red" is the proposition "this board is not red." The contradictory is not any proposition like "this board is blue," because quite obviously both "this board is red" and "this board is blue" can be false at the same time—for example, if the board is green.

A word of caution may be in order about the first logical principle (that a false conclusion is a sign of a false premise). The opposite is not true; that is, a true conclusion is not a sign of true premises. If, using a set of premises and valid reasoning, you arrive at a true conclusion, it may still be the case that one or more of your premises are false. An example may be helpful. Each of the two following premises is false:

(1) All Americans speak French fluently; (2) General de Gaulle is an American. But these two premises combine correctly to give the following true conclusion: General de Gaulle speaks French fluently.

There are many variations of reduction to the absurd. We shall encounter some of them later on in this book. The important thing is to be sure that the logical processes involved are valid and to be certain that the conclusion which you claim to be absurd is so in fact. In Proposition 6 it is worth noting that the discovery of the absurdity depends on visual intuition; that is, Euclid asks us to look at the diagram and to see that the two triangles clearly cannot be equal because the one is totally within the other. Once more this raises the question of how appropriate it is for Euclid to depend on sight and on the diagram in his book when, as we have repeatedly pointed out, Euclidean geometry is *not* concerned with visible lines, triangles, etc.

Although there are many more propositions in Book I, we shall not examine most of them in detail, since they present neither much difficulty nor any new principles. In the next chapter, however, we shall examine another group of propositions from Book I that *does* exhibit a new principle.

CHAPTER TWO

Lobachevski—Non-Euclidean Geometry

PART I

The following selection consists of two sections. First, we have six more propositions from Book I of Euclid's *Elements* (Propositions 27–32). These are propositions dealing with parallel lines. With these Euclidean propositions we have placed some pages from Lobachevski's *Theory of Parallels*. This work discusses Euclid's theory of parallels, finds fault with it, and substitutes another theory for it. In so doing, Lobachevski develops a version of "non-Euclidean geometry."

Euclid:

*Elements of Geometry**

BOOK I

PROPOSITION 27

If a straight line falling on two straight lines make the alternate angles equal to one another, the straight lines will be parallel to one another.

For let the straight line *EF* falling on the two straight lines *AB*, *CD* make the alternate angles *AEF*, *EFD* equal to one another;

* From *The Thirteen Books of Euclid's Elements,* trans. by Sir Thomas L. Heath (2nd ed.; London: Cambridge University Press, 1926). Reprinted by permission.

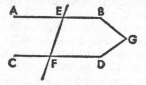

I say that *AB* is parallel to *CD*.

For, if not, *AB*, *CD* when produced will meet either in the direction of *B*, *D* or towards *A*, *C*.

Let them be produced and meet, in the direction of *B*, *D*, at *G*.

Then, in the triangle *GEF*, the exterior angle *AEF* is equal to the interior and opposite angle *EFG*:
which is impossible. [I. 16]

Therefore *AB*, *CD* when produced will not meet in the direction of *B, D*.

Similarly it can be proved that neither will they meet towards *A, C*.

But straight lines which do not meet in either direction are parallel; [Def. 23]
therefore *AB* is parallel to *CD*.

Therefore etc. Q.E.D.

PROPOSITION 28

If a straight line falling on two straight lines make the exterior angle equal to the interior and opposite angle on the same side, or the interior angles on the same side equal to two right angles, the straight lines will be parallel to one another.

For let the straight line *EF* falling on the two straight lines *AB*, *CD* make the exterior angle *EGB* equal to the interior and opposite angle *GHD*, or the interior angles on the same

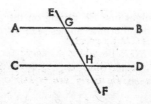

side, namely *BGH*, *GHD*, equal to two right angles; I say that *AB* is parallel to *CD*.

For, since the angle *EGB* is equal to the angle *GHD*, while the angle *EGB* is equal to the angle *AGH*,   [I. 15]
the angle *AGH* is also equal to the angle *GHD*; and they are alternate; therefore *AB* is parallel to *CD*.   [I. 27]

Again, since the angles *BGH*, *GHD* are equal to two right angles, and the angles *AGH*, *BGH* are also equal to two right angles,   [I. 13]
the angles *AGH*, *BGH* are equal to the angles *BGH*, *GHD*.

Let the angle *BGH* be subtracted from each; therefore the remaining angle *AGH* is equal to the remaining angle *GHD*; and they are alternate; therefore *AB* is parallel to *CD*.   [I. 27]

Therefore etc.   Q.E.D.

PROPOSITION 29

A straight line falling on parallel straight lines makes the alternate angles equal to one another, the exterior angle equal to the interior and opposite angle, and the interior angles on the same side equal to two right angles.

For let the straight line *EF* fall on the parallel straight lines *AB*, *CD*; I say that it makes the alternate angles *AGH*, *GHD* equal, the exterior angle *EGB* equal to the interior and opposite angle *GHD*, and the interior angles on the same side, namely *BGH*, *GHD*, equal to two right angles.

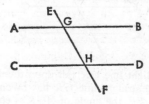

For, if the angle *AGH* is unequal to the angle *GHD*, one of them is greater.

Let the angle *AGH* be greater.

Let the angle *BGH* be added to each; therefore the angles *AGH*, *BGH* are greater than the angles *BGH*, *GHD*.

But the angles *AGH*, *BGH* are equal to two right angles;   [I. 13] therefore the angles *BGH*, *GHD* are less than two right angles.

But straight lines produced indefinitely from angles less than two right angles meet;   [Post. 5]
therefore *AB*, *CD*, if produced indefinitely, will meet; but they do not meet, because they are by hypothesis parallel.

Therefore the angle *AGH* is not unequal to the angle *GHD*, and is therefore equal to it.

Again, the angle *AGH* is equal to the angle *EGB*;   [I. 15]
therefore the angle *EGB* is also equal to the angle *GHD*.
                                                                                    [C.N. 1]
Let the angle *BGH* be added to each; therefore the angles *EGB*, *BGH* are equal to the angles *BGH*, *GHD*.   [C.N. 2]

But the angles *EGB*, *BGH* are equal to two right angles;
                                                                                    [I. 13]
therefore the angles *BGH*, *GHD* are also equal to two right angles.

Therefore etc.   Q.E.D.

PROPOSITION 30

Straight lines parallel to the same straight line are also parallel to one another.

Let each of the straight lines *AB*, *CD* be parallel to *EF*; I say that *AB* is also parallel to *CD*.

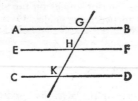

For let the straight line *GK* fall upon them.

Then, since the straight line *GK* has fallen on the parallel straight lines *AB*, *EF*, the angle of *AGK* is equal to the angle *GHF*.   [I. 29]

Again, since the straight line *GK* has fallen on the parallel straight lines *EF*, *CD*, the angle *GHF* is equal to the angle *GKD*.   [I. 29]

But the angle *AGK* was also proved equal to the angle *GHF*; therefore the angle *AGK* is also equal to the angle *GKD*;
                                                                                    [C.N. 1]
and they are alternate.

Therefore *AB* is parallel to *CD*.*   Q.E.D.

PROPOSITION 31

Through a given point to draw a straight line parallel to a given straight line.

Let *A* be the given point, and *BC* the given straight line; thus it is required to draw through the point *A* a straight line parallel to the straight line *BC*.

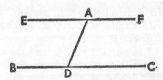

Let a point *D* be taken at random on *BC*, and let *AD* be joined; on the straight line *DA*, and at the point *A* on it, let the angle *DAE* be constructed equal to the angle *ADC* [I. 23]; and let the straight line *AF* be produced in a straight line with *EA*.

Then, since the straight line *AD* falling on the two straight lines *BC*, *EF* has made the alternate angles *EAD*, *ADC* equal to one another, therefore *EAF* is parallel to *BC*.   [I. 27]

Therefore through the given point *A* the straight line *EAF* has been drawn parallel to the given straight line *BC*.   Q.E.F.

PROPOSITION 32

In any triangle, if one of the sides be produced, the exterior angle is equal to the two interior and opposite angles, and the three interior angles of the triangle are equal to two right angles.

Let *ABC* be a triangle, and let one side of it *BC* be produced to *D*; I say that the exterior angle *ACD* is equal to the two interior and opposite angles *CAB*, *ABC*, and the three interior angles of the triangle *ABC*, *BCA*,*CAB* are equal to two right angles.

* The usual *conclusion* in general terms ("Therefore etc.") repeating the enunciation is, curiously enough, wanting at the end of this proposition.

For let *CE* be drawn through the point *C* parallel to the straight line *AB*.   [I. 31]

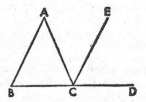

Then, since *AB* is parallel to *CE*, and *AC* has fallen upon them, the alternate angles *BAC*, *ACE* are equal to one another.   [I. 29]

Again, since *AB* is parallel to *CE*, and the straight line *BD* has fallen upon them, the exterior angle *ECD* is equal to the interior and opposite angle *ABC*.   [I. 29]

But the angle *ACE* was also proved equal to the angle *BAC*; therefore the whole angle *ACD* is equal to the two interior and opposite angles *BAC*, *ABC*.

Let the angle *ACB* be added to each; therefore the angles *ACD*, *ACB* are equal to the three angles *ABC*, *BCA*, *CAB*.

But the angles *ACD*, *ACB* are equal to two right angles;
           [I. 13]
therefore the angles *ABC*, *BCA*, *CAB* are also equal to two right angles.

Therefore etc.   Q.E.D.

Nicholas Lobachevski: *The Theory of Parallels**

In geometry I find certain imperfections which I hold to be the reason why this science, apart from transition into analytics, can as yet make no advance from that state in which it has come to us from Euclid.

As belonging to these imperfections, I consider the obscurity in the fundamental concepts of the geometrical magnitudes and in the manner and method of representing the measuring of these magnitudes, and finally the momentous gap in the theory

   * From *Geometrical Researches on the Theory of Parallels*, trans. by George B. Halsted (Chicago-London: The Open Court Publishing Co., 1914; copyright by The Open Court Publishing Co., La Salle, Ill., 1942), pp. 11-19. Reprinted by permission.

of parallels, to fill which all efforts of mathematicians have been so far in vain.

For this theory Legendre's endeavors have done nothing, since he was forced to leave the only rigid way to turn into a side path and take refuge in auxiliary theorems which he illogically strove to exhibit as necessary axioms. My first essay on the foundations of geometry I published in the Kasan *Messenger* for the year 1829. In the hope of having satisfied all requirements, I undertook hereupon a treatment of the whole of this science, and published my work in separate parts in the *"Gelehrten Schriften der Universitaet Kasan"* for the years 1836, 1837, 1838, under the title "New Elements of Geometry, with a complete Theory of Parallels." The extent of this work perhaps hindered my countrymen from following such a subject, which since Legendre had lost its interest. Yet I am of the opinion that the Theory of Parallels should not lose its claim to the attention of geometers, and therefore I aim to give here the substance of my investigations, remarking beforehand that contrary to the opinion of Legendre, all other imperfections—for example, the definition of a straight line—show themselves foreign here and without any real influence on the Theory of Parallels.

In order not to fatigue my reader with the multitude of those theorems whose proofs present no difficulties, I prefix here only those of which a knowledge is necessary for what follows.

1. A straight line fits upon itself in all its positions. By this I mean that during the revolution of the surface containing it the straight line does not change its place if it goes through two unmoving points in the surface: (*i. e.*, if we turn the surface containing it about two points of the line, the line does not move.)

2. Two straight lines can not intersect in two points.

3. A straight line sufficiently produced both ways must go out beyond all bounds, and in such way cuts a bounded plain into two parts.

4. Two straight lines perpendicular to a third never intersect, how far soever they be produced.

5. A straight line always cuts another in going from one side of it over to the other side: (*i. e.*, one straight line must cut another if it has points on both sides of it.)

6. Vertical angles, where the sides of one are productions of the sides of the other, are equal. This holds of plane recti-

lineal angles among themselves, as also of plane surface angles: (*i. e.*, dihedral angles.)

7. Two straight lines can not intersect, if a third cuts them at the same angle.

8. In a rectilineal triangle equal sides lie opposite equal angles, and inversely.

9. In a rectilineal triangle, a greater side lies opposite a greater angle. In a right-angled triangle the hypothenuse is greater than either of the other sides, and the two angles adjacent to it are acute.

10. Rectilineal triangles are congruent if they have a side and two angles equal, or two sides and the included angle equal, or two sides and the angle opposite the greater equal, or three sides equal.

11. A straight line which stands at right angles upon two other straight lines not in one plane with it is perpendicular to all straight lines drawn through the common intersection point in the plane of those two.

12. The intersection of a sphere with a plane is a circle.

13. A straight line at right angles to the intersection of two perpendicular planes, and in one, is perpendicular to the other.

14. In a spherical triangle equal sides lie opposite equal angles, and inversely.

15. Spherical triangles are congruent (or symmetrical) if they have two sides and the included angle equal, or a side and the adjacent angles equal.

From here follow the other theorems with their explanations and proofs.

16. All straight lines which in a plane go out from a point can with reference to a given straight line in the same plane, be divided into two classes—into *cutting* and *not-cutting*.

The *boundary lines* of the one and the other class of those lines will be called *parallel to the given line*.

From the point *A* (Fig. 1) let fall upon the line *BC* the perpendicular *AD*, to which again draw the perpendicular *AE*.

In the right angle *EAD* either will all straight lines which go out from the point *A* meet the line *DC*, as for example *AF*, *or* some of them, like the perpendicular *AE*, will not meet the line *DC*. In the uncertainty whether the perpendicular *AE* is the only line which does not meet *DC*, we will assume it may be possible that there are still other lines, for example *AG*, which do not cut *DC*, how far soever they may be prolonged. In passing over from the cutting lines, as *AF*, to the not-cutting

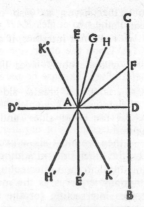

Figure 1

lines, as *AG*, we must come upon a line *AH*, parallel to *DC*, a boundary line, upon one side of which all lines *AG* are such as do not meet the line *DC*, while upon the other side every straight line *AF* cuts the line *DC*.

The angle *HAD* between the parallel *HA* and the perpendicular *AD* is called the parallel angle (angle of parallelism), which we will here designate *II* (*p*) for *AD = p*.

If *II* (*p*) is a right angle, so will the prolongation *AE'* of the perpendicular *AE* likewise be parallel to the prolongation *DB* of the line *DC*, in addition to which we remark that in regard to the four right angles, which are made at the point *A* by the perpendiculars *AE* and *AD*, and their prolongations *AE'* and *AD'*, every straight line which goes out from the point *A*, either itself or at least its prolongation, lies in one of the two right angles, which are turned toward *BC*, so that except the parallel *EE'* all others, if they are sufficiently produced both ways, must intersect the line *BC*.

If *II* (*p*) < ½ π, then upon the other side of *AD*, making the same angle *DAK = II* (*p*) will lie also a line *AK*, parallel to the prolongation *DB* of the line *DC*, so that under this assumption we must also make a distinction of *sides in parallelism*.

All remaining lines or their prolongations within the two right angles turned toward *BC* pertain to those that intersect, if they lie within the angle *HAK = 2 II* (*p*) between the parallels; they pertain on the other hand to the non-intersecting

AG, if they lie upon the other sides of the parallels *AH* and *AK,* in the opening of the two angles $EAH = \frac{1}{2}\pi - II\,(p)$, $E'AK = \frac{1}{2}\pi - II\,(p)$, between the parallels and *EE'* the perpendicular to *AD.* Upon the other side of the perpendicular *EE'* will in like manner the prolongations *AH'* and *AK'* of the parallels *AH* and *AK* likewise be parallel to *BC;* the remaining lines pertain, if in the angle *K'AH',* to the intersecting, but if in the angles *K'AE, H'AE'* to the non-intersecting.

In accordance with this, for the assumption $II\,(p) = \frac{1}{2}\pi$, the lines can be only intersecting or parallel; but if we assume that $II\,(p) < \frac{1}{2}\pi$, then we must allow two parallels, one on the one and one on the other side; in addition we must distinguish the remaining lines into non-intersecting and intersecting.

For both assumptions it serves as the mark of parallelism that the line becomes intersecting for the smallest deviation toward the side where lies the parallel, so that if *AH* is parallel to *DC,* every line *AF* cuts *DC,* how small soever the angle *HAF* may be.

17. *A straight line maintains the characteristic of parallelism at all its points.*

Given *AB* (Fig. 2) parallel to *CD,* to which latter *AC* is perpendicular. We will consider two points taken at random on the line *AB* and its production beyond the perpendicular.

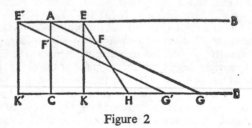

Figure 2

Let the point *E* lie on that side of the perpendicular on which *AB* is looked upon as parallel to *CD.*

Let fall from the point *E* a perpendicular *EK* on *CD* and so draw *EF* that it falls within the angle *BEK.*

Connect the points *A* and *F* by a straight line, whose production then (by Theorem 16) must cut *CD* somewhere in *G.* Thus we get a triangle *ACG,* into which the line *EF* goes; now since this latter, from the construction, can not cut *AC,* and can not cut *AG* or *EK* a second time (Theorem 2), therefore it must meet *CD* somewhere at *H* (Theorem 3).

Now let E' be a point on the production of AB and $E'K'$ perpendicular to the production of the line CD; draw the line $E'F'$ making so small an angle $AE'F'$ that it cuts AC somewhere in F'; making the same angle with AB, draw also from A the line AF, whose production will cut CD in G (Theorem 16).

Thus we get a triangle AGC, into which goes the production of the line $E'F'$; since now this line can not cut AC a second time, and also can not cut AG, since the angle $BAG = BE'G'$ (Theorem 7), therefore must it meet CD somewhere in G'.

Therefore from whatever points E and E' the lines EF and $E'F'$ go out, and however little they may diverge from the line AB, yet will they always cut CD, to which AB is parallel.

18. *Two lines are always mutually parallel.*

Let AC be a perpendicular on CD, to which AB is parallel; if we draw from C the line CE making any acute angle ECD with CD, and let fall from A the perpendicular AF upon CE, we obtain a right-angled triangle ACF, in which AC, being the hypothenuse, is greater than the side AF (Theorem 9).

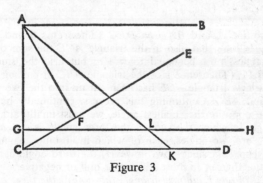

Figure 3

Make $AG = AF$, and slide the figure $EFAB$ until AF coincides with AG, when AB and FE will take the position AK and GH, such that the angle $BAK = FAC$, consequently AK must cut the line DC somewhere in K (Theorem 16), thus forming a triangle AKC, on one side of which the perpendicular GH intersects the line AK in L (Theorem 3), and thus determines the distance AL of the intersection point of the lines AB and CE on the line AB from the point A.

Hence it follows that CE will always intersect AB, how small

soever may be the angle *ECD*, consequently *CD* is parallel to
AB (Theorem 16).

19. *In a rectilineal triangle the sum of the three angles can
not be greater than two right angles.*

Suppose in the triangle *ABC* (Fig. 4) the sum of the three
angles is equal to $\pi + a$; then choose in case of the inequality
of the sides the smallest *BC*, halve it in *D*, draw from *A*
through *D* the line *AD* and make the prolongation of it, *DE*,
equal to *AD*, then join the point *E* to the point *C* by the straight
line *EC*. In the congruent triangles *ADB* and *CDE*, the angle

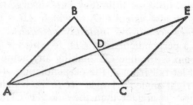

Figure 4

ABD = *DCE*, and *BAD* = *DEC* (Theorems 6 and 10);
whence follows that also in the triangle *ACE* the sum of the
three angles must be equal to $\pi + a$; but also the smallest
angle *BAC* (Theorem 9) of the triangle *ABC* in passing over
into the new triangle *ACE* has been cut up into the two parts
EAC and *AEC*. Continuing this process, continually halving
the side opposite the smallest angle, we must finally attain to
a triangle in which the sum of the three angles is $\pi + a$, but
wherein are two angles, each of which in absolute magnitude
is less than $\frac{1}{2} a$; since now, however, the third angle can not
be greater than π, so must *a* be either null or negative.

20. *If in any rectilineal triangle the sum of the three angles
is equal to two right angles, so is this also the case for every
other triangle.*

If in the rectilineal triangle *ABC* (Fig. 5) the sum of
the three angles $= \pi$, then must at least two of its angles, *A* and
C, be acute. Let fall from the vertex of the third angle *B* upon
the opposite side *AC* the perpendicular *p*. This will cut the
triangle into two right-angled triangles, in each of which the
sum of the three angles must also be π, since it can not in
either be greater than π, and in their combination not less
than π.

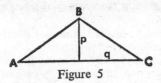

Figure 5

So we obtain a right-angled triangle with the perpendicular sides p and q, and from this quadrilateral whose opposite sides are equal and whose adjacent sides p and q are at right angles (Fig. 6).

By repetition of this quadrilateral we can make another with sides np and mq. and finally a quadrilateral $ABCD$ with sides at right angles to each other, such that $AB = np$, $AD = mq$.

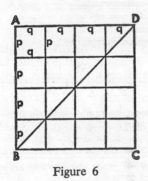

Figure 6

$DC = np$, $BC = mq$, where m and n are any whole numbers. Such a quadrilateral is divided by the diagonal DB into two congruent right-angled triangles, BAD and BCD, in each of which the sum of the three angles $= \pi$.

The numbers n and m can be taken sufficiently great for the right-angled triangle ABC (Fig. 7) whose perpendicular sides $AB = np$, $BC = mq$, to enclose within itself another given (right-angled) triangle BDE as soon as the right-angles fit each other.

Drawing the line DC, we obtain right-angled triangles of which every successive two have a side in common.

The triangle ABC is formed by the union of the two triangles ACD and DCB, in neither of which can the sum of the angles be greater than π; consequently it must be equal to π, in order that the sum in the compound triangle may be equal to π.

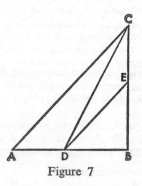

Figure 7

In the same way the triangle BDC consists of the two triangles DEC and DBE, consequently must in DBE the sum of the three angles be equal to π, and in general this must be true for every triangle, since each can be cut into two right-angled triangles.

From this it follows that only two hypotheses are allowable: Either is the sum of the three angles in all rectilineal triangles equal to π, or this sum is in all less than π.

21. *From a given point we can always draw a straight line that shall make with a given straight line an angle as small as we choose.*

Let fall from the given point A (Fig. 8) upon the given line BC the perpendicular AB; take upon BC at random the point D; draw the line AD; make $DE=AD$, and draw AE.

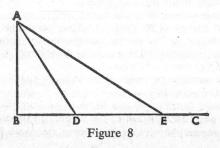

Figure 8

In the right-angled triangle ABD let the angle $ADB = a$; then must in the isosceles triangle ADE the angle AED be either ½ a or less (Theorems 8 and 20). Continuing thus we finally attain to such an angle, AEB, as is less than any given angle.

22. *If two perpendiculars to the same straight line are parallel to each other, then the sum of the three angles in a rectilineal triangle is equal to two right angles.*

Let the lines AB and CD (Fig. 9) be parallel to each other and perpendicular to AC.

Draw from A the lines AE and AF to the points E and F, which are taken on the line CD at any distance $FC > EC$ from the point C.

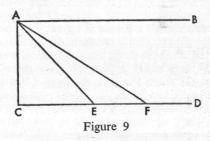

Figure 9

Suppose in the right-angled triangle ACE the sum of the three angles is equal to $\pi - \alpha$, in the triangle AEF equal to $\pi - \beta$, then must it in the triangle ACF equal $\pi - \alpha - \beta$, where α and β can not be negative.

Further, let the angle $BAF = a$, $AFC = b$, so is $\alpha + \beta = a - b$; now by revolving the line AF away from the perpendicular AC we can make the angle a between AF and the parallel AB as small as we choose; so also can we lessen the angle b, consequently the two angles α and β can have no other magnitude than $\alpha = 0$ and $\beta = 0$.

It follows that in all rectilineal triangles the sum of the three angles is either π and at the same time also the parallel angle $II(p) = \frac{1}{2}\pi$ for every line p, or for all triangles this sum is $< \pi$ and at the same time also $II(p) < \frac{1}{2}\pi$.

The first assumption serves as *foundation for the ordinary geometry and plane trigonometry.*

The second assumption can likewise be admitted without leading to any contradiction in the results, and founds a new geometric science, to which I have given the name *Imaginary*

Geometry, and which I intend here to expound as far as the development of the equations between the sides and angles of the rectilineal and spherical triangle.

PART II

If ever there was a scandal in the intellectual world, Euclid's fifth postulate constituted such a scandal. The very existence of this postulate seemed offensive to a great many people; even those who did not completely condemn the postulate nevertheless considered it a blemish on Euclid's otherwise elegant edifice. Indeed, there exists a book by an eighteenth-century Italian Jesuit, Girolamo Saccheri, the English title of which is *Euclid Freed of Every Fleck.* This book, published in 1733, is not a mere curiosity written by a crank; it is a very serious work which plays an important role in the controversy surrounding the postulate. Now, however, this controversy no longer exists. The fifth postulate has become quite acceptable, and Euclid, instead of being chastized for having formulated it, is praised for having recognized the need for it. Indeed, mathematicians hold that the fifth postulate is characteristic of Euclid's geometry. It is now recognized that Saccheri and all the other mathematicians who felt uncomfortable about the fifth postulate were really searching for a form of generalized non-Euclidean geometry.

Let us take a close look at Euclid's famous—or infamous— postulate:

Let it be postulated that, if a straight line falling on two straight lines make the interior angles on the same side less than two right angles, the two straight lines, if produced indefinitely, meet on that side on which are the angles less than the two right angles (p. 17).

Whereas the first four postulates are brief and easily understood, Euclid's fifth postulate is as lengthy as a proposition and as complicated. The complication and length constitute the major objections to the postulate. Its statement begins with something that is given—the interior angles on the same side are less than two right angles—and then proceeds to a conclusion—the two lines will meet on the side where the angles are less than two right angles. (See Figure 2–1.) Objectors

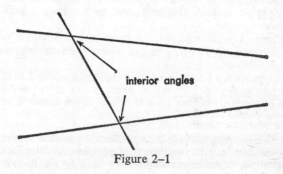

interior angles

Figure 2–1

feel that it is not at all self-evident that the conclusion follows from the premises. Hence, whereas we can easily accept the validity of the first four postulates, there is no reason why we should consider the fifth postulate valid. Objectors feel that its truth should be *proved*, just as though it were a proposition.

The matter is worse if the postulate is called an axiom (as it frequently is in early Latin translations of Euclid), for, as we noted in Chapter I, axioms are statements of self-evident truths; but the fifth postulate is not self-evident, and so the name "axiom" should not be applied to it. Thus Saccheri, after stating the "axiom," writes as follows:

> No one doubts the truth of this proposition; but . . .
> they accuse Euclid . . . because he has used for it the
> name axiom, as if obviously from the right understand·
> ing of its terms alone came conviction. Whence not ı
> few (withal retaining Euclid's definition of parallels)
> have attempted its demonstration from those proposi·
> tions of Euclid's First Book alone which precede the
> twenty-ninth, wherein begins the use of the controverted
> proposition.*

* Girolamo Saccheri's *Euclides Vindicatus,* ed. and trans. by George Bruce Halsted. Chicago, 1920: Open Court Publishing Co., pp. 5-7.

Here the objections and the proposed remedy are quite clearly stated. Saccheri states that the fifth postulate or axiom is true but that it is wrong to call it by the name "axiom" (that is, to claim self-evidence for it); hence the postulate must be proved to be true. To accomplish this proof, we have available to us all the propositions in Book I which precede Proposition 29, the first one in which the postulate is used. Saccheri attempts to accomplish this task, and to a certain extent he succeeds.

Nicholas Lobachevski, writing more than a hundred years after Saccheri (in 1840), employs almost the same language:

> In geometry I find certain imperfections which I hold to be the reason why this science . . . can as yet make no advance from that state in which it has come to us from Euclid.

> As belonging to these imperfections, I consider . . . the momentous gap in the theory of parallels, to fill which all efforts of mathematicians have been so far in vain (pp. 68-9).

The man who wrote these words was born at Makariev, Russia, in the year 1793. Lobachevski went to the gymnasium in the city of Kazan, and then entered the university there. All of his active intellectual life was spent at the University of Kazan; he was first a student, then a professor, and finally the rector of the University. Lobachevski carried a tremendous load of teaching and administrative responsibilities (the latter being especially heavy in bureaucratic Russia), so that we wonder how he ever found time for his own research. His first writings on the subject of parallels go back to 1826, but the *Theory of Parallels* was not published until 1840. Incidentally, almost the same results as those obtained by Lobachevski were found by John Bolyai, a Hungarian mathematician. His work on parallelism was published in 1831, but it is thought that Bolyai's first ideas on the subject go back to 1823. Neither Lobachevski's nor Bolyai's works attracted much attention when they were first published; not until 1867, when Bernhard Riemann's essay on the basic hypotheses that support geometry was posthumously published, did mathematicians generally take an interest in non-Euclidean geometries. Lobachevski died in the year 1856.

Let us begin with a look at Euclid's theory of parallels. The

first proposition involving parallel lines—Proposition 27—
does not make use of Postulate 5. The proposition states that,
if a line intersects two other lines in such a way that the alternate angles are equal, then the two lines are parallel. (See
Figure 2–2. In that figure, alternate angles are designated by
the same letters.)

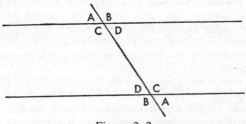

Figure 2–2

To prove this proposition, Euclid employs the method of
reduction to the absurd: if two lines are not parallel, then of
course they must meet. Assume, therefore, that they do meet
(it does not matter on which side) at the point *G* (see Figure
2–3). A triangle, *EFG*, is then formed. One of the pairs of
alternate angles is *AEF* and *EFD*; it is given that they are
equal. However, it is impossible that they be equal, since in

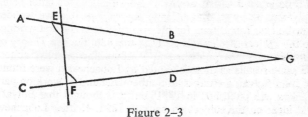

Figure 2–3

the triangle *EFG* the angle *AEF* is an exterior angle, whereas
angle *EFG* is an interior angle. According to Proposition 16
of Book I, an exterior angle of a triangle is always greater than
either of the two opposite interior angles. Hence, the same
angle (*AEF*) must be both equal to, and greater than, *EFG*—
a conclusion which is absurd. Thus the original assumption

—that the two lines meet to form a triangle—must be false, and so the given two lines must be non-meeting or parallel.

Let us skip Proposition 28, which is just another version of Proposition 27, and hurry on to Proposition 29, in which the parallel postulate is used for the first time. Proposition 29 is the converse of Proposition 27. What is given in the first proposition becomes what is proved in the second proposition, and what is proved in the first proposition becomes what is given in the second one. Thus it is given in Proposition 27 that the alternate angles are equal, and it is proved that the two lines in question are parallel. On the other hand, in Proposition 29 it is given that the two lines are parallel, and it is proved that the alternate angles are equal.

The proof is by reduction to the absurd, just as is the proof of Proposition 27. Let us assume, Euclid says, that the alternate angles are not equal. Then one of them must be greater than the other one (it does not matter which one it is). Let the greater angle be AGH. (See Figure 2–4.) Add the angle BGH to both the angle AGH and the angle GHD. Then angle AGH + angle BGH is greater than angle GHD + angle BGH.

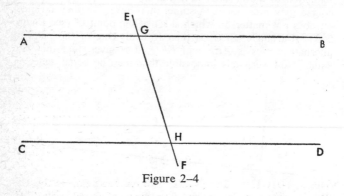

Figure 2–4

But angle AGH + angle BGH is equal to two right angles. Hence the two angles GHD + BGH are less than two right angles. And so, by Postulate 5 the lines AB and CD, if extended, must meet toward BD. However, this is absurd, since the lines are given to be parallel. And so the assumption that the alternate angles are not equal must be false.

Since Propositions 27 and 29 are converses, we should expect their proofs to be similar. And so they are: both proceed by reduction to the absurd. The element which produces the absurdity, however, is different: in the case of Proposition 27, it is Proposition 16 that is the keystone to the proof, whereas in the case of Proposition 29 it is Postulate 5 that provides the absurdity.

In order to overcome the "flaws" of Euclid's geometry, Lobachevski substitutes a new postulate for Euclid's fifth one. Unfortunately, he is not very explicit in his manner of doing it. To understand Lobachevski's procedure, we must first realize that there are several different but equivalent ways in which Euclid's fifth postulate can be stated. One of the equivalent statements of Postulate 5 is this: "In a plane, through a given point, there is one and just one parallel line to a given line."

To see how this statement is equivalent to Euclid's fifth postulate, let us restate the proof of Proposition 29, using the postulate of the uniqueness of the parallel line. It is to be proved that if a line intersects two parallel lines, then the alternate angles are equal. Let *AB* and *CD* be the parallel lines, and let *EF* intersect them. (See Figure 2–5.) It is to be proved

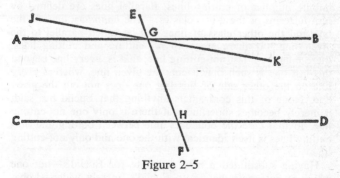

Figure 2–5

that angle *AGH* = angle *GHD*. We use reduction to the absurd. If the two angles are not equal, then construct angle *JGH* so that it is equal to angle *GHD*. Extend line *JG* so that the line *JK* is formed. Now, because of the equality of angle *JGH* and angle *GHD*, the two lines *JK* and *CD* are parallel, according to Proposition 27. But line *AB* is also parallel to line *CD*. Thus we have arrived at an absurdity—for two lines, *JK* and *AB*, are both parallel to the same line, *CD*. According to the postulate of the "uniqueness of parallel lines," this is impossible.

The postulate Lobachevski substitutes for Euclid's may be expressed in this form: "In a plane, through a given point, there exists an infinite number of lines that do not cut a given line." Thus Lobachevski postulates an infinite number of parallel lines to a given line, in Euclid's sense of the word "parallel." Lobachevski himself, however, reserves the term "parallel" for two special not-cutting lines.

In section 16 (p. 70) Lobachevski defines parallelism. However, he first makes a distinction:

> All straight lines which in a plane go out from a point can, with reference to a given straight line in the same plane, be divided into two classes—into *cutting* and *not-cutting*.

Of course, Euclid would agree with this definition, but he would add that the class of not-cutting lines has just one member, that not-cutting line being the one which Euclid calls the parallel. Lobachevski, as we have said, postulates that there is an infinite number of not-cutting lines, just as there is an infinite number of cutting lines. Parallel lines are defined by him in terms of these two classes: "The *boundary* lines of the one and the other class of lines will be called parallel to the given line." If there are both not-cutting and cutting lines, there must be a last not-cutting line; that is, every line beyond this last one is such that it cuts the given line, whereas every line on the other side of this last one does not cut the given line. None of this contradicts anything that Euclid has said; it merely becomes superfluous if there is only one not-cutting line. In that case the boundary line between cutting and not-cutting lines is itself identical with the one and only not-cutting line.

Having substituted a new postulate for Euclid's—but one which is not contradictory to Euclid's, merely wider—Lobachevski proceeds to prove propositions concerning the same matters as Euclid. Naturally, his results are not the same as Euclid's; however, they are not contradictory to Euclid's. Just as Euclid's postulate is a special case of Lobachevski's postulate (that is, the special case when the not-cutting lines number only one), so Euclid's propositions are special cases of Lobachevski's. For example, Euclid finds that the sum of the angles in a triangle is equal to two right angles; Lobachevski finds this sum to be either two right angles or less than two right angles. Since Lobachevski's postulate is more complicated than Euclid's, it should not be surprising that the proofs of his propositions are also more complex.

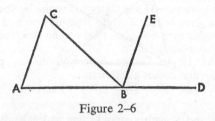

Figure 2–6

Euclid proves that the angles of a triangle are equal to two right angles in the following manner: If the triangle is ABC, Euclid first extends the line AB to D. (See Figure 2–6.) Then, through B, he draws BE parallel to AC. From Proposition 29 it follows that angle CBE is equal to angle ACB, and that EBD is equal to angle CAB. Hence the three angles ABC, CBE, and EBD are equal to the three interior angles of the triangle. But the former angles, being the angles on a straight line, are equal to two right angles; consequently the interior angles of a triangle must also be equal to two right angles. In Lobachevski's geometry this proof fails, of course, because of the unavailability of Proposition 29.

What does Lobachevski substitute for Proposition 32? In any triangle, Lobachevski tells us, the sum of the angles is *at most* equal to two right angles. Thus there may be triangles in which the sum of the interior angles is less than two right angles, or there may be triangles in which the sum is exactly equal to two right angles. But there are no triangles in which the sum of the angles is greater than two right angles. The proof is found in Section 19. The method used is that of reduction to the absurd. (Note that the methods of Euclid and Lobachevski are the same, even though some of their crucial assumptions are different.) Lobachevski assumes that the sum of the angles in a triangle is greater than two right angles. (For "two right angles" Lobachevski uses the expression π; this is merely a different way of measuring angles. A third way of expressing the assumption is to say that the sum of the angles of the triangles is greater than 180°. We shall adhere to Euclid's way of measuring angles—in terms of right angles.)

To arrive at an absurdity, Lobachevski bisects one of the sides of the triangle, BC, at a point D. (See Figure 2–7.) He

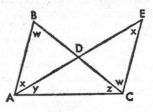

Figure 2–7

connects A and D with a straight line and extends AD to E
so that AD equals DE. Then it is easy to prove that triangles
ABD and DCE are congruent (this does not involve any reference to parallelism). Now consider the newly formed triangle AEC. The sum of its angles—EAC, ACE, and CEA—
is equal to the sum of the angles of the original triangle. For
the sake of convenience, we have given letters to the various
angles. Equal angles have been designated by the same letter.
In the original triangle the sum of the interior angles, starting at
point B and running counterclockwise, is $w + x + y + z$. In the
new triangle, starting at E and going counterclockwise, the sum
is $x + y + z + w$. It follows that the sum of the angles in the new
triangle AEC is also greater than two right angles. If the sum of
the angles in the first triangle ABC is, for example, 2 right
angles $+ a$, then it is also 2 right angles $+ a$ in the new triangle AEC. At the same time, it is clear that the angle EAC
(or y) is smaller than the angle BAC (or $x + y$).By proceeding
in the same manner with triangle AEC (that is, by dividing
the side EC in half), we arrive at yet another triangle with the
sum of its angles equal to 2 right angles $+ a$; this triangle will
have an angle at A even smaller than EAC or y. By proceeding in this manner, it is possible to finally arrive at a triangle
which has an angle at A smaller than the quantity $\frac{1}{2} a$. We
can proceed in the same manner with the other small angle
(such as the one E) and, while keeping the sum of the angles
in the triangle constant, have the other small angle also equal
to less than $\frac{1}{2} a$. Since the sum of the three angles of the final
triangle must be equal to 2 right angles $+ a$, while the two
small angles together are less than a (each separately being
less than $\frac{1}{2} a$), the remaining third angle will have to be greater
than two right angles. This is absurd, for if this third angle
ever becomes so large as to be equal to two right angles, there
will be no angle—and no triangle—left. We conclude, then,

that the original assumption is wrong and that the sum of the angles in a triangle cannot be greater than two right angles.

In Section 20, Lobachevski points out that he does not know what the sum of the angles in a triangle amounts to, except that the sum cannot be greater than two right angles. He then adds this: if there is just one triangle concerning which it is known that the sum of its angles is exactly equal to two right angles, then *all* triangles must have the sum of their angles equal to two right angles. Let the triangle concerning which it is known that the sum of its angles is equal to two right angles be *ABC*. (See Figure 2–8.) Let *MNO* be any other right-angled triangle. (We are changing Lobachevki's terminology, since

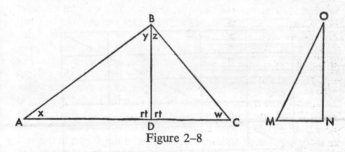

Figure 2–8

he uses the same letters in several triangles, thereby creating unnecessary confusion.) From the vertex opposite the largest side of *ABC* drop the perpendicular *BD*. This divides the triangle *ABC* into two right-angled triangles, *ABD* and *BDC*. From the previous proposition, the sum of the angles in either of the right-angled triangles cannot be greater than two right angles. Thus we have

    (1) $x + y$ + right angle is equal to or less than 2 right angles.

and

    (2) $z + w$ + right angle is equal to or less than 2 right angles.

If we now add these two lines together, we get

    (3) $x + y + z + w$ + 2 right angles is equal to or less than 4 right angles.

But since it is given that $x + y + z + w$ is equal to 2 right angles, it is clear that in statement (3) the relation of being "equal" rather than that of being "less than" holds. In other words, statement (3) should be written as follows:

    (3) $x + y + z + w$ + 2 right angles = 4 right angles.

Therefore, in lines (1) and (2), we must also have the relation of equality; for if in either of them the relation of being "less than" obtained, we could not by adding obtain line (3) with the equal sign. Thus triangle *BDC* has the sum of its angles equal to two right angles, as does triangle *ADB*. By placing two triangles such as *BDC* together, we can form a rectangle (Lobachevski uses the term "quadrilateral") with sides *BC* = *p*, and *DC* = *q*. From many rectangles equal to this one, we can form one with sides *np* and *nq*, where *n* is a whole number. (Lobachevski says to make the rectangle with sides *np* and *mq*, where *n* and *m* are different whole numbers; however, he then is not entitled to take the following step,

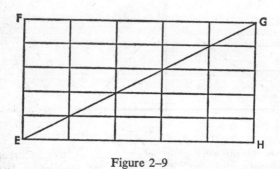

Figure 2–9

although he seems unaware of it.) Let this large rectangle be called *EFGH*. (See Figure 2–9.) The diagonal *EG* divides this rectangle into two congruent triangles, *EFG* and *EGH*. The sum of the angles in each of these two big triangles is equal to

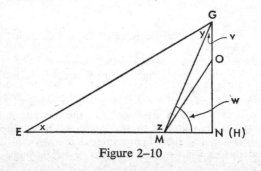

Figure 2–10

two right angles, because the angles of the big triangles are equal to the angles of the original triangle *BDC* with the sides *p* and *q*.

Now choose the number *n* large enough so that *EH* is greater than *MN* and *GH* is greater than *NO*. Draw the triangle *EGH* so that it wholly encloses the triangle *MNO*. (See Figure 2–10.) Thus points *H* and *N* coincide. Join *M* and *G*. We shall now show that, since the big triangle, *EGH*, has angles equal to two right angles, the two triangles which together make it up—*EGM* and *MGN*—must each have angles equal to two right angles. Similarly, since the sum of the angles in *MGN* is equal to two right angles, the angles in triangle *MNO* must amount to the same sum.

We already know that the angles of any triangle must be either less than two right angles or exactly equal to two right angles. But if the angles $x + y + z$ are less than two right angles or if the angles $w + v$ are less than a right angle (it is given that the angle at *N* is right), an impossibility results. For if we add all these angles up, we find that $x + y + v + z + w$ are less than three right angles. Now it is known from Euclid's Proposition 13 that $z + w$ is equal to two right angles. That would leave $x + y + v$ as equal to less than one right angle. But this cannot be, since these three angles, together with the right angle at *N*, are supposed to make two right angles. Thus our assumption has led to an absurdity, and we see that all the triangles enclosed in *EGH* must have their angles equal to two right angles.

Since *MNO* was any right triangle, we can conclude that if any right triangle has the sum of its interior angles equal to two right angles, then all right triangles have their angular sum equal to two right angles. If all right triangles have their angular sum equal to two right angles, then all triangles have the same angular sum, for any triangle can be divided into two right triangles.

From this Lobachevski concludes that "only two hypotheses are allowable: Either is the sum of the three angles in all rectilineal triangles equal to π [two right angles], or this sum is in all less than π." In other words, either all geometry is Euclidean, or all geometry is Lobachevskian. There cannot be a mixture of the two geometries. "It follows," Lobachevski writes,

> that in all rectilineal triangles the sum of the three angles is either π [two right angles] . . . , or for all triangles this sum is less than π. . . .

The first assumption serves as the *foundation for the ordinary geometry and plane trigonometry*.

The second assumption can likewise be admitted without leading to any contradiction in the results, and founds a new geometric science, to which I have given the name *Imaginary Geometry*, and which I intend here to expound . . . (pp. 77-8).

We have merely Lobachevski's word for the fact that his geometry can be developed without contradition; he has not proved this. At the same time, it is only fair to note that Euclid nowhere proves that *his* geometry will never lead to contradictions. Euclid's "proof" consists in the actual development of hundreds of propositions without contradictions; Lobachevski's "proof" is of the same sort. The pages following Section 22 are a verification of his boast that a non-contradictory geometry can be developed from his postulate.

Let us re-examine Section 19. This is the section in which Lobachevski proves that the sum of the angles of any triangle cannot be greater than two right angles. Compare the proof of this proposition with the proof of Euclid's sixteenth proposition, which shows that in a triangle the exterior angle is always greater than either of the two opposite interior angles. You will notice that the two proofs are almost the same. Both depend on the same construction: the side *BC* of the triangle *ABC* is bisected; *A* is joined to *D* and then extended so that *AD = DE*. Then *E* is joined to *C*. (See Figure 2–11.) The two triangles *ABD* and *DEC* are easily shown to be congruent. Euclid and Lobachevski use this congruency for different purposes.

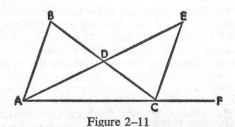

Figure 2–11

Euclid concludes that since angle ABD is equal to angle DCE, therefore the exterior angle DCF must be greater than the interior angle ABD.

Now let us make a slight change in the diagram for Proposition 16 (of Euclid) or Section 19 (of Lobachevski). Instead of drawing the figure with straight lines, as we have so far done, let us draw the figure on the surface of a sphere. Here the place of straight lines is taken by great circles—circles that have the same center as the sphere itself. Examples of great circles on the Earth are the equator and all of the meridians. A great circle is like a straight line, in that it constitutes the shortest distance between two points on a sphere, just as a straight line is the shortest distance between two points on a plane.

Look at Figure 2–12. We have drawn a triangle ABC consisting of parts of great circles. The base AC is part of the "equator" of the sphere; the two sides AB and BC are each "meridians"; thus the point B is the "north pole" of the sphere. In order to give some definiteness to the figure, we have made the angle at B equal to 120°. (We shall here use the degree measurement of angles for simplicity's sake.) Notice that no matter what the angle at B is made to be, the two angles at A and at C are right angles. Thus no matter what the angle at B is, the sum of the angles of the triangle ABC is certainly going to be greater than two right angles or 180°. In our example, it is three and a third right angles, or 300°. Thus Lobachevski's Section 19 does not apply to spherical triangles. If we now extend the base AC, say to F, it is also apparent at once that Euclid's Proposition 16 does not hold true for spherical triangles. For the exterior angle BCF is a right angle; it is therefore equal to one of the opposite interior angles—the one at A—and is smaller than the other opposite interior angle—the one at B.

If we complete the figure so that, on the sphere, we duplicate the constructions of Proposition 16 or Section 19, we can see why their statements cannot be proved here. Bisect BC at D. Join A and D (with a great circle), and extend the great circle segment to E so that AD = DE. Join E and C with the segment of a great circle. (It takes a little practice to see the diagram properly. The point E is on the far side of the sphere; to understand why EC is drawn the way it is, remember that the circle of which EC is a part has its center at the center of the sphere. Below the main diagram we have placed another one, in which the spherical triangle has been "flattened out" and placed in the plane. This may help in visualizing the spherical

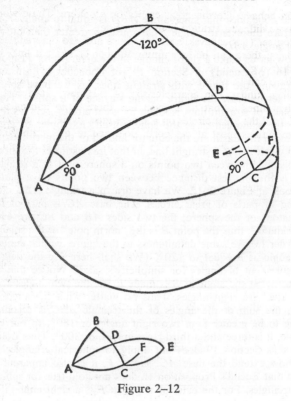

Figure 2–12

diagram. Another aid would be to draw the diagram on a truly spherical surface such as a ball.)

Looking at Figure 2–12, it is obvious why the proof of Proposition 16 or Section 19 fails. The line *EC* does not fall within the angle *BCF* but outside of it. Thus Euclid could not here conclude that angle *DCF* is greater than angle *DCE*. (In fact we know that *DCF* is 90° and that *DCE*, being equal to the angle at *B*, is 120°.) And Lobachevski cannot conclude that there is a limit to how large the angle *ACE* can become; in fact, this angle in our diagram is greater than 180°, and there is still a triangle *AEC*. (Angle *ACE* is 210° in our example.)

Now imagine that there are *straight* lines—not great circles—

which behave like the great circles on a sphere. These would be quite different straight lines from Euclid's or Lobachevski's, of course. (Lobachevski's straight lines are also different from Euclid's; there can be an infinite number of straight lines not meeting a given line, if the lines are Lobachevski's sort, whereas there can be only one such non-meeting line if the lines are Euclid's kind.) The characteristic of this new, third sort of straight lines is that to a given line there is *no* non-meeting line. (All the great circles on a sphere meet twice; for example, all meridians meet at the north pole and at the south pole.) It turns out to be possible to have a geometrical system in which the straight lines in a plane are of this "quasi-spherical" sort. This new geometry is called "Riemannian" after the German mathematician Bernhard Riemann (1826-1866), who first studied it. It is, of course, different from both Euclid's geometry and Lobachevski's. For example, the sum of the angles in a Riemannian triangle is found to be greater than two right angles.

Just as the sphere provides a way of visualizing a plane geometry in which there are no parallel lines, there is another surface which enables us to visualize Lobachevski's geometry, in which there is an infinite number of parallel lines. This surface is called a "pseudosphere"; it is shown in Figure 2–13. On the pseudosphere those lines which are the shortest dis-

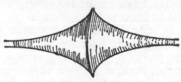

Figure 2–13

tance between two points behave like the straight lines in a Lobachevskian plane. There are many non-meeting lines to a given line, and the sum of the angles of a triangle is less than two right angles.

Those lines on a surface which constitute the shortest distance between two points are called the "geodesics" of that surface. The straight lines in Riemannian geometry have many of the properties of the geodesics of a sphere, whereas the straight lines in Lobachevskian geometry have many of the properties of the geodesics of a pseudosphere. However, it is most important to realize that these non-Euclidean geometries are *plane* geometries; the sphere, the pseudosphere, and their geodesics are useful only in order to visualize these geometries. Riemannian geometry is not spherical geometry, nor is Lobachevskian geometry pseudospherical geometry.

To sum up, there are three possibilities as regards parallel lines, each possibility giving rise to a different geometry: (1) Through a given point there is an infinite number of non-meeting lines to a given line—Lobachevskian geometry. (2) Through a given point there is one and only one non-meeting line to a given point—Euclidean geometry. (3) Through a given point there is no non-meeting line to a given line—Riemannian geometry.

Any system of geometry in which Euclid's Proposition 16 is valid eliminates the possibility of Riemannian geometry. This is the reason why, as we noted earlier, Saccheri had a certain amount of success in proving Euclid's fifth postulate. Saccheri accepted Proposition 16; consequently, he was able to demonstrate absurd conclusions from (the equivalent of) Riemann's postulate.

A system of geometry in which Euclid's Postulate 5 holds eliminates Lobachevski's hypothesis. Thus Euclid rids himself of the possibility of Riemannian geometry by means of Proposition 16, and of Lobachevskian geometry by means of Postulate 5. We should add that Proposition 16 is, in turn, based on Postulate 2 (that is, on the assumption that straight lines are infinite in length); Proposition 16 (or Lobachevski's Section 19) cannot be proved in Riemannian geometry, because in the latter straight lines are finite in length. We can now see that the proofs of Euclid's Propositions 27 and 29 are really quite similar. Both, as we have already noted, are demonstrated by use of reduction to the absurd. But the keystone to the absurdity is Proposition 16 in the first case, and Postulate 5 in the second case. Proposition 16 is the equivalent of another postulate concerning parallelism, namely, "To a given line, through a given point, there exists at least one parallel (non-meeting) line." In both Proposition 27 and Proposition 29, therefore, the absurdity is reached by the use of a postulate concerning parallel lines.

Finally, we must touch on a question that has no doubt already occurred to the reader: Which of these geometries is true? Or are any of them true? The answer is in one way simple, yet also complicated. All three geometries are in themselves equally valid. That is, each can be shown to be a consistent system. Each system contains equivalent propositions; that is, each proposition in one system has a corresponding proposition in the other systems. No one of these geometries is more true than another; this statement is not so hard to accept if we remember that geometry is not concerned with physical lines or points, but rather with ideal, mental entities. These things of the mind can, of course, be shaped by the mind (as long as no contradictions develop). If we wish, therefore, we can choose to geometrize with lines that behave like those of Riemann or those of Lobachevski rather than those of Euclid.

Yet we may also ask, which geometry applies to the things and the space around us? We are used to employing Euclidean geometry; engineers and architects certainly assume that Euclid's geometry and no other is true. Yet this is not conclusive, for it is apparent that for small figures the results which the three geometries yield would be almost indistinguishable. A small triangle on a vast sphere is very much like a plane triangle in Euclidean space. Similarly, it may be that space is Lobachevskian in character; yet it may be so large that for the small areas in human purview, the geometrical results would not be noticeably different from those of Euclidean geometry.

The question of which geometry is most suitable for physical applications is an experimental one. The German mathematician Gauss (1777-1855) performed some measurements on large triangles to determine whether the sum of their angles was 180° or not. However, his results were inconclusive; such differences from 180° as he found were so small that they might have been due to experimental error.

CHAPTER THREE

Descartes—Geometry and Algebra Joined

PART I

The following selection consists of a few pages from the beginning of Descartes' *Geometry*. That title may be slightly misleading; the subject being developed here is actually what we nowadays call analytic geometry. Descartes worked out the method of analytic geometry in response to a need: he felt that geometry as practiced by the ancients was too obscure and difficult to understand. Though Descartes knew Euclid's work, of course, the charge of obscurity is leveled not so much against the *Elements* as against later Greek mathematicians and their works, especially Apollonius' work on conic sections. The conic sections are figures obtained by slicing a cone with a plane surface. As the result of such slicing we may obtain either a circle, an ellipse, a parabola, or a hyperbola. These four figures are the "conic sections." Ever since Descartes' time, these conic sections have been elegantly treated by the method of analytic geometry.

René Descartes
Geometry[*]

BOOK I

PROBLEMS THE CONSTRUCTION OF WHICH REQUIRES ONLY STRAIGHT LINES AND CIRCLES

Any problem in geometry can easily be reduced to such terms that a knowledge of the lengths of certain straight lines is sufficient for its construction. Just as arithmetic consists of only four or five operations, namely, addition, subtraction, multiplication, division and the extraction of roots, which may be considered a kind of division, so in geometry, to find required lines it is merely necessary to add or subtract other lines; or else, taking one line which I shall call unity in order to relate it as closely as possible to numbers, and which can in general be chosen arbitrarily, and having given two other lines, to find a fourth line which shall be to one of the given lines as the other is to unity (which is the same as multiplication); or, again, to find a fourth line which is to one of the given lines as unity is to the other (which is equivalent to division); or, finally, to find one, two, or several mean proportionals between unit and some other line (which is the same as extracting the square root, cube root, etc., of the given line). And I shall not hesitate to introduce these arithmetical terms into geometry, for the sake of greater clearness.

For example, let AB be taken as unity, and let it be required to multiply BD by BC. I have only to join the points A and C, and draw DE parallel to CA; then BE is the product of BD and BC.

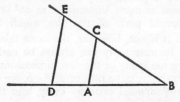

[*] From *The Geometry of Rene Descartes*, trans. by David E. Smith and Marcia L. Latham (Chicago-London: The Open Court Publishing Company, 1925), pp. 2-17. Reprinted by permission.

If it be required to divide *BE* by *BD*, I join *E* and *D*, and draw *AC* parallel to *DE*; then *BC* is the result of the division.

If the square root of *GH* is desired, I add, along the same straight line, *FG* equal to unity; then, bisecting *FH* at *K*, I describe the circle *FIH* about *K* as a center, and draw from *G* a perpendicular and extend it to *I*, and *GI* is the required root. I do not speak here of cube root, or other roots, since I shall speak more conveniently of them later.

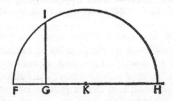

Often it is not necessary thus to draw the lines on paper, but it is sufficient to designate each by a single letter. Thus, to add the lines *BD* and *GH*, I call one a and the other b, and write $a + b$. Then $a - b$ will indicate that b is subtracted from a; ab that a is multiplied by b; $\frac{a}{b}$ that a is divided by b; aa or a^2 that a is multiplied by itself; a^3 that this result is multiplied by a, and so on, indefinitely. Again, if I wish to extract the square root of $a^2 + b^2$, I write $\sqrt{a^2 + b^2}$; if I wish to extract the cube root of $a^3 - b^3 + ab^2$, I write $\sqrt[3]{a^3 - b^3 + ab^2}$, and similarly for other roots. Here it must be observed that by a^2, b^3, and similar expressions, I ordinarily mean only simple lines, which, however, I name squares, cubes, etc., so that I may make use of the terms employed in algebra.

It should also be noted that all parts of a single line should always be expressed by the same number of dimensions, provided unity is not determined by the conditions of the problem. Thus, a^3 contains as many dimensions as ab^2 or b^3, these being the component parts of the line which I have called $\sqrt[3]{a^3 - b^3 + ab^2}$. It is not, however, the same thing when unity is determined, because unity can always be understood, even where there are too many or too few dimensions; thus, if it be required to extract the cube root of $a^2b^2 - b$, we must consider the quantity a^2b^2 divided once by unity, and the quantity b multiplied twice by unity.

Finally, so that we may be sure to remember the names of these lines, a separate list should always be made as often as names are assigned or changed. For example, we may write, $AB = 1$, that is AB is equal to 1; $GH = a$, $BD = b$, and so on.

If, then, we wish to solve any problem, we first suppose the solution already effected, and give names to all the lines that seem needful for its construction, to those that are unknown as well as to those that are known. Then, making no distinction between known and unknown lines, we must unravel the difficulty in any way that shows most naturally the relations between these lines, until we find it possible to express a single quantity in two ways. This will constitute an equation, since the terms of one of these two expressions are together equal to the terms of the other.

We must find as many such equations as there are supposed to be unknown lines; but if, after considering everything involved, so many cannot be found, it is evident that the question is not entirely determined. In such a case we may choose arbitrarily lines of known length for each unknown line to which there corresponds no equation.

If there are several equations, we must use each in order, either considering it alone or comparing it with the others, so as to obtain a value for each of the unknown lines; and so we must combine them until there remains a single unknown line which is equal to some known line, or whose square, cube, fourth power, fifth power, sixth power, etc., is equal to the sum or difference of two or more quantities, one of which is known, while the others consist of mean proportionals between unity and this square, or cube, or fourth power, etc., multiplied by other known lines. I may express this as follows:

$$z = b,$$
$$\text{or } z^2 = -az + b^2,$$
$$\text{or } z^3 = az^2 + b^2z - c^3,$$
$$\text{or } z^4 = az^3 - c^3z + d^4, \textit{ etc.}$$

That is, z, which I take for the unknown quantity, is equal to b; or, the square of z is equal to the square of b diminished by a multiplied by z; or, the cube of z is equal to a multiplied by the square of z, plus the square of b multiplied by z, diminished by the cube of c; and similarly for the others.

Thus, all the unknown quantities can be expressed in terms of a single quantity, whenever the problem can be constructed by means of circles and straight lines, or by conic sections, or even by some other curve of degree not greater than the third or fourth.

But I shall not stop to explain this in more detail, because I should deprive you of the pleasure of mastering it yourself, as well as of the advantage of training your mind by working over it, which is in my opinion the principal benefit to be derived from this science. Because I find nothing here so difficult that it cannot be worked out by any one at all familiar with ordinary geometry and with algebra, who will consider carefully all that is set forth in this treatise.

I shall therefore content myself with the statement that if the student, in solving these equations, does not fail to make use of division wherever possible, he will surely reach the simplest terms to which the problem can be reduced.

And if it can be solved by ordinary geometry, that is, by the use of straight lines and circles traced on a plane surface, when the last equation shall have been entirely solved there will remain at most only the square of an unknown quantity, equal to the product of its root by some known quantity, increased or diminished by some other quantity also known. Then this root or unknown line can easily be found. For example, if I have $z^2 = az + b^2$, I construct a right triangle NLM with one side LM, equal to b, the square root of the known quantity b^2 and the other side, LN, equal to ½ a, that is, to

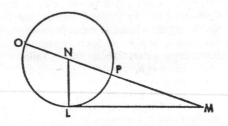

half the other known quantity which was multiplied by z, which I supposed to be the unknown line. Then prolonging MN, the hypotenuse of this triangle, to O, so that NO is equal to NL, the whole line OM is the required line z. This is expressed in the following way:

$$z = \frac{1}{2} a + \sqrt{\frac{1}{4} a^2 + b^2}.$$

But if I have $y^2 = -ay + b^2$, where y is the quantity whose value is desired, I construct the same right triangle NLM, and on the hypotenuse MN lay off NP equal to NL, and the remainder PM is y, the desired root. Thus I have

$$y = -\frac{1}{2}a + \sqrt{\frac{1}{4}a^2 + b^2}.$$

In the same way, if I had

$$x^4 = -ax^2 + b^2,$$

PM would be x^2 and I should have

$$x = \sqrt{-\frac{1}{2}a + \sqrt{\frac{1}{4}a^2 + b^2}},$$

and so for other cases.

Finally, if I have $z^2 = az - b^2$, I make NL equal to ½ a and LM equal to b as before; then, instead of joining the points M and N, I draw MQR parallel to LN, and with N as a center

describe a circle through L cutting MQR in the points Q and R; then z, the line sought, is either MQ or MR, for in this case it can be expressed in two ways, namely:

$$z = \frac{1}{2}a + \sqrt{\frac{1}{4}a^2 - b^2},$$

and

$$z = \frac{1}{2}a - \sqrt{\frac{1}{4}a^2 - b^2}.$$

And if the circle described about N and passing through L neither cuts nor touches the line MQR, the equation has no root, so that we may say that the construction of the problem is impossible.

These same roots can be found by many other methods; I have given these very simple ones to show that it is possible to construct all the problems of ordinary geometry by doing no more than the little covered in the four figures that I have explained. This is one thing which I believe the ancient mathematicians did not observe, for otherwise they would not have put so much labor into writing so many books in which the very sequence of the propositions shows that they did not have a sure method of finding all, but rather gathered together those propositions on which they had happened by accident.

PART II

Histories of culture place the beginning of modern times around the year 1600. Such a date is, of course, arbitrary. There were men and events before 1600 that clearly belong to modern times, such as the discovery of America and the revolutionary work in astronomy by Copernicus. Still, the number of those who gained fame in all fields of knowledge increased impressively from 1600 on. In philosophy we may mention Descartes, Spinoza, Leibniz, and Locke; in mathematics, Fermat, the Bernouilli family, Descartes, and Pascal; in chemistry, Boyle, Priestley, Stahl, and Lavoisier; in physics, Kepler, Galileo, Newton, and Huygens.

Without doubt, one of the most famous of all these men is Descartes. No other man so justly deserves the title of "the first of the moderns." Descartes not only initiated modern thought and modern methods in philosophy and mathematics; he also was remarkably aware of the fact that he was discarding the traditions and errors of earlier times.

René Descartes (1596–1650) was educated at the Jesuit school of La Flèche. All his life, Descartes remained friendly toward the Jesuits, and one of them, Marin Mersenne, also a former pupil at La Flèche, became an intimate friend of his. Descartes traveled through much of Europe, living not only in his native France, but also in Germany, Sweden, Holland, Austria, Bohemia, and Italy. Much of his life after 1628 was spent in Holland, where most of his works were written.

Descartes contributed to almost all major branches of

knowledge. Among his philosophical works are the *Meditations,* the *Discourses,* and the *Principles of Philosophy.* Other famous works of Descartes are the *Rules for the Direction of the Mind,* a treatise dealing with the methodology of speculative thought; the *Passions of the Soul,* a work in psychology; and the *Geometry,* the book with which we are here concerned.

Descartes also wrote about various scientific subjects; he developed a theory of optics, a theory of the motion of the heart, and a theory of the motion of the planets. Since Descartes was a contemporary of Johann Kepler, Galileo Galilei, and William Harvey, he was acquainted with the work of these scientists, and they with his. His philosophical works were circulated among the philosophers of his age and aroused much admiration as well as controversy. Philosophers such as Thomas Hobbes, Antoine Arnauld, and Pierre Gassendi wrote lengthy objections to Descartes' *Meditations,* and he in turn replied to these. (Both objections and replies are included in many editions of the *Meditations.*) In short, the work of Descartes created a stir even in his lifetime, and the *Geometry* did so no less than his other books.

Descartes was a proud and vain man; he delights in showing his readers that he knows something that they do not. Consequently, he very frequently does not explain his methods and procedures in any detail. For instance, he writes, concerning the basic principles of his *Geometry*:

> But I shall not stop to explain this in more detail, because I should deprive you of the pleasure of mastering it yourself, as well as of the advantage of training your mind by working over it, which is in my opinion the principal benefit to be derived from this science (p. 99).

In spite of Descartes' reluctance to say much about his geometry, we can easily state its aim: to join geometry and algebra, to solve geometrical problems by algebraic methods, and, conversely, to solve arithmetical or algebraic problems by geometrical methods.

Descartes was not the first to recognize that geometry and arithmetic are closely related. The very fact that both are branches of mathematics indicates that they have a great deal in common—namely, that their subject matter is quantity. Euclid deals with arithmetic in Books 7–9 of the *Elements,* indicating that he, too, considered geometry and arithmetic to be closely affiliated. When we measure the length of lines and calculate the areas of figures, we are applying arithmetic to geometry. When we use the words "square" and "cube" to indicate certain kinds of numbers—those which are obtained when a number is multiplied by itself either once or twice —we are using an obvious analogy between arithmetic and geometry.

Descartes systematizes the relation between geometry and arithmetic. He develops in the *Geometry* a method for dealing with any geometrical problem—a method now known as *analytic geometry*. This method, properly applied, abolishes the need for geometrical ingenuity; the solution to a geometrical problem no longer depends on the geometer's ability to draw certain lines and see certain connections. It is necessary only to apply Descartes' method, and the solution must appear. (Ingenuity may still have a role in that an ingenious mathematician may arrive at the solution more rapidly and more smoothly than an unskilled one, even if both use the methods of analytic geometry.)

Descartes states the heart of the method as follows:

> If, then, we wish to solve any problem, we first suppose the solution already effected, and give names to all the lines that seem needful for its construction—to those that are unknown as well as to those that are known (p. 99).

We should notice that this is a method for solving *construction* problems. In the typical problem which Descartes has in mind, a certain line (or other figure) is to be constructed. This line is defined in terms of some of its properties; a circle, for example, would be defined as a line all of whose points are equidistant from a given point.

Although Descartes solves construction problems, he does not employ any of Euclid's construction postulates. The reason for this apparent paradox is that Descartes' understanding of the term "construction" is quite different from Euclid's. For Euclid, to construct a figure means to draw it (or to understand how one would draw it), using the postulates of his system. For Descartes, to construct a geometrical figure means to find an algebraic equation for that figure.

Let us illustrate Descartes' method with an example. A few pages beyond the portion of the *Geometry* which we reprint, Descartes writes:

Let AB, AD, ... be any number of straight lines given in position, and let it be required to find a point C, from which straight lines CB, CD, ... can be drawn, making angles CBA, CDA, ... respectively, with the given lines, and such that the product of certain of them is equal to the product of the rest, or at least such that these two products shall have a given ratio, for this condition does not make the problem any more difficult. (See Figure 3–1.)

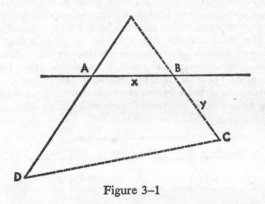

Figure 3–1

He continues as follows:

First, I suppose the thing done, and since so many lines are confusing, I may simplify matters by considering one of the given lines and one of those to be drawn (as, for example, AB and BC) as the principal lines, to which I shall try to refer all the others. Call the segment of the line AB between A and B, x, and call BC, y.

Descartes actually uses more given lines than the two we have drawn, and consequently, more lines are also to be drawn from point C. We have simplified the example and the diagram in order to make it more intelligible. The problem which Descartes poses is that of finding all those points C (he says *the* point C) which are such that the product of BC and CD (where these two lines make given angles with the given lines) is a given quantity. Let the product of BC and CD be, say, 24. In other words, if we let $AB = x$ and $BC = y$, as Descartes proposes, then the problem is to find points C such that $y \cdot DC = 24$. Now all that remains to be done is to express the line DC in terms of x and y; then we shall have an equation of the kind that Descartes is looking for. It is theoretically simple to express DC in terms of x and y, since all the angles of the quadrilateral $ABCD$ are known. In practice, however, the expression would be quite complicated, involving trigonometric functions such as sines and cosines.

Let us investigate another problem of the kind that Descartes wants to solve, but a problem which is less complex than the one above: Given a straight line, and a point not on that line, to construct a line all of whose points are equidistant from the point and the line. First let us indicate that this is the sort of problem that Descartes wishes to solve. Where he has two given lines, AB and AD, we have one given line AB, and a given point F. (See Figure 3–2.) The points C, which we assume have been found, are such that the lines which are drawn from C to F and from C perpendicular to AB are equal.

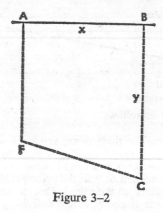

Figure 3–2

Since the line from C to AB is called "the distance," the angle which line BC makes with AB is a right angle. The basic equation then is $\dfrac{BC}{FC} = 1$.

Pause for a moment and consider whether, and how, Euclid would solve this problem. Euclid would be stumped, for it is apparent that the line which we are looking for must be curved and that, at the same time, the line is not a circle. Euclid, therefore, could not draw the wanted line, for the only curved lines which he can draw are circles (with the help of Postulate 3).

However, though Euclid could not draw the entire line, he could find several points of it. For example, one point of the

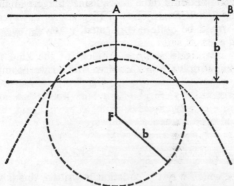

Figure 3-3

line must be halfway between the given point F and the given line AB. Other points of the line for which we are looking can be found by drawing a circle with any radius b around the given point F, and then finding the two points on this circle which are also at the distance b from the given line AB. (This can be done by drawing a line parallel to AB, at a distance b from AB. See Figure 3-3.)

Descartes solves the problem by beginning with the assumption that C is one of the points he is looking for. (See Figure

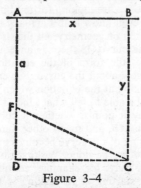

Figure 3-4

3-4.) We have already noted that he calls AB "x" and BC "y."

(*A* is the point at which the perpendicular from *F* meets *AB*. The distance *AF* is fixed; let us call it *a*. Now drop a perpendicular from *C* to *AF* extended; let it intersect this extension at *D*. *CDF* is a right triangle; hence, according to Proposition 47 of Euclid, Book I (the so-called Pythagorean theorem),

$$\overline{CF}^2 = \overline{FD}^2 + \overline{DC}^2.$$

Note that $FD = y - a$, and that $DC = x$. We can write, therefore,

$$\overline{CF}^2 = (y - a)^2 + x^2.$$

We also know that $CF = CB = y$. And so we have

$$y^2 = (y - a)^2 + x^2.$$
$$y^2 = y^2 - 2ya + a^2 + x^2.$$
$$2ya = a^2 + x^2.$$

This can also be written as follows:

$$2ya - a^2 = x^2$$
$$2a\left(y - \frac{a}{2}\right) = x^2$$

No matter which way the equation is written, this is the solution to the problem.

How is this a solution? We pointed out earlier that no construction of the desired line by strictly Euclidean means was possible, and Descartes' solution certainly is not Euclidean. Descartes solves the problem—but only if we revise our understanding of what it means to solve a problem. For Euclid, it means to construct, by means of the given postulates, the desired figure. For Descartes, it means to find an equation which reveals all of the characteristics of the desired figure (usually a curve).

Employing Euclid's conception of geometry, we know nothing about the curve we are looking for until it has been drawn. In fact, we do not even know that it actually exists. Employing Descartes' conception of geometry, all that is needed is to find the equation of the curve. If there is an equation, there is a curve; furthermore, the form of the equation reveals everything there is to know about the curve. For example, a trained mathematician looking at the equation which we derived from Figure 3–4 would be able to tell what kind of curve it is (a parabola), which way it points, whether it curves very steeply, whether it intersects *AB*, and many other things.

The actual drawing of the curve becomes quite unimportant, though it can of course be done. We first divide *x* and *y* into arbitrary units. We may, for example, count off units on *AB* (the "*x*-axis"), by starting at *A* (calling *A* the 0-point) and going to the right. The 0-point for the "*y*-axis" must also be at *A*, so that *AF* becomes the *y*-axis. By choosing random values for x, we can find the corresponding values for y, and in that way find points on the curve. For example, if $x = 0$, we substitute this value in the formula and find that $y = \dfrac{a}{2}$. Similarly, by substituting 1, 2, 3, etc., for x in the formula, we can find the corresponding values of y, and consequently other points C. However, the important innovation in Descartes' method is that the actual drawing of the curve becomes unimportant. The curve is in fact identified with its equation, and the equation reveals all the important facts concerning the curve.

Descartes' method is tremendously powerful. Evidence of this is the fact that no one nowadays develops geometry in the Euclidean fashion; instead, geometry is developed analytically. What gives the method this power? First, analytic geometry has freed itself from the restrictions of Euclid's construction postulates, or from any other set of construction postulates. Such postulates, whether they are Euclid's, Lobachevski's, or any other geometer's, restrict the number of operations that can be performed. Certain constructions are permitted, others are not. Descartes' geometry, since it is basically algebraical, is not affected by any of these restrictions. This is not to say that it operates without any restrictions. The postulates of algebra apply to the algebraical operations. Furthermore, Descartes uses certain geometrical properties of his figures; on page 108 we used Euclid's 47th proposition in Book I of the *Elements* in order to derive the formula for the parabola. Employing this theorem means, of course, that we are operating in the realm of Euclidean geometry (for this theorem is dependent on the parallel postulate). Analytic geometry cannot escape all postulates; any geometrical problem must be solved within a set of postulates. However, analytic geometry can equally well solve problems in Lobachevskian and in Euclidean geometry. The important advantage which analytic geometry has lies in the realm of constructions. Euclid could draw only straight lines and circles, and Lobachevski, for all his differences with Euclid on parallelism, permitted himself no different constructions. Descartes, however, permits himself to draw any figure whatsoever, because he pays no attention to construction postulates.

The second reason for the power of Descartes' method is the trick of assuming, when a problem needs to be solved, that the solution has already been effected. Then, with the required line already drawn, Descartes works backwards. If a certain line is to be drawn, Descartes simply says, "Let it be done."

It is easy to see how greatly this method increases his ability to solve problems. All constructions involving curved lines other than circles remained completely foreign to Euclid, but they are definitely part of Descartes' sphere of interest.

Is this "backwards" method of solving problems legitimate? If the problem is to contruct a line of such-and-such properties, to say "Let the construction be done" seems simply to circumvent the problem. To understand the sense in which Descartes (and analytic geometry) provides legitimate solutions, we must investigate the meaning of "solution."

For Euclid, to solve a geometrical problem means to begin with what is given or known and then, gradually, piece by piece, to add other valid assertions (either propositions or postulates), until he arrives at the required answer. Because this method arrives at its goal by the compilation of various pieces of previously acquired knowledge, it is called the "synthetic" method. This method puts together, or synthesizes, many small pieces in order to arrive at a result which before was unknown.

For Descartes, to solve a geometrical problem means to look at the solution as though he had already found it, and breaking it up—or analyzing it—into small parts each of which is known to us. This method, therefore, is called the "analytic" method, and when it is applied to geometry it gives us analytic geometry.

Is Descartes' method better or worse than Euclid's? Both methods have their advantages and disadvantages. Euclid's has the advantage of being more orderly; slowly, he proceeds from what is known to new and unknown things. On the other hand, Descartes' method has the advantage of being more easily learned and of being very fruitful for new discoveries. Euclid's method suffers from the fact that, as we read along in a series of propositions or in a single proposition, we very often cannot understand why the geometer takes a particular direction. Quite frequently it comes as a surprise to the reader when Euclid arrives at his desired result. Descartes, who loved to impugn the motives of other mathematicians, claimed that this was precisely the reason why the ancient geometers employed the synthetic method: their achievement seemed all the greater because the student could not understand how the result had even been discovered. Although we may not agree with Descartes' view of the ancients' motives, we must concede that his method clarifies to a much greater extent the reason for each step undertaken.

II

arithmetic

CHAPTER FOUR

Archimedes—Numbers and Counting

PART I

We have already mentioned that Euclid's *Elements* contains arithmetical as well as geometrical material. In the present selection, we present two short excerpts from the three number books (Books VII–IX). First, there are all the definitions that Euclid puts down at the beginning of Book VII; and secondly, there is one very important proposition from Book IX. Of course, the number books contain a great deal more than this, but much of it is very ordinary arithmetical stuff and some of it is also not of much interest to us any more. But the two excerpts which we have selected retain their validity and their utility.

In addition to Euclid, we also make the acquaintance here of Archimedes, with the little treatise called *The Sand-Reckoner*. Archimedes wrote many treatises, and quite a few of them have come down to us. Many deal with with problems of physics; others deal with pure mathematics. *The Sand-Reckoner* attacks a fairly simple problem, but one that is nevertheless important: how to count up to large numbers, and how to name large numbers in a consistent fashion.

Euclid:
*Elements of Geometry**

BOOK VII

DEFINITIONS

1. An **unit** is that by virtue of which each of the things that exist is called one.

2. A **number** is a multitude composed of units.

3. A number is a **part** of a number, the less of the greater, when it measures the greater;

4. but **parts** when it does not measure it.

5. The greater number is a **multiple** of the less when it is measured by the less.

6. An **even number** is that which is divisible into two equal parts.

7. An **odd number** is that which is not divisible into two equal parts, or that which differs by an unit from an even number.

8. An **even-times even number** is that which is measured by an even number according to an even number.

9. An **even-times odd number** is that which is measured by an even number according to an odd number.

10. An **odd-times odd number** is that which is measured by an odd number according to an odd number.

11. A **prime number** is that which is measured by an unit alone.

12. Numbers **prime to one another** are those which are measured by an unit alone as a common measure.

13. A **composite number** is that which is measured by some number.

14. Numbers **composite to one another** are those which are measured by some number as a common measure.

15. A number is said to **multiply** a number when that which is multiplied is added to itself as many times as there are units in the other, and thus some number is produced.

16. And, when two numbers having multiplied one another

* From *The Thirteen Books of Euclid's Elements,* trans. by Sir Thomas L. Heath (2nd ed.; London: Cambridge University Press, 1926). Reprinted by permission.

make some number, the number so produced is called **plane,** and its sides are the numbers which have multiplied one another.

17. And, when three numbers having multiplied one another make some number, the number so produced is **solid,** and its sides are the numbers which have multiplied one another.

18. A **square number** is equal multiplied by equal, or a number which is contained by two equal numbers.

19. And a **cube** is equal multiplied by equal and again by equal, or a number which is contained by three equal numbers.

20. Numbers are **proportional** when the first is the same multiple, or the same part, or the same parts, of the second that the third is of the fourth.

21. **Similar plane and solid numbers** are those which have their sides proportional.

22. A **perfect number** is that which is equal to its own parts . . .

BOOK IX

PROPOSITION 20

Prime numbers are more than any assigned multitude of prime numbers.

Let *A*, *B*, *C* be the assigned prime numbers; I say that there are more prime numbers than *A*, *B*, *C*.

For let the least number measured by *A*, *B*, *C* be taken, and let it be *DE*; let the unit *DF* be added to DE.

Then *EF* is either prime or not.

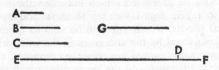

First, let it be prime; then the prime numbers *A*, *B*, *C*, *EF* have been found which are more than *A*, *B*, *C*.

Next, let *EF* not be prime; therefore it is measured by some prime number.

[VII. 31]

Let it be measured by the prime number *G*.

I say that *G* is not the same with any of the numbers *A*, *B*, *C*.

For, if possible, let it be so.

Now *A*, *B*, *C* measure *DE*; therefore *G* also will measure *DE*.

But it also measures *EF*.

Therefore *G*, being a number, will measure the remainder, the unit *DF*: which is absurd.

Therefore *G* is not the same with any one of the numbers *A*, *B*, *C*.

And by hypothesis it is prime.

Therefore the prime numbers *A*, *B*, *C*, *G* have been found which are more than the assigned multitude of *A*, *B*, *C*.

Q.E.D.

Archimedes: *The Sand Reckoner**

"There are some, king Gelon, who think that the number of the sand is infinite in multitude; and I mean by the sand not only that which exists about Syracuse and the rest of Sicily but also that which is found in every region whether inhabited or uninhabited. Again there are some who, without regarding it as infinite, yet think that no number has been named which is great enough to exceed its multitude. And it is clear that they who hold this view, if they imagined a mass made up of sand in other respects as large as the mass of the earth, including in it all the seas and the hollows of the earth filled up to a height equal to that of the highest of the mountains, would be many times further still from recognising that any number could be expressed which exceeded the multitude of the sand so taken. But I will try to show you by means of geometrical proofs, which you will be able to follow, that, of the numbers named by me and given in the work which I sent to Zeuxippus, some exceed not only the number of the mass of sand equal in magnitude to the earth filled up in the way described, but also that of a mass equal in magnitude to the universe. Now you are aware that 'universe' is the name given by most astronomers to the sphere whose centre is the centre of the earth and whose radius is equal to the straight

* From *The Works of Archimedes*, ed. by Sir Thomas L. Heath (Cambridge: at the University Press, 1897). Reprinted by permission.

line between the centre of the sun and the centre of the earth. This is the common account as you have heard from astronomers. But Aristarchus of Samos brought out a book consisting of some hypotheses, in which the premises lead to the result that the universe is many times greater than that now so called. His hypotheses are that the fixed stars and the sun remain unmoved, that the earth revolves about the sun in the circumference of a circle, the sun lying in the middle of the orbit, and that the sphere of the fixed stars, situated about the same centre as the sun, is so great that the circle in which he supposes the earth to revolve bears such a proportion to the distance of the fixed stars as the centre of the sphere bears to its surface. Now it is easy to see that this is impossible; for, since the centre of the sphere has no magnitude, we cannot conceive it to bear any ratio whatever to the surface of the sphere. We must however take Aristarchus to mean this: since we conceive the earth to be, as it were, the centre of the universe, the ratio which the earth bears to what we describe as the 'universe' is the same as the ratio which the sphere containing the circle in which he supposes the earth to revolve bears to the sphere of the fixed stars. For he adapts the proofs of his results to a hypothesis of this kind, and in particular he appears to suppose the magnitude of the sphere in which he represents the earth as moving to be equal to what we call the 'universe.'

I say then that, even if a sphere were made up of the sand, as great as Aristarchus supposes the sphere of the fixed stars to be, I shall still prove that, of the numbers named in the *Principles,* some exceed in multitude the number of the sand which is equal in magnitude to the sphere referred to, provided that the following assumptions be made.

1. *The perimeter of the earth is about* 3,000,000 *stadia and not greater.*

It is true that some have tried, as you are of course aware, to prove that the said perimeter is about 300,000 stadia. But I go further and, putting the magnitude of the earth at ten times the size that my predecessors thought it, I suppose its perimeter to be about 3,000,000 stadia and not greater.

2. *The diameter of the earth is greater than the diameter of the moon, and the diameter of the sun is greater than the diameter of the earth.*

In this assumption I follow most of the earlier astronomers.

3. *The diameter of the sun is about* 30 *times the diameter of the moon and not greater.*

It is true that, of the earlier astronomers, Eudoxus declared it to be about nine times as great, and Pheidias my father twelve times, while Aristarchus tried to prove that the diameter of the sun is greater than 18 times but less than 20 times the diameter of the moon. But I go even further than Aristarchus in order that the truth of my proposition may be established beyond dispute, and I suppose the diameter of the sun to be about 30 times that of the moon and not greater.

4. *The diameter of the sun is greater than the side of the chiliagon inscribed in the greatest circle in the (sphere of the) universe.*

I make this assumption because Aristarchus discovered that the sun appeared to be about $\frac{1}{720}$th part of the circle of the zodiac, and I myself tried, by a method which I will now describe, to find experimentally the angle subtended by the sun and having its vertex at the eye."

[Up to this point the treatise has been literally translated because of the historical interest attaching to the *ipsissima verba* of Archimedes on such a subject. The rest of the work can now be more freely reproduced, and, before proceeding to the mathematical contents of it, it is only necessary to remark that Archimedes next describes how he arrived at a higher and a lower limit for the angle subtended by the sun. This he did by taking a long rod or ruler, fastening on the end of it a small cylinder or disc, pointing the rod in the direction of the sun just after its rising (so that it was possible to look directly at it), then putting the cylinder at such a distance that it just concealed, and just failed to conceal, the sun, and lastly measuring the angles subtended by the cylinder. He explains also the correction which he thought it necessary to make because "the eye does not see from one point but from a certain area."

The result of the experiment was to show that the angle subtended by the diameter of the sun was less than $\frac{1}{164}$th part, and greater than $\frac{1}{200}$th part, of a right angle.

To prove that (on this assumption) the diameter of the sun is greater than the side of a chiliagon, or figure with 1000 equal sides, inscribed in a great circle of the 'universe.'

Suppose the plane of the paper to be the plane passing through the centre of the sun, the centre of the earth and the eye, at the time when the sun has just risen above the horizon. Let the plane cut the earth in the circle *EHL* and the sun in the circle *FKG*, the centres of the earth and sun being *C*, *O* respectively, and *E* being the position of the eye.

Further, let the plane cut the sphere of the 'universe' (i.e. the sphere whose centre is C and radius CO) in the great circle AOB.

Draw from E two tangents to the circle FKG touching it at P, Q, and from C draw two other tangents to the same circle touching it in F, G respectively.

Let CO meet the sections of the earth and sun in H, K respectively; and let CF, CG produced meet the great circle AOB in A, B.

Join EO, OF, OG, OP, OQ, AB, and let AB meet CO in M.

Now $CO > EO$, since the sun is just above the horizon. Therefore $\angle PEQ > \angle FCG$.

And $\angle PEQ > \frac{1}{200}R$
but $< \frac{1}{164}R$ } where R represents a right angle.

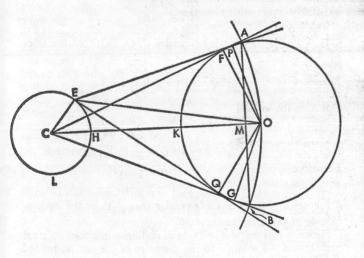

Thus $\angle FCG < \frac{1}{164}R$, *a fortiori,*
and the chord AB subtends an arc of the great circle which is less than $\frac{1}{656}$th of the circumference of that circle, i.e.

$AB <$ (side of 656-sided polygon inscribed in the circle).

Now the perimeter of any polygon inscribed in the great circle is less than $\frac{44}{7}CO$. [Cf. *Measurement of a circle*, Prop. 3.]

Therefore $\qquad AB : CO < 11 : 1148$,

and, *a fortiori*, $\qquad AB < \frac{1}{100}CO \dots\dots\dots\dots (a)$.

Again, since $CA = CO$, and AM is perpendicular to CO, while OF is perpendicular to CA, $AM = OF$.

Therefore $\qquad AB = 2AM = $ (diameter of sun).

Thus $\qquad$ (diameter of sun) $< \frac{1}{100}CO$, by (a),

and, *a fortiori*

$\qquad$ (diameter of earth) $< \frac{1}{100}CO$. $\qquad$ [Assumption 2]

Hence $\qquad CH + OK < \frac{1}{100}CO$,

so that $\qquad HK > \frac{99}{100}CO$,

or $\qquad CO : HK < 100 : 99$.

And $\qquad CO > CF$,

while $\qquad HK < EQ$.

Therefore $\qquad CF : EQ < 100 : 99 \dots\dots\dots\dots (\beta)$.

Now in the right-angled triangles CFO, EQO, of the sides about the right angles,

$OF = OQ$, but $EQ < CF$ (*since* $EO < CO$).

Therefore $\qquad \angle OEQ : \angle OCF > CO : EO$.

but $\qquad\qquad\qquad\qquad < CF : EQ$.

Doubling the angles,

$\qquad\qquad \angle PEQ : \angle ABC < CF : EQ$

$\qquad\qquad\qquad\qquad\qquad < 100 : 99$, by (β) above.

But $\qquad\qquad\qquad \angle PEQ > \frac{1}{200}R$, by hypothesis.

Therefore $\qquad\qquad \angle ACB > \frac{99}{20000}R$

$\qquad\qquad\qquad\qquad\qquad > \frac{1}{203}R$.

It follows that the arc AB is greater than $\frac{1}{812}$th of the circumference of the great circle AOB.

Hence, *a fortiori*, $AB > $ (side of chiliagon inscribed in great circle), and AB is equal to the diameter of the sun, as proved above.

———————

The following results can now be proved:

$\qquad$ (*diameter of 'universe'*) $< 10,000$ (*diameter of earth*),

and (*diameter of 'universe'*) $< 10,000,000,000$ *stadia*.

(1) Suppose, for brevity, that d_u represents the diameter of the 'universe,' d_s that the sun, d_e that of the earth, and d_m that of the moon.

By hypothesis, $d_s > 30d_m$,   [Assumption 3]
and $d_e > d_m$;   [Assumption 2]
therefore $d_s < 30d_e$.

Now, by the last proposition,

$d_s > $ (side of chiliagon inscribed in great circle),

so that   (perimeter of chiliagon) $< 1000d_s$
$< 30,000d_e$.

But the perimeter of any regular polygon with more sides than 6 inscribed in a circle is greater than that of the inscribed regular hexagon, and therefore greater than three times the diameter. Hence (perimeter of chiliagon) $> 3d_u$.

It follows that $d_u < 10,000d_e$.

(2) (Perimeter of earth) $> 3,000,000$ stadia.   [Assumption 1]
and   (perimeter of earth) $> 3d_e$.

Therefore $d_e < 1,000,000$ stadia,
whence $d_u < 10,000,000,000$ stadia.

Assumption 5.

Suppose a quantity of sand taken not greater than a poppy-seed, and suppose that it contains not more than 10,000 grains.

Next suppose the diameter of the poppy-seed to be not less than $\frac{1}{40}$th of a finger-breadth.

Orders and periods of numbers.

I. We have traditional names for numbers up to a myriad (10,000); we can therefore express numbers up to a myriad myriads (100,000,000). Let these numbers be called numbers of the *first order*.

Suppose the 100,000,000 to be the unit of the *second order*, and let the *second order* consist of the numbers from that unit up to $(100,000,000)^2$.

Let this again be the unit of the *third order* of numbers ending with $(100,000,000)^3$; and so on, until we reach the 100,000,000*th order* of numbers ending with $(100,000,000)^{100,000,000}$, which we will call P.

II. Suppose the numbers from 1 to P just described to form the *first period*.

Let P be the unit of the *first order of the second period*, and let this consist of the numbers from P up to $100,000,000\ P$.

Let the last number be the unit of the *second order of the second period*, and let this end with $(100,000,000)^2 P$.

We can go on in this way till we reach the 100,000,000*th order of the second period* ending with $(100,000,000)^{100,000,000}$ P, or P^2.

III. Taking P^2 as the unit of the *first order of the third period*, we proceed in the same way till we reach the 100,000,000*th order of the third period* ending with P^3.

IV. Taking P^3 as the unit of the *first order of the fourth period*, we continue the same process until we arrive at the 100,000,000*th order of the* 100,000,000*th period* ending with $P^{100,000,000}$. This last number is expressed by Archimedes as "a myriad-myriad units of the myriad-myriad-th order of the myriad-myriad-th period, which is easily seen to be 100,000,000 times the product of $(100,000,000)^{99,999,999}$ and $P^{99,999,999}$, i.e. $P^{100,000,000}$.

[The scheme of numbers thus described can be exhibited more clearly by means of *indices* as follows.

FIRST PERIOD.

First order. Numbers from 1 to 10^8.
Second order. "   " 10^8 to 10^{16}.
Third order.   "   " 10^{16} to 10^{24}.
$\vdots$
(10^8)*th order.* "   " $18^{8 \cdot (10^8 - 1)}$ to $10^{8 \cdot 10^8}$ (P, say).

SECOND PERIOD.

First order.   "   " $P \cdot 1$ to $P \cdot 10^8$.
Second order. "   " $P \cdot 10^8$ to $P \cdot 10^{16}$.
$\vdots$
(10^8)*th order.* "   " $P \cdot 10^{8 \cdot (10^8 - 1)}$ to
$P \cdot 10^{8 \cdot 10^8}$ (or P^2).

$\vdots$

(10^8)TH PERIOD.

First order.   "   " $P^{10^8 - 1} \cdot 1$ to $P^{10^8 - 1} \cdot 10^8$.
Second order. "   " $P^{10^8 - 1} \cdot 10^8$ to $P^{10^8 - 1} \cdot 10^{16}$.
$\vdots$
(10^8)*th order.* "   " $P^{10^8 - 1} \cdot 10^{8 \cdot (10^8 - 1)}$ to
$P^{10^8 - 1} \cdot 10^{8 \cdot 10^8}$ (i.e. P^{10^8}).

The prodigious extent of this scheme will be appreciated when it is considered that the last number in the *first period* would be represented now by 1 followed by 800,000,000 ciphers, while the last number of the (10^8)*th period* would require 100,000,000 times as many ciphers, i.e. 80,000 million millions of ciphers.]

Octads.

Consider the series of terms in continued proportion of which the first is 1 and the second 10 [i.e. the geometrical progression 1, 10^1, 10^2, 10^3, ...]. The *first octad* of these terms [i.e. 1, 10^1, 10^2, ... 10^7] fall accordingly under the *first order of the first period* above described, the *second octad* [i.e. 10^8, 10^9, ... 10^{15}] under the *second order of the first period*, the first term of the octad being the unit of the corresponding order in each case. Similarly for the *third octad*, and so on. We can, in the same way, place any number of octads.

Theorem.

If there be any number of terms of a series in continued proportion, say A_1, A_2, A_3, ... A_m, ... A_n, ... A_{m+n-1}, ... of which $A_1 = 1$, $A_2 = 10$ [so that the series forms the geometrical progression 1, 10^1, 10^2, ... 10^{m-1}, ... 10^{n-1}, ... 10^{m+n-2}, ...], and if any two terms as A_m, A_n be taken and multiplied, the product $A_m \cdot A_n$ will be a term in the same series and will be as many terms distant from A_n as A_m is distant from A_1; also it will be distant from A_1 by a number of terms less by one than the sum of the numbers of terms by which A_m and A_n respectively are distant from A_1.

Take the term which is distant from A_n by the same number of terms as A_m is distant from A_1. This number of terms is m (the first and last being both counted). Thus the term to be taken is m terms distant from A_n, and is therefore the term A_{m+n-1}.

We have therefore to prove that

$$A_m \cdot A_n = A_{m+n-1}.$$

Now terms equally distant from other terms in the continued proportion are proportional.

Thus $$\frac{A_m}{A_1} = \frac{A_{m+n-1}}{A_n}.$$

But $A_m = A_m \cdot A_1$, since $A_1 = 1$.

Therefore $A_{m+n-1} = A_m \cdot A_n \ldots \ldots \ldots (1).$

The second result is now obvious, since A_m is m terms distant from A_1, A_n is n terms distant from A_1, and A_{m+n-1} is $(m + n - 1)$ terms distant from A_1.

Application to the number of the sand.

By Assumption 5 [p. 121],

(diam. of poppy-seed) $\not< \frac{1}{40}$ (finger-breadth);

and, since spheres are to one another in the triplicate ratio of their diameters, it follows that sphere of diam. 1 finger-breadth $\not\gg$ 64,000 poppy-seeds

$$\not\gg 64,000 \times 10,000$$
$$\not\gg 640,000,000$$
$\not\gg$ 6 units of *second order* + 40,000,000 units of *first order* } grains of sand.

(*a fortiori*) $<$ 10 units of *second order* of numbers.

We now gradually increase the diameter of the supposed sphere, multiplying it by 100 each time. Thus, remembering that the sphere is thereby multiplied by 100^3 or 1,000,000, the number of grains of sand which would be contained in a sphere with each successive diameter may be arrived at as follows.

Diameter of sphere.	*Corresponding number of grains of sand.*
(1) 100 finger-breadths	$<$ 1,000,000 $\times$ 10 units of *second order*.
	$<$ (7th term of series) $\times$ (10th term of series)
	$<$ 16th term of series [i.e. 10^{15}]
	$<$ [10^7 or] 10,000,000 units of the *second order*.
(2) 10,000 finger-breadths	$<$ 1,000,000 $\times$ (last number)
	$<$ (7th term of series) $\times$ (16th term)
	$<$ 22nd term of series [i.e. 10^{21}]
	$<$ [10^5 or] 100,000 units of *third order*.
(3) 1 stadium ($<$10,000 finger-breadths)	$<$ 100,000 units of *third order*.
(4) 100 stadia	$<$ 1,000,000 $\times$ (last number)
	$<$ (7th term of series) $\times$ (22nd term)
	$<$ 28th term of series [10^{27}]
	$<$ [10^3 or] 1,000 units of *fourth order*.
(5) 10,000 stadia	$<$ 1,000,000 $\times$ (last number)
	$<$ (7th term of series) $\times$ (28th term)
	$<$ 34th term of series [10^{33}]
	$<$ 10 units of *fifth order*.
(6) 1,000,000 stadia	$<$ (7th term of series) $\times$ (34th term)

	$< $ 40th term $\qquad$ [10^{39}]
	$< $ [10^7 or] 10,000,000 units of *fifth order*.
(7) 100,000,000 stadia	$< $ (7th term of series) $\times$ (40th term)
	$< $ 46th term $\qquad$ [10^{45}]
	$< $ [10^5 or] 100,000 units of *sixth order*.
(8) 10,000,000,000 stadia	$< $ (7th term of series) $\times$ (46th term)
	$< $ 52nd term of series $\qquad$ [10^{51}]
	$< $ [10^3 or] 1,000 units of *seventh order*.

But, by the proposition above [p. 120],

(diameter of 'universe') $< $ 10,000,000,000 stadia.

Hence *the number of grains of sand which could be contained in a sphere of the size of our 'universe' is less than* 1,000 *units of the seventh order of numbers* [or 10^{51}].

From this we can prove further that *a sphere of the size attributed by Aristarchus to the sphere of the fixed stars would contain a number of grains of sand less than* 10,000,000 *units of the eighth order of numbers* [or $10^{56+7} = 10^{63}$].

For, by hypothesis,

(earth) : ('universe') = ('universe') : (sphere of fixed stars).

And [p. 120]

(diameter of 'universe') $< $ 10,000 (diam. of earth);

whence

(diam. of sphere of fixed stars) $< $ 10,000 (diam. of 'universe').

Therefore

(sphere of fixed stars) $< $ $(10,000)^3$. ('universe').

It follows that the number of grains of sand which would be contained in a sphere equal to the sphere of the fixed stars

$< $ $(10,000)^3 \times$ 1,000 units of *seventh order*

$< $ (13th term of series) $\times$ (52nd term of series)

$< $ 64th term of series $\qquad$ [i.e. 10^{63}]

$< $ [10^7 or] 10,000,000 units of *eighth order* of numbers.

Conclusion.

"I conceive that these things, king Gelon, will appear incredible to the great majority of people who have not studied mathematics, but that to those who are conversant therewith and have given thought to the question of the distances and sizes of the earth and the sun and moon and the whole universe the proof will carry conviction. And it was for this reason that I thought the subject would be not inappropriate for your consideration."

PART II

In the light of the achievements of the Greek geometers, we sometimes forget that the Greeks also devoted a great deal of study to numbers. This chapter illustrates their theoretical as well as their practical interest in numbers. The selection from Euclid has to do with number theory; the selection from Archimedes deals with the more mundane problem of how to name numbers.

We will begin with the brief selection from Euclid. His approach to arithmetic is very similar to his approach to geometry; in both sciences he begins with a long series of definitions which define both terms the reader is already familiar with and terms that are probably new to him. As was the case in Book I, the early definitions, because they deal with the basic terms, present the greatest difficulty; see, for example, Euclid's definitions of "unit" and "number."

The definitions are not followed by postulates or axioms. The absence of axioms can easily be explained: axioms are no different for arithmetic than for geometry; having been set down in Book I, they need not be repeated here. The lack of postulates is a different matter, however. It seems as though Euclid did not think that he needed to postulate anything here as he did in geometry. Yet this is clearly wrong. Just as there are geometrical constructions the possibility of which must be granted to Euclid in geometry, so there are a number of operations in arithmetic which must be granted to him if he is to prove anything here. For example, there should be a postulate which says: "Let it be granted that if a, b, and c are three numbers, then the sum of a and b added to c is the same as the number obtained by adding a to the sum of b and c." Or,

"$(a + b) + c = a + (b + c)$." There are several other, similar arithmetical postulates which are also omitted by Euclid. Euclid, who was so careful and precise in his formulation of the geometrical postulates, is apparently quite careless and happy-go-lucky here. In contrast to this, modern arithmetic and algebra pay much attention to the problem of finding the right postulates.

Definition 11 defines a *prime number* as one "which is measured by an unit alone." Another definition of a prime number is that it is not divisible by any number (except itself and unity). Examples of prime numbers are 2 (the only even prime number), 3, 5, 7, 11, 13, 17, 19, 23, 29, 31, 37, and so on. Even from these few examples it is obvious that prime numbers become more scarce as we count higher. Between 23 and 29 five not-prime numbers (composite numbers) intervene. These intervals become larger and larger; between 199 and 211, there are 11 composite numbers. This increasing rarity of prime numbers naturally leads to the question whether perhaps beyond a certain point in the number scale, there might be no more prime numbers at all. Is it possible that all numbers beyond a certain one (probably very large) are composite numbers? Or do prime numbers keep recurring, although less and less frequently?

Proposition 20 of Book IX of the *Elements* answers this question: The quantity of prime numbers is infinitely large. Euclid's way of stating the proposition does not immediately reveal what he has in mind: "Prime numbers are more than any assigned multitude of prime numbers." This means the following: Suppose it is claimed that the number of prime numbers is finite, say equal to n. Then Euclid proves that there must be more than n prime numbers.

The last statement is a rather curious one. On the assumption that something is the case, namely, that there are just n prime numbers, the opposite is proved, namely, that there are more than n prime numbers. This oddity in the proof, together with the intrinsic interest in the statement of the proposition, constitutes the reason for our including this single proposition from the arithmetical books of Euclid's *Elements*. The proof is also remarkable for the fact that it depends on nothing previously proved; it is an exercise in pure logic alone.

Instead of stating the proof in general terms, let us first exemplify it. Suppose that someone said: "The number of prime numbers is finite." We would then be justified in asking him: "How many prime numbers are there?" His answer would have to be some number; let us assume that he answers: "There are just four prime numbers." Using Euclid's method, we will now show that if there are four prime numbers, then there is at least another, a fifth prime number.

The four prime numbers claimed to be the only ones would have to be the first four primes, of course; that is, they would have to be 2, 3, 5, 7. Form the product of these four numbers—namely, $2 \cdot 3 \cdot 5 \cdot 7 = 210$. Add 1 to this product: $210 + 1 = 211$. This new number is either a prime number or not. In this case, 211 is a prime number and, therefore, the proposition has been proved, for we have found a fifth prime number.

Suppose it had been claimed that there are just six prime numbers—namely, 2, 3, 5, 7, 11, 13. Form the product of these numbers. $2 \cdot 3 \cdot 5 \cdot 7 \cdot 11 \cdot 13 = 30,030$. Add 1 to this product: $30,030 + 1 = 30,031$. Again we say that this number is either prime or not. In this case, it is a composite number and therefore divisible by some prime number. This prime number cannot be any of the original six, for if any of them is divided into 30,031, it leaves a remainder of 1. (This is the case because all of the original six prime numbers are divisible into 30,030.) Therefore, the proposition has again been proved, since a seventh prime number has been found. This seventh prime number is the one which is a factor of 30,031. In this example, the number would be 59, since $30,031 = 59 \cdot 509$. (509 is also prime, so that we have actually found not only a seventh but also an eighth prime number.)

Euclid's proof is merely a generalization of this. If it is asserted that there are just n prime numbers, form the product of these n prime numbers. Add 1 to this product. This number —call it K—is itself either prime or not. If K is prime, the proposition has already been proved. If K is not a prime number, then it must be divisible by some prime number. This prime number is not one of the original n primes, for any of these n primes, if divided into K, leaves the remainder 1. Hence a new prime number has been found—namely, the one which is the factor of K.

What is the method of this proof? It somewhat resembles reduction to the absurd. We are to prove that the number of primes is larger than any given number, and so we begin by assuming the contradictory, namely that the number of primes is equal to a given number. But the conclusion which we come to is not in itself absurd; it merely contradicts the original assumption. From the assumption that there are just n prime numbers, we are able to demonstrate that there are at least $n + 1$ prime numbers. We might call this method "reduction to the opposite." Although this method is powerful, the number of instances where it can be applied is small.

Now we turn our attention to Archimedes. There was probably no branch of mathematics known to him to which Archimedes did not make a valuable contribution. Living in the third century B.C. (from aproximately 287 to 212 B.C.), Archimedes displayed a dazzling skill in geometry, in arithmetic, in the calculus, in the physics of the lever, and of floating bodies—a skill that was not matched until two thousand years later.

Archimedes lived in Syracuse in Sicily, though he had studied at Alexandria. *The Sand Reckoner* is addressed to Gelon, the king of Syracuse; Archimedes was on friendly terms with both Gelon and his father, Hiero. On behalf of the kings of Syracuse, Archimedes constructed many clever mechanical devices, especially for repelling besieging armies. Archimedes attached little importance to these ingenious machines; he considered himself a mathematician and requested that on his tombstone there be displayed a sphere with a circumscribed cylinder—thus commemorating what he considered to be his outstanding achievement, namely, the discovery of the relation of the volume of a sphere and a cylinder.

Archimedes died when Syracuse was conquered by the Romans under the command of Marcellus in 212 B.C. Although Marcellus had given orders that Archimedes was not to be harmed, in the confusion of the battle Archimedes was slain. Marcellus was chagrined by the unfortunate event and gave Archimedes a decent burial. Much of our knowledge of Archimedes as a person stems from Plutarch's *Life of Marcellus*. He is best seen, however, through his works, of which a great many have survived. *The Sand-Reckoner,* though it is a short work, displays his general scientific erudition as well as his skill as a mathematician.

All of us have at one time or another encountered someone given to constant exaggeration. One of the most common exaggerations is the substitution of the word "infinite" for the phrase "very large." Many people say that something is "infinitely better than something else," or that "a modern ballistic missile is infinitely more complicated than the airplane of the brothers Wright," or that "the number of atoms in a given piece of matter is infinite." All of these expressions are not merely inaccurate, but wrong. Nothing on this earth is infinitely more complicated or infinitely better than anything else, and there is *no* number that is infinite. (Throughout this chapter, we use the word "number" to stand for "whole number" or "integer.") An infinite amount—leaving aside the question of whether or not there is such a thing—would mean an amount that cannot be counted, no matter how much time is taken to do it. An infinite quantity is not enumerable—it cannot be counted. And conversely, anything which *can* be counted—any quantity, no matter how large, to which a number *can* be assigned—is by that token not infinite. No number can ever be said to be infinite, for every number always has a next one; hence the former number cannot be called infinite, since there is at least one number greater than it. In fact, a good definition of infinity states that infinity is larger than any number that you may name and that consequently, infinity itself is not a number.

King Gelon, to whom *The Sand-Reckoner* is addressed, was evidently a person for whom "very large" and "infinite" were synonymous, especially when "very large" means something of the order of millions or even more. One of the major tasks that Archimedes sets for himself in this little treatise is to show the king that "large"—no matter how large—is not infinite, but very definitely finite. Archimedes takes a quantity which seems to the uneducated to be so large as to be indistinguishable from infinity—the number of grains of sand in the universe—and *counts* it. At least, he shows that this quantity cannot possibly exceed a certain number which he names. And so, if the quantity can be numbered, it is not infinite.

In order to accomplish his purpose, Archimedes must first have some notion of the size of the universe. He must tell us what he means by "the universe," and how large he conceives it to be. He must also tell us how large he takes a grain of sand to be. Then Archimedes must find a way of naming very large numbers, so that he can tell us in a definite way the number of grains of sand in the universe. It will not do for him simply to say "it's a very large number"; for nobody denies this. What is desired is a definite number to be assigned to the quantity of sand; this will show that the quantity is finite.

By "universe" Archimedes means the space enclosed by the sphere of the fixed stars. (In ancient astronomy, all fixed stars were thought to be attached or "fixed" to one celestial sphere.)

In defining what he means by "universe," Archimedes writes as follows (remember that the entire work is addressed to King Gelon):

> Now you are aware that "universe" is the name given by most astronomers to the sphere whose centre is the centre of the earth and whose radius is equal to the straight line between the centre of the sun and the centre of the earth (p. 116).

This view of the universe is based on the geocentric hypothesis: The earth is thought to be in the center of the universe, with sun, moon, planets, and the fixed stars all revolving around the earth. In this hypothesis, the fixed stars are usually considered to be farther out than any other heavenly body, but as Archimedes states the theory here, it appears that the sun is at the greatest distance from the earth.

Archimedes then reports that there is also another view of the universe:

> Aristarchus of Samos brought out a book consisting of some hypotheses, in which the premises lead to the result that the universe is many times greater than that now so called. His hypotheses are that the fixed stars and the sun remain unmoved, that the earth revolves about the sun in the circumference of a circle, the sun lying in the middle of the orbit, and that the sphere of the fixed stars, situated about the same centre as the sun, is so great that the circle in which he supposes the earth to revolve bears such a proportion to the distance of the fixed stars as the centre of the sphere bears to its surface (p. 117).

This is a heliocentric view: the sun is the center of the universe and the earth revolves around the sun. The fixed stars are truly fixed—that is, motionless—but appear to move because of the daily rotation of the earth. This is, of course, exactly the theory put forth by Copernicus some 1,700 years later. Aristarchus' theory apparently could not hold its own against the rival geocentric theory and was not generally accepted. (We may surmise that the reason for Aristarchus' failure lay in the apparent greater simplicity of the geocentric theory. In the course of time, however, the geocentric theory needed so many modifications and additions that, by the time of Copernicus, it was far more complicated than the rediscovered heliocentric theory.)

If the heliocentric theory is adopted, the fixed stars must be far more distant from the earth than they need be in the geocentric theory. Although the earth is sometimes closer to, and sometimes farther from, a given star (depending on where the earth is in the course of its annual revolution around the sun), the earth always *seems* to be exactly in the center of the universe. This can be the case only if the distance to the fixed stars is so great that in relation to it, the distance from the earth to the sun is so small as to be negligible. This is what Archimedes means when he writes that "the sphere of the fixed stars . . . is so great that the circle in which he supposes the earth to revolve bears such a proportion to the distance of the fixed stars as the centre of the sphere bears to its surface."

Now Archimedes begins to put down some hypothetical figures about the actual size of the universe. He is not so much concerned to give accurate figures for the astronomical distances as to be sure always to give a *greater* distance than anyone has proposed. In this way—if he succeeds in showing that the grains of sand in such a universe are enumerable—it will certainly be obvious that the quantity of sand in the actual universe, being smaller, must be also enumerable.

Archimedes begins by giving a value for the circumference of the earth. He assumes that it is no larger than 3 million stadia. A stadium is a Greek unit of length; it was not everywhere the same length. (Just as "mile" can mean a statute mile or a nautical mile, and just as "gallon" designates a different volume in the United States and in Canada.) For our purposes we may say that a stadium is approximately 600 feet long. Consequently, as brief calculation will show, the figure of 3 million stadia is far too large for the circumference of the earth; in fact, 300,000 stadia, which, as Archimedes notes, some other astronomers proposed for the size of the earth, is much closer. But Archimedes is only interested in giving estimates that are not too small.

Further, Archimedes notes that the diameter of the sun is greater than the diameter of the earth, while the diameter of the earth is greater than that of the moon. In addition, Archimedes assumes that the diameter of the sun is about 30 times as great as the diameter of the moon, but not more than that. For this result he relies on experimental work by various astronomers; again, to be on the safe side he elects a value which makes the sun greater than any of the astronomers has found it to be.

So far all the assumptions have dealt with the diameters

of three bodies: the earth, the sun, and the moon. Since Archimedes is interested in the size of the "universe," he must connect these diameters with the diameter or with the circumference of the universe. This he does in Assumption 4, in which he tells us that if a regular chiliagon (figure of a thousand sides) is inscribed in the "equator" of the universe, then the diameter of the sun is greater than the side of the chiliagon. Actually, Archimedes proves this statement by means of experimental evidence. Then he goes on:

Since

the diameter of the sun is equal to or less than 30 diameters of the moon

and

the diameter of the moon is less than the diameter of the earth

or

30 diameters of the moon are less than 30 diameters of the earth,

it follows that

the diameter of the sun is less than 30 diameters of the earth.

Assumption 4 states that

the diameter of the sun is greater than the side of the chiliagon inscribed in the universe.

Thus

1000 diameters of the sun are greater than 1000 sides of the chiliagon

which means that

1000 diameters of the sun are greater than the circumference of the chiliagon.

Turning this last inequality around, we have

the circumference of the chiliagon is less than 1000 diameters of the sun

or

the circumference of the chiliagon is less than 30,000 diameters of the earth.

The circumference of a regular hexagon (six-sided figure) inscribed in a circle is three times the diameter of the circle. Any regular figure which has more than six sides has a circumference larger than that of the hexagon, but smaller than that of the circle. Consequently, the circumference of a regular chiliagon inscribed in the equator of the universe is greater than three times the diameter of the universe. Let us write this down:

The circumference of the chiliagon is greater than 3 diameters of the universe

or, turning this around,

3 diameters of the universe are less than the circumference of the chiliagon.

Dividing by three, we have

the diameter of the universe is less than ⅓ of the circumference of the chiliagon.

Reverting to the relation between the circumference of the
chiliagon and the diameter of the earth, we have

the diameter of the universe is less than ⅓ of 30,000
diameters of the earth,

or

the diameter of the universe is less than 10,000 diameters
of the earth.

Since the circumference of the earth has been assumed to
be at most 3 million stadia, the diameter of the earth must be
less than 1 million stadia. (This is true because the diameter
of a circle is multiplied by π, which is greater than 3, in order
to obtain the circumference of a circle.)

Hence, if

the diameter of the earth is less than 1 million stadia,

it follows that

the diameter of the universe is less than 10,000 million
stadia,

or

the diameter of the universe is less than 10 billion stadia.

Since, as we noted earlier, a stadium is about 600 feet or
1/9 of a mile, the "universe" in this calculation turns out to
have a diameter of about 1.1 billion miles. Imagine the vast
quantity of sand, if this entire universe were filled with sand!
Nevertheless, Archimedes proposes to tell us the number of
grains of sand if this universe contained nothing but sand.

Let us simplify Archimedes' statements just a little. Let us
say, for example, that he maintains that

1 stadium equals 10,000 fingerbreadths.

Since

1 fingerbreadth equals 40 diameters of a poppy seed,

it follows that

1 stadium equals 400,000 diameters of a poppy seed.

Now the volumes of spheres are to each other as the cubes
of their diameters. Hence we have

$$\frac{\text{Volume of a sphere with the diameter of 1 stadium}}{\text{Volume of a sphere with the diameter of 1 poppy seed}} =$$

$$\frac{(400,000)^3}{1}$$

But

$$\frac{(400,000)^3}{1} = \frac{(4 \cdot 10^5)^3}{1} = 64 \cdot 10^{15}.$$

Since, according to Archimedes, a sphere with the diameter of one poppy seed contains 10,000 grains of sand, it follows that a sphere with a diameter of 1 stadium contains $64 \cdot 10^{15} \cdot 10,000$ grains of sand, or $64 \cdot 10^{15} \cdot 10^4 = 64 \cdot 10^{19}$ grains of sand.

How many grains of sand are there in a sphere the size of the universe, or 10 billion stadia? Again we use the relation between volumes of spheres:

$$\frac{\text{Volume of a sphere with a diameter of } 10^{10} \text{ stadia}}{\text{Volume of a sphere with the diameter of 1 stadium}} =$$

$$\frac{(10^{10})^3}{1} = 10^{30}.$$

Since the smaller sphere (with the diameter of 1 stadium) contains $64 \cdot 10^{19}$ grains of sand, the larger sphere must contain 10^{30} times as many grains. Now $10^{19} \cdot 10^{30} = 10^{49}$. Thus the number of grains of sand in the universe, using Archimedes' assumptions, is $64 \cdot 10^{49}$ (written as 64 followed by 49 zeros).

In making this calculation, we have employed the decimal system of numerical notation. This system is based on the powers of 10—10, 100, 1000, and so on. Each power of 10 gives its name to a whole series of numbers; there are units, tens, hundreds, thousands, and so on. However, we very quickly run out of names for the powers of ten, and in any case it becomes difficult to remember just what we mean, for example, by a quadrillion. For that reason, mathematicians do not even try to name very large numbers with words. They merely write them as powers of ten. Thus 5 million is very often written as $5 \cdot 10^6$. For numbers larger than a million, this manner of notation is almost mandatory. The reader will have noticed that we employed this notation for the number of grains in the universe.

Let us now take a look at the system of naming numbers that Archimedes devised and see whether it is adequate to his purpose. That is, can numbers as large as $64 \cdot 10^{49}$ (or even larger) be written in his notation? The Greeks, unlike us, had a single name for the number 10,000, namely "myriad." Thus they had distinct names up to the fourth power of ten, namely, ten, a hundred, a thousand, and a myriad. Apparently they had no names for larger numbers; for instance, they had no name for a million. But given the names they had, they could give distinct names, Archimedes notes, up to a myriad myriads. For example, there might be a number as follows:

4838 myriads, 659 thousands, 76 hundreds, 3 tens, 5.

This number means:

4838 · 10,000 plus 659 · 1000 plus 76 · 100 plus 3 · 10 plus 5 or

48,380,000 plus 659,000 plus 7600 plus 30 plus 5.

In the decimal system this number would be written as 49,046,635.

Since a myriad myriads (100,000,000) is the last number that can be given a distinct name, Archimedes proposes that this number become the unit of a second group of numbers, which he calls numbers of the second order. (Numbers from 1 to 100,000,000 he calls numbers of the first order.) Numbers of the second order run from 100,000,000 to (100,000,000)^2. This last number becomes the unit of numbers of the third order. In general, the numbers of the nth order are those beginning with (100,000,000)$^{n-1}$ and ending with (100,000,000)^n. We can continue until we reach the 100,000,000th order of numbers, which will end with the number (100,000,000)^{100,000,000}. Archimedes calls this number P. In decimal notation, P would be written as $(10^8)^{10^8}$ or $10^{(8 \cdot 10^8)}$.

Archimedes now calls the entire group of numbers from 1 to P the *first period* of numbers. Then he considers the number P as the unit of the first order of the second period. The first order of the second unit would go from P up to 100,000,000P. There is no need to describe the rest of the scheme, since Archimedes does it adequately. But what is of interest is this: although Archimedes at this point has barely begun to develop his scheme, we are already far past the number needed to express the number of grains of sand in the universe. As we saw, this number was approximately 64 · 10^{49}, or less than 10^{52}. Where does this number fall in Archimedes' scheme?

The first order of numbers goes from 1 to 10^8 (1 to a myriad).

The second order of numbers goes from 10^8 to 10^{16} (a myriad to a myriad of myriads).

The third order of numbers goes from 10^{16} to 10^{24}.

. . . .

The seventh order of numbers goes from 10^{48} to 10^{56}.

The number of grains of sand in the universe can be expressed, therefore, by a number of the seventh order. There is no need even to go to the end of the first period of numbers!

To appreciate Archimedes' achievement in developing such a scheme, remember that in explaining it, we constantly had recourse to the decimal system. We expressed all of Archimedes' numbers in terms of powers of ten. Archimedes, it must be remembered, did not possess the symbol "0" for writing numbers. What seems easy to us, therefore, required a tremendous effort of imagination and insight. Even without the symbol "0" Archimedes took the basic step in the writing of numbers: he uses each number that he can express as the unit for a new group of numbers. This is exactly what is done in the decimal system, or in any other system that writes its numbers by reference to the powers of some unit.

CHAPTER FIVE

Dedekind—Irrational Numbers

PART I

Whereas the previous selection dealt with some fairly simple problems in the realm of numbers—whether they are prime, how many prime numbers there are, how to count numbers—the selection now before us deals with a very sophisticated problem. It establishes, in very rigorous and convincing fashion, that there is a kind of number which is very special. It is called "irrational," and its defining property is that there is no number, no matter how small, which can be a factor of both an irrational number and a rational number. No matter how tiny a fraction you choose, you can never find one that will go into both the number 2 (a rational number) and the number $\sqrt{2}$ (an irrational number). The existence of such numbers had been known long before Dedekind, but he put the theory of irrational numbers on a rigorous and respectable footing.

Richard Dedekind:
Continuity and Irrational Numbers*

My attention was first directed toward the considerations which form the subject of this pamphlet in the autumn of 1858. As professor in the Polytechnic School in Zürich I found

* From *Essays on the Theory of Numbers*, trans. by Wooster Woodruff Beman (3rd printing; Chicago-London: The Open Court Publishing Company, 1924), pp. 1-19. Reprinted by permission.

myself for the first time obliged to lecture upon the elements of the differential calculus and felt more keenly than ever before the lack of a really scientific foundation for arithmetic. In discussing the notion of the approach of a variable magnitude to a fixed limiting value, and especially in proving the theorem that every magnitude which grows continually, but not beyond all limits, must certainly approach a limiting value, I had recourse to geometric evidences. Even now such resort to geometric intuition in a first presentation of the differential calculus, I regard as exceedingly useful, from the didactic standpoint, and indeed indispensable, if one does not wish to lose too much time. But that this form of introduction into the differential calculus can make no claim to being scientific, no one will deny. For myself this feeling of dissatisfaction was so overpowering that I made the fixed resolve to keep meditating on the question till I should find a purely arithmetic and perfectly rigorous foundation for the principles of infinitesimal analysis. The statement is so frequently made that the differential calculus deals with continuous magnitude, and yet an explanation of this continuity is nowhere given; even the most rigorous expositions of the differential calculus do not base their proofs upon continuity but, with more or less consciousness of the fact, they either appeal to geometric notions or those suggested by geometry, or depend upon theorems which are never established in a purely arithmetic manner. Among these, for example, belongs the above-mentioned theorem, and a more careful investigation convinced me that this theorem, or any one equivalent to it, can be regarded in some way as sufficient basis for infinitesimal analysis. It then only remained to discover its true origin in the elements of arithmetic and thus at the same time to secure a real definition of the essence of continuity. I succeeded Nov. 24, 1858, and a few days afterward I communicated the results of my meditations to my dear friend Durege with whom I had a long and lively discussion. Later I explained these views of a scientific basis of arithmetic to a few of my pupils, and here in Braunschweig read a paper upon the subject before the scientific club of professors, but I could not make up my mind to its publication, because, in the first place, the presentation did not seem altogether simple, and further, the theory itself had little promise. Nevertheless I had already half determined to select this theme as subject for this occasion, when a few days ago, March 14, by the kindness of the author, the paper *Die Elemente der Funktionenlehre* by E. Heine (*Crelle's Journal*, Vol. 74) came into my hands and confirmed me in my decision. In the main I fully agree with the substance of this memoir, and indeed I could hardly do otherwise, but I will frankly acknowledge that my own presentation seems to me to be simpler in form and to bring out the vital point more clearly. While writing this preface (March 20, 1872), I am just in receipt of the interesting paper *Ueber die Ausdehnung eines Satzes aus der Theorie der trigonometrischen Reihen,* by G. Cantor (*Math. Annalen,* Vol. 5), for which I owe the ingenious author my hearty thanks. As I find on a hasty perusal, the axiom given in Section II of that paper, aside from the form of presentation, agrees with what I designate in Section III as the essence of continuity. But what advantage will be gained by even a purely abstract definition of real numbers of a higher type, I am as yet unable to see, conceiving as I do of the domain of real numbers as complete in itself.

I PROPERTIES OF RATIONAL NUMBERS

The development of the arithmetic of rational numbers is here presupposed, but still I think it worth while to call attention to certain important matters without discussion, so as to show at the outset the standpoint assumed in what follows. I regard the whole of arithmetic as a necessary, or at least natural, consequence of the simplest arithmetic act, that of counting, and counting itself as nothing else than the successive creation of the infinite series of positive integers in which each individual is defined by the one immediately preceding; the simplest act is the passing from an already-formed individual to the consecutive new one to be formed. The chain of these numbers forms in itself an exceedingly useful instrument for the human mind; it presents an inexhaustible wealth of remarkable laws obtained by the introduction of the four fundamental operations of arithmetic. Addition is the combination of any arbitrary repetitions of the above-mentioned simplest act into a single act; from it in a similar way arises multiplication. While the performance of these two operations is always possible, that of the inverse operations, subtraction and division, proves to be limited. Whatever the immediate occasion may have been, whatever comparisons or analogies with experience, or intuition, may have led thereto; it is certainly true that just this limitation in performing the indirect operations has in each case been the real motive for a new creative act; thus negative and fractional numbers have been created by the human mind; and in the system of all rational numbers there has been gained an instrument of infinitely greater perfection. This system, which I shall denote by R, possesses first of all a completeness and self-containedness which I have designated in another place* as characteristic of a *body of numbers* [Zahlkörper] and which consists in this that the four fundamental operations are always performable with any two individuals in R, i. e., the result is always an individual of R, the single case of division by the number zero being excepted.

For our immediate purpose, however, another property of the system R is still more important; it may be expressed by saying that the system R forms a well-arranged domain of one dimension extending to infinity on two opposite sides. What is meant by this is sufficiently indicated by my use of expressions borrowed from geometric ideas; but just for this reason it will be necessary to bring out clearly the corresponding purely arithmetic properties in order to avoid even the appearance as if arithmetic were in need of ideas foreign to it.

To express that the symbols a and b represent one and the same rational number we put $a=b$ as well as $b=a$. The fact that two rational numbers a, b are different appears in this that the difference $a - b$ has either a positive or negative value. In the former case a is said to be *greater* than b, b *less* than a; this is also indicated by the symbols $a > b$, $b < a$.† As in the latter case $b - a$ has a positive value it follows that $b > a$, $a < b$. In regard to these two ways in which two numbers may differ the following laws will hold:

I. If $a > b$, and $b > c$, then $a > c$. Whenever a, c are two different (or unequal) numbers, and b is greater than the one and less than the other, we shall, without hesitation because of the suggestion of geometric ideas, express this briefly by saying: b lies between the two numbers a, c.

II. If a, c are two different numbers, there are infinitely many different numbers lying between a, c.

III. If a is any definite number, then all numbers of the system R fall into two classes, A_1 and A_2, each of which contains infinitely many individuals; the first class A_1 comprises all num-

---

* *Vorlesungen uber Zahlentheorie,* by P. G. Lejeune Dirichlet, 2d ed. § 159.
† Hence in what follows the so-called "algebraic" greater and less are understood unless the word "absolute" is added.

bers a_1 that are $< a$, the second class A_2 comprises all numbers a_2 that are $> a$; the number a itself may be assigned at pleasure to the first or second class, being respectively the greatest number of the first class or the least of the second. In every case the separation of the system R into two classes A_1, A_2 is such that every number of the first class A_1 is less than every number of the second class A_2.

II COMPARISON OF THE RATIONAL NUMBERS WITH THE POINTS OF A STRAIGHT LINE

The above-mentioned properties of rational numbers recall the corresponding relations of position of the points of a straight line L. If the two opposite directions existing upon it are distinguished by "right" and "left," and p, q are two different points, then either p lies to the right of q, and at the same time q to the left of p, or conversely q lies to the right of p and at the same time p to the left of q. A third case is impossible, if p, q are actually different points. In regard to this difference in position the following laws hold:

I. If p lies to the right of q, and q to the right of r, then p lies to the right of r; and we say that q lies between the points p and r.

II. If p, r are two different points then there always exist infinitely many points that lie between p and r.

III. If p is a definite point in L, then all points in L fall into two classes, P_1, P_2, each of which contains infinitely many individuals; the first class P_1 contains all the points p_1, that lie to the left of p, and the second class P_2 contains all the points p_2 that lie to the right of p; the point p itself may be assigned at pleasure to the first or second class. In every case the separation of the straight line L into the two classes or portions P_1, P_2, is of such a character that every point of the first class P_1 lies to the left of every point of the second class P_2.

This analogy between rational numbers and the points of a straight line, as is well known, becomes a real correspondence when we select upon the straight line a definite origin or zero-point 0 and a definite unit of length for the measurement of segments. With the aid of the latter to every rational number a a corresponding length can be constructed and if we lay this off upon the straight line to the right or left of 0 according as a is possitive or negative, we obtain a definite end-point *p*, which may be regarded as the point corresponding to the number *a*; to the rational number zero corresponds the point *0*. In this way to every rational number *a*, i. e., to every individual in *R*, corresponds one and only one point *p*, i. e., an individual in *L*. To the two numbers *a*, *b* respectively correspond the two points *p*, *q*, and if *a* > *b*, then *p* lies to the right of *q*. To the laws I, II, III of the previous Section correspond completely the laws I, II, III of the present

III CONTINUITY OF THE STRAIGHT LINE

Of the greatest importance, however, is the fact that in the straight line *L* there are infinitely many points which correspond to no rational number. If the point *p* corresponds to the rational number *a*, then, as is well known, the length *0p* is commensurable with the invariable unit of measure used in the construction, i. e., there exists a third length, a so-called common measure, of which these two lengths are integral multiples. But the ancient Greeks already knew and had demonstrated that there are lengths incommensurable with a given unit of length, e. g., the diagonal of the square whose side is the unit of length. If we lay off such a length from point *0* upon the line we obtain an end-point which corresponds to no rational number. Since further it can be easily shown that there are infinitely many lengths which are incommensurable with the unit of length, we may affirm: The straight line *L* is infinitely richer in point-individuals than the domain *R* of rational numbers in number-individuals.

If now, as is our desire, we try to follow up arithmetically all phenomena in the straight line, the domain of rational numbers is insufficient and it becomes absolutely necessary that the instrument *R* constructed by the creation of the rational numbers be essentially improved by the creation of new numbers such that the domain of numbers shall gain the same completeness, or as we may say at once, the same *continuity*, as the straight line.

The previous considerations are so familiar and well known to all that many will regard their repetition quite superfluous. Still I regarded this recapitulation as necessary to prepare properly for the main question. For, the way in which the irrational numbers are usually introduced is based directly upon the conception of extensive magnitudes—which itself is nowhere carefully defined—and explains numbers as the result of measuring such a magnitude by another of the same kind.* Instead of this I demand that arithmetic shall be developed out of itself.

That such comparison with non-arithmetic notions have furnished the immediate occasion for the extension of the number-concept may, in a general way, be granted (though this was certainly not the case in the introduction of complex numbers); but this surely is no sufficient ground for introducing these foreign notions into arithmetic, the science of numbers. Just as negative and fractional rational numbers are formed by a new creation, and as the laws of operating with these numbers must and can be reduced to the laws of operating with positive integers, so we must endeavor completely to define irrational numbers by means of the rational numbers alone. The question only remains how to do this.

The above comparison of the domain R of rational numbers with a straight line has led to the recognition of the existence of gaps, of a certain incompleteness or discontinuity of the former, while we ascribe to the straight line completeness, absence of gaps, or continuity. In what then does this continuity consist? Everything must depend on the answer to this question, and only through it shall we obtain a scientific basis for the investigation of *all* continuous domains. By vague remarks upon the unbroken connection in the smallest parts obviously nothing is gained; the problem is to indicate a precise characteristic of continuity that can serve as the basis for valid deductions. For a long time I pondered over this in vain, but finally I found what I was seeking. This discovery will, perhaps, be differently estimated by different people; the majority may find its substance very commonplace. It consists of the following. In the preceding section attention was called to the fact that every point p of the straight line produces a separation of the same into two portions such that every point of one portion lies to the left of every point of the other. I find the essence of continuity in the converse, i. e., in the following principle:

"If all points of the straight line fall into two classes such that every point of the first class lies to the left of every point of the second class, then there exists one and only one point

---

* The apparent advantage of the generality of this definition of number disappears as soon as we consider complex numbers. According to my view, on the other hand, the notion of the ratio between two numbers of the same kind can be clearly developed only after the introduction of irrational numbers.

which produces this division of all points into two classes, this severing of the straight line into two portions."

As already said I think I shall not err in assuming that every one will at once grant the truth of this statement; the majority of my readers will be very much disappointed in learning that by this commonplace remark the secret of continuity is to be revealed. To this I may say that I am glad if every one finds the above principle so obvious and so in harmony with his own ideas of a line; for I am utterly unable to adduce any proof of its correctness, nor has any one the power. The assumption of this property of the line is nothing else than an axiom by which we attribute to the line its continuity, by which we find continuity in the line. If space has at all a real existence it is *not* necessary for it to be continuous; many of its properties would remain the same even were it discontinuous. And if we knew for certain that space was discontinuous there would be nothing to prevent us, in case we so desired, from filling up its gaps, in thought, and thus making it continuous; this filling up would consist in a creation of new point-individuals and would have to be effected in accordance with the above principle.

IV CREATION OF IRRATIONAL NUMBERS

From the last remarks it is sufficiently obvious how the discontinuous domain R of rational numbers may be rendered complete so as to form a continuous domain. In Section I it was pointed out that every rational number a effects a separation of the system R into two classes such that every number a_1 of the first class A_1 is less than every number a_2 of the second class A_2; the number a is either the greatest number of the class A_1 or the least number of the class A_2. If now any separation of the system R into two classes A_1, A_2, is given which possesses only *this* characteristic property that every number a_1 in A_1 is less than every number a_2 in A_2, then for brevity we shall call such a separation a *cut* [Schnitt] and designate it by (A_1, A_2). We can then say that every rational number a produces one cut or, strictly speaking, two cuts, which, however, we shall not look upon as essentially different; this cut possesses, *besides*, the property that either among the numbers of the first class there exists a greatest or among the numbers of the second class a least number. And conversely, if a cut possesses this property, then it is produced by this greatest or least rational number.

But it is easy to show that there exist infinitely many cuts not produced by rational numbers. The following example suggests itself most readily.

Let D be a positive integer but not the square of an integer, then there exists a positive integer λ such that

$$\lambda^2 < D < (\lambda + 1)^2.$$

If we assign to the second class A_2, every positive rational number a_2 whose square is $> D$, to the first class A_1 all other rational numbers a_1, this separation forms a cut (A_1, A_2), i. e., every number a_1 is less than every number a_2. For if $a_1 = 0$, or is negative, then on that ground a_1 is less than any number a_2, because, by definition, this last is positive; if a_1 is positive, then is its square $\leqq D$, and hence a_1 is less than any positive number a_2 whose square is $> D$.

But this cut is produced by no rational number. To demonstrate this it must be shown first of all that there exists no rational number whose square $= D$. Although this is known from the first elements of the theory of numbers, still the following indirect proof may find place here. If there exist a rational number whose square $= D$, then there exist two positive integers t, u, that satisfy the equation

$$t^2 - Du^2 = 0,$$

and we may assume that u is the *least* positive integer possessing the property that its square, by multiplication by D, may be converted into the square of an integer t. Since evidently

$$\lambda u < t < (\lambda + 1)u,$$

the number $u' = t - \lambda u$ is a positive integer certainly *less* than u. If further we put

$$t' = Du - \lambda t,$$

t' is likewise a positive integer, and we have

$$t^2 - Du'^2 = (\lambda^2 - D)(t^2 - Du^2) = 0,$$

which is contrary to the assumption respecting u.

Hence the square of every rational number x is either $< D$ or $> D$. From this it easily follows that there is neither in the class A_1 a greatest, nor in the class A_2 a least number. For if we put

$$y = \frac{x(x^2 + 3D)}{3x^2 + D},$$

we have

$$y - x = \frac{2x(D - x^2)}{3x^2 + D}$$

and

$$y^2 - D = \frac{(x^2 - D)^3}{(3x^2 + D)^2}$$

If in this we assume x to be a positive number from the class A_1, then $x^2 < D$, and hence $y > x$ and $y^2 < D$. Therefore y likewise belongs to the class A_1. But if we assume x to be a number from the class A_2, then $x^2 > D$, and hence $y < x$, $y > 0$, and $y^2 > D$. Therefore y likewise belongs to the class A^2. This cut is therefore produced by no rational number.

In this property that not all cuts are produced by rational numbers consists the incompleteness or discontinuity of the domain R of all rational numbers.

Whenever, then, we have to do with a cut (A_1, A_2) produced by no rational number, we create a new, an *irrational* number a, which we regard as completely defined by this cut (A_1, A_2); we shall say that the number a corresponds to this cut, or that it produces this cut. From now on, therefore, to every definite cut there corresponds a definite rational or irrational number, and we regard two numbers as *different* or *unequal* always and only when they correspond to essentially different cuts.

In order to obtain a basis for the orderly arrangement of all *real*, i. e., of all rational and irrational numbers we must investigate the relation between any two cuts (A_1, A_2) and (B_1, B_2) produced by any two numbers a and β. Obviously a cut (A_1, A_2) is given completely when one of the two classes, e. g., the first, A_1, is known, because the second, A_2, consists of all rational numbers not contained in A_1, and the characteristic property of such a first class lies in this: that if the number a_1 is contained in it, it also contains all numbers less than a_1. If now we compare two such first classes A_1, B_1 with each other, it may happen

1. That they are perfectly identical, i. e., that every number contained in A_1 is also contained in B_1, and that every number contained in B_1 is also contained in A_1. In this case A_2 is necessarily identical with B_2, and the two cuts are perfectly identical, which we denote in symbols by $a = \beta$ or $\beta = a$.

But if the two classes A_1, B_1 are not identical, then there exists in the one, e. g., in A_1, a number $a'_1 = b'_2$ not contained in the other B_1 and consequently found in B_2; hence all numbers b_1 contained in B_1 are certainly less than this number $a'_1 = b'_2$ and therefore all numbers b_1 are contained in A_1.

2. If now this number a'_1 is the only one in A_1 that is not

contained in B_1, then is every other number a_1 contained in A_1 also contained in B_1 and is consequently $< a'_1$, i. e., a'_1 is the greatest among all the numbers a_1, hence the cut (A_1, A_2) is produced by the rational number $a = a'_1 = b'_2$. Concerning the other cut (B_1, B_2) we know already that all numbers b_1 in B_1 are also contained in A_1 and are less than the number $a'_1 = b'_2$ which is contained in B_2; every other number b_2 contained in B_2 must, however, be greater than b'_2, for otherwise it would be less than a'_1, therefore contained in A_1 and hence in B_1; hence b'_2 is the least among all numbers con-in B_2, and consequently the cut (B_1, B_2) is produced by the same rational number $\beta = b'_2 = a'_1 = a$. The two cuts are then only unessentially different.

3. If, however, there exist in A_1 at least two different numbers $a'_1 = b'_2$ and $a''_1 = b''_2$, which are not contained in B_1, then there exist infinitely many of them, because all the infinitely many numbers lying between a'_1 and a''_1 are obviously contained in A_1 (Section I, II) but not in B_1. In this case we say that the numbers a and β corresponding to these two essentially different cuts (A_1, A_2) and (B_1, B_2) are *different*, and further that a is *greater* than β, that β is *less* than a, which we express in symbols by $a > \beta$ as well as $\beta < a$. It is to be noticed that this definition coincides completely with the one given earlier, when a, β are rational.

The remaining possible cases are these:

4. If there exists in B_1 one and only one number $b' = a'_2$, that is not contained in A_1 then the two cuts (A_1, A_2) and (B_1, B_2) are only unessentially different and they are produced by one and the same rational number $a = a'_2 = b'_1 = \beta$.

5. But if there are in B_1 at least two numbers which are not contained in A_1, then $\beta > a$, $a < \beta$.

As this exhausts the possible cases, it follows that of two different numbers one is necessarily the greater, the other the less, which gives two possibilities. A third case is impossible. This was indeed involved in the use of the *comparative* (greater, less) to designate the relation between a, β; but this use has only now been justified. In just such investigations one needs to exercise the greatest care so that even with the best intention to be honest he shall not, through a hasty choice of expressions borrowed from other notions already developed, allow himself to be led into the use of inadmissible transfers from one domain to the other.

If now we consider again somewhat carefully the case $a > \beta$ it is obvious that the less number β, if rational, certainly belongs to the class A_1; for since there is in A_1 number $a'_1 = b'_2$ which belongs to the class B_2, it follows that the number β, whether the greatest number in B_1 or the least in B_2 is certainly $\leqq a'_1$ and hence contained in A_1. Likewise it is obvious from $a > \beta$ that the greater number a, if rational, certainly belongs to the class B_2, because $a \geqq a'_1$. Combining these two considerations we get the following result: If a cut is produced by the number a then any rational number belongs to the class A_1 or to the class A_2 according as it is less or greater than a; if the number a is itself rational it may belong to either class.

From this we obtain finally the following: If $a > \beta$, i. e., if there are infinitely many numbers in A_1 not contained in B_1 then there are infinitely many such numbers that at the same time are different from a and from β; every such rational number c is $< a$, because it is contained in A_1 and at the same time it is $> \beta$ because contained in B_2.

PART II

The name of Pythagoras of Samos, a Greek mathematician and philosopher of the sixth century B.C., is indelibly associated with the discovery of irrational numbers. According to tradition, Pythagoras discovered that the side and the diagonal of a square are incommensurable: if the length of the side of the square is called "1," then the length of the diagonal is given by the value of the square root of 2, a value that is an irrational number.

There are several terms in the preceding paragraph which need clearing up. Foremost among them is "irrational"; next in importance, because of its close relation to irrationality, is "incommensurable." The way to understand the problem of irrationality among numbers is to understand first of all what rational numbers are. This in turn requires us to go back and begin with the simplest of all numbers, the positive integers, 1, 2, 3, 4, ..., etc. (Actually, even these numbers are not simple;

in the next chapter we shall see that it is quite difficult to define the allegedly simple term "number"; for the time being, however, we shall rely on our intuitive understanding of the meaning of number.) The positive integers are what Euclid had in mind when he defined "number." Note, incidentally, that Euclid does not include "1," or the unit, among the numbers. Thereby he avoids circularity in his definition of number, which is "multitude of units." The positive integers are often referred to as "natural numbers."

Mathematics cannot get along well just using the natural numbers. Suppose we start with any natural number a and add another natural number b to it. The result c—whatever it may be—will be another natural number. Similarly, if a given natural number d is multiplied by a natural number e, the result f is again a natural number. Thus the operations of addition and multiplication are such that if they are performed on two or more members of the natural number system they will give results that are also members of the natural number system. Another way of saying the same thing is that for addition and multiplication the natural number system is closed; these operations, when performed on natural numbers, do not take us out of the system.

We run into trouble, however, when we turn to the other two basic arithmetical operations—subtraction and division. Sometimes, these two operations when performed on natural numbers give results that are themselves natural numbers. If the natural number from which we subtract is greater than the natural number which we subtract, then the result is another natural number. For example, $8 - 5 = 3$; $56,734 - 39,001 = 17,733$. And similarly if the natural number which we divide is a multiple of the natural number which we divide it by, then the result is another natural number. $40 \div 5 = 8$; $306 \div 17 = 18$, and so on.

But if things are the other way around, we must leave the natural number system in order to get an answer. If in a subtraction problem of natural numbers the first number is smaller than the second number, then the resulting difference is not a natural number. We can only say in such a case either that there is no answer, or that the answer is a new kind of number, a negative number. Either "$5 - 8$" must be considered as a problem without a solution, or if we want it to have a solution, we must admit that a problem involving two natural numbers can result in something *not* a natural number, namely a negative number. Either way of looking at subtraction is perfectly legitimate; mathematicians prefer, however, the second answer, since they like to leave as few insoluble problems as possible. In this case, the price of finding a solution is a new definition of number with a consequent expansion of the number system.

If we reckon all integers—both positive and negative (as well as 0)—as belonging to the number system, then the operation of subtraction can always be performed within that system. For subtraction, the system of natural numbers is not closed, but the system of all integers is. Subtracting an integer from an integer always results in another integer. Certain rules must be established, of course, to indicate how the operations are to be performed, but these rules present no difficulties. For example, $-5 - (-8) = -5 + 8$, according to the rules. We do not intend here to investigate whether these rules are good, clear, or self-explanatory. We only want to point out that the rules are such that any subtraction problem has just one answer, and that the answer—if the problem involves integers—is always an integer.

This expansion of the number system to include negative integers not only makes subtraction among *natural* numbers always possible; it also is the case that this new system of *all* integers is closed for subtraction, so that subtraction among integers (whether positive or negative) is always possible.

We have already indicated that the system of natural numbers is not closed for division. How about the system of all integers? Is it closed for division? The answer again is No. The introduction of negative integers has done nothing toward solving the problem of making division always possible. What needs to be done, if we are faced with division problems such as $40 \div 7$, is either the declaration that this problem has no solution, or else another expansion of the number system to include *fractions*. If we are willing to modify our definition of number once more and to expand our number system accordingly, then we can give an answer to division problems such as $40 \div 7$; the answer is, of course $5\frac{5}{7}$.

By introducing not only positive but also negative fractions we can make division always possible as long as it involves only positive or negative integers or fractions. There is one exception however: If division by 0 is called for, there is no answer. Division by 0 is declared not possible. We mention this mainly to indicate that this way of dealing with a difficulty—declaring the problem impossible—is one that is, in fact, occasionally used by mathematicians.

The system of the numbers we have so far introduced—positive and negative integers, as well as positive and negative fractions—is called the system of rational numbers. It is closed for the operations of addition, subtraction, multiplication, and division, with the single exception of division by 0, which is never permitted.

It is obvious that the system of rational numbers includes a great many numbers. For example, between any two rational numbers there is always a third one which is greater than one of the original numbers and smaller than the other one. (This is not true of integers; for example, there is no integer between 21 and 22.) It it also intuitively obvious that in any given interval, say between two integers like 5 and 6, there is an infinite number of rational numbers.

But interestingly enough, the system of rational numbers does not yet include all numbers. There are two ways of seeing this: First, we could show that there are some "numbers" such as the length of the diagonal of a square whose side is 1, which are not equal to any rational numbers. We could show that there are a great many other numbers of this sort, which obviously are not rational. The second way consists of looking at the system of rational numbers and finding that in fact there are "holes" in it: there are some places in the interval between 1 and 2 which are not taken up by any rational number. Another way of saying this is that the system of rational numbers is not continuous. If we compare the interval between 1 and 2 with the points on a line, we should find that we cannot assign a rational number to every point. There are, so to speak, "too many" points on the line. The points to which no rational numbers correspond have irrational numbers corresponding to them.

It was the German mathematician Richard Dedekind who first rigorously analyzed the concept of irrational number. Dedekind (1831-1916) was a student of Gauss—perhaps his greatest—at the University of Göttingen. Though Dedekind spent most of his life in a relatively obscure teaching position, his works have that simplicity and abstractness that mark the mathematician of genius.

In defining irrational numbers, Dedekind chose the second of the two ways we mentioned above. He began with the system of rational numbers and then showed that by means of that system he could define numbers which did not belong in that system. The method he used is that of making a *Schnitt* (German for "cut") in the rational number system. This cut serves to define an irrational number; accordingly this method is referred to as the "Dedekind Schnitt."

Dedekind's procedure is very simple and very difficult to understand. What he does is apparently so unexciting that it is difficult to realize the significance of it.

Dedekind begins by noting three laws that are true for any two rational numbers a and b, which are not equal.

1. If a is greater than b and b is greater than c, then also a is greater than c. The property of being "greater than" is transitive, as we would now say.

2. Between any two rational numbers, there lies an infinite number of other rational numbers. We have already mentioned this property of the rational number system.

3. Any rational number a divides the entire system of rational numbers into two classes. One class contains all those rational numbers smaller than a; the other class, those numbers greater than a. These are two completely distinct classes, having no members in common. To which of these two classes does a itself belong? We may assign it to either class; it makes no difference. No matter where we place a itself, it is true that any member of the first class is smaller than any member of the second class. The only difference is this: if we assign a to the first class, then this class has a greatest member, namely a, while the second class has no least member (for between any member of the second class and a, there always exists an infinite number of other rational numbers). If, on the other hand, we assign a to the second class, then this second class has a least member, namely a, while the first class has no greatest member. (For again, if we put forward any rational number in the first class as allegedly the greatest, it is always possible to find infinitely many other rational numbers which are larger than this number but still smaller than a, and so belong to the first class.)

Dedekind summarizes the significance of this kind of cut as follows:

We can then say that every rational number a produces one cut, or, strictly speaking, two cuts, which, however, we shall not look upon as essentially different; this cut possesses, besides, the property that either among the numbers of the first class there exists a greatest or among the numbers of the second class a least number. And conversely, if a cut possesses this property, then it is produced by this greatest or least rational number (p. 145).

Then he continues with the most important statement in the entire work:

> But it is easy to show that there exist infinitely many cuts not produced by rational numbers.

Before going on, let us examine what one of Dedekind's cuts looks like, when it is made by a rational number. Let us consider the number ⅘. This is, of course, a rational number. According to Dedekind, it divides all rational numbers into two classes, namely, those smaller than ⅘, and those greater than ⅘. Examples of numbers in the first class are ⅔, ½, 0, − ¼, − 2, etc. Examples of numbers in the second class are 1, 1½, 756, etc. All numbers in the first group are smaller than all numbers in the second group. Conversely, all numbers in the second group are greater than all numbers in the first group. Now it only remains to assign a place to ⅘ itself. If we assign it to the first class, it is still true that every member of the first group is smaller than any member of the second group. Suppose that we now assign ⅘ to the second group instead; it will still be true that any member of the first group is smaller than any member of the second group. If we assign ⅘ to the first group, then the first group has a greatest member, namely ⅘. If, instead, we assign ⅘ to the second group, then the second group has a least member, namely ⅘.

Dedekind's method of showing that "in the holes" of the rational number system there are other, irrational, numbers, is as follows: He proposes to show us a cut made *in* the rational number system, but not *by* a rational number. This cut, as before, produces two classes. As before, it will be the case that any member of the first class is less than any member of the second class (and any member of the second class is greater than any member of the first class). So far all is the same as before. Here is the difference: The cut which Dedekind proposes to show us is such that the first class has no greatest member, while the second class has no least member. If he can succeed in showing us such a cut, then it is clear that no rational number has produced it; for any rational number produces a cut in which either the first group has a greatest, or the second group, a least, member.

Dedekind begins by choosing a positive integer, but one which is not the square of another integer. An example of such an integer would be the number 18. Dedekind calls this number D. The number D then lies between two square numbers, such as λ^2 and $(\lambda + 1)^2$. If $D = 18$, then $\lambda = 4$, and $\lambda + 1 = 5$; 18 lies between 16 and 25.

Now Dedekind divides all rational numbers into two classes, in terms of D. He calls these two classes A_1 and A_2. The second class, A_2, includes all positive rational numbers whose square is greater than D; the first class, A_1, includes all other rational numbers. Every number in A_1 is less than any number in A_2. A_1 contains all negative numbers, since A_2 contains only positive numbers and any negative number is, of course, smaller than any positive number. The positive numbers which A_1 contains are smaller than the positive numbers in A_2, for the only positive numbers in A_1 are those whose square is less than D, whereas A_2 contains all those positive numbers whose square is greater than D.

Thus A_1 and A_2 are two classes of the kind which Dedekind has discussed earlier: any member of A_1 is less than any member of A_2, and any member of A_2 is greater than any member of A_1. But A_1 *has no greatest member* and A_2 *has no least member*. This last fact still remains to be shown; but if Dedekind succeeds in demonstrating it, he will also have succeeded in proving that here is a cut in the rational number system not made by a rational number.

Everything, then, depends on the absence of both a least (in A_2) and a greatest (in A_1) member. To show that these numbers are absent, Dedekind begins by first showing that there is no *rational* number whose square is D. The proof is by reduction to the absurd.

Let us assume that in fact there is a rational number whose square is D. Since, by assumption D lies between the squares of two adjacent integers (λ and $\lambda + 1$), the rational number whose square is D must be a fraction. Let it be $\dfrac{t}{u}$. Let these be the least positive numbers in which that fraction can be expressed; that is, let it not be possible to do any more "canceling." Thus

$$\frac{t^2}{u^2} = D$$

or

$$t^2 = Du^2$$

or

$$t^2 - Du^2 = 0.$$

If we substitute the value $\dfrac{t^2}{u^2}$ for D in the inequality

$$\lambda^2 < D < (\lambda + 1)^2$$

we get

$$\lambda^2 < \frac{t^2}{u^2} < (\lambda + 1)^2$$

or

$$\lambda^2 u^2 < t^2 < (\lambda + 1)^2 u^2$$

or

$$\lambda u < t < (\lambda + 1)u.$$

Regarding first only the left side of the last inequality, we see that

$$0 < t - \lambda u.$$

This means that $t - \lambda u$ is a positive quantity. Furthermore, since t, λ, u are all integers, $t - \lambda u$ must also be an integer.

Looking now at the right side of the above inequality, we see that

$$t < \lambda u + u$$

or again

$$t - \lambda < u.$$

Let us give the quantity $t - \lambda u$ the name u'. Let us also give the name t' to the quantity $Du - \lambda t$. This last quantity is certainly an integer, since D, u, λ, and t are all integers. It is also a positive integer, for Du is greater than λt. This may be seen as follows:

$$Du^2 = t^2$$

or

$$Du = \frac{t^2}{u}.$$

The last line may be written as

$$Du = t \cdot \frac{t}{u}.$$

Now $\frac{t}{u}$, when squared, makes D, while λ when squared makes λ^2, and D is greater than λ^2; therefore $\frac{t}{u}$ is greater than λ.

Hence Du, which equals $t \cdot \frac{t}{u}$, is greater than $t \cdot \lambda$.

Now form the quantity $t'^2 - Du'^2$. This is equal to

$$(Du - \lambda t)^2 - D(t - \lambda u)^2.$$

This last quantity is equal to

$$D^2 u^2 - 2Du\lambda t + \lambda^2 t^2 - Dt^2 + 2Dt\lambda u - D\lambda^2 u^2$$

or

$$D^2 u^2 + \lambda^2 t^2 - Dt^2 - D\lambda^2 u^2.$$

This last quantity can be written as
$$(\lambda^2 - D)(t^2 - Du^2).$$
But we know that $(t^2 - Du^2) = 0$, by the assumption that $\frac{t}{u}$ when squared equals D. Therefore the whole product is equal to 0. And therefore also
$$t'^2 - Du'^2 = 0.$$
This means that
$$\frac{t'^2}{u'^2} = D$$
And since u' is smaller than u, this contradicts the original assumption that $\frac{t}{u}$ was the fraction in the smallest terms which, when squared, gives D.

Hence we conclude that the number whose square is D is not rational—that is, that it cannot be expressed as a fraction of integers. Having established this, we can show that the class A_1 has no greatest, and the class A_2 no least, member.

The method of proof is another reduction to the absurd. Suppose there is a number x which is the greatest in A_1. (It will, of course, be a positive number.) Now form the quantity

$$y = \frac{x(x^2 + 3D)}{3x^2 + D}$$

Then

$$\begin{aligned}
y - x &= \frac{x(x^2 + 3D)}{3x^2 + D} - x = \frac{x(x^2 + 3D) - x(3x^2 + D)}{3x^2 + D} \\
&= \frac{x^3 + 3Dx - 3x^3 - xD}{3x^2 + D} = \frac{2Dx - 2x^3}{3x^2 + D} \\
&= \frac{2x(D - x^2)}{3x^2 + D}.
\end{aligned}$$

Consider this last quantity: x is positive, and since x is assumed to belong to the class A_1, D is greater than x^2. Therefore, the numerator of the fraction is positive, and the entire fraction is positive, since the denominator is clearly positive. But if the quantity $y - x$ is positive, then y is greater than x.

Furthermore, y^2 is less than D and therefore y belongs to A_1. To see this, consider the same quantity y as before, namely,

$$y = \frac{x(x^2 + 3D)}{3x^2 + D}.$$

Then

$$y^2 = \frac{x^2(x^2 + 3D)^2}{(3x^2 + D)^2} = \frac{x^2(x^4 + 6x^2D + 9D^2)}{(3x^2 + D)^2}$$

$$= \frac{x^6 + 6x^4D + 9D^2x^2}{(3x^2 + D)^2}$$

Then

$$y^2 - D = \frac{x^6 + 6x^4D + 9D^2x^2\ Gx^4D - D}{(3x^2 + D)^2}$$

$$= \frac{x^6 + 6x^4D + 9D^2x^2 - D(3x^2 + D)^2}{(3x^2 + D)^2}$$

$$= \frac{x^6 + 6x^4D + 9D^2x^2 - 9Dx^4 - 6x^2D^2 - D^3}{(3x^2 + D)^2}$$

$$= \frac{x^6 - 3x^4D + 3x^2D^2 - D^3}{(3x^2 + D)^2} = \frac{(x^2 - D)^3}{(3x^2 + D)^2}$$

The numerator of the last fraction is negative. For x^2 is less than D, so that $x^2 - D$ is negative. And a negative number raised to the third power gives another negative number. (For example, -5 raised to the third power is -125.) The denominator of the fraction is positive, and therefore the fraction as a whole is negative. This means that $y^2 - D$ is negative; in other words, y^2 is less than D.

This proves that there is no greatest member in A_1. For on the assumption that there was a greatest member x, we have found another number, y, which is greater than x and also belongs to A_1. (Note that the method of this proof is much like that of Proposition 20 in Euclid's Book IX: assuming that something is the case, we prove that it is not.)

In exactly similar fashion, we can prove that A_2 has no least member. To prove this, let us again assume that there is a least member x. Form the quantity y as before, and also $y - x$. The fraction

$$y - x = \frac{2x(D - x^2)}{3x^2 + D}$$

now is negative, for in the numerator D is smaller than x^2, making the whole fraction negative. Consequently, y is less than x.

To show y is a member of A_2, we must prove that y^2 is greater than D. Form again the expression $y^2 - D$. As before,

$$y^2 - D = \frac{(x^2 - D)^3}{(3x^2 + D)^2}.$$

This time, since x^2 is greater than D, the expression $x^2 - D$ is positive, and hence its cube is also positive. Therefore, the entire expression $y^2 - D$ is positive, which means that y^2 is greater than D, or y belongs to A_2.

These two demonstrations together show that neither does A_1 have a greatest member, nor does A_2 have a least member. Consequently, the cut (A_1, A_2) is not made by any rational number.

But if the cut (A_1, A_2) is not made by any rational number, then it must be made by another, new kind of number, since in all respects the cut is like the cut made by a rational number, except for the property that A_1 has no greatest, and A_2 no least, member. This new type of number is called an irrational number. The word "irrational" is not meant to suggest anything unreasonable or strange about these numbers; it merely means that these numbers have no ratio to the number 1 that can be expressed in whole numbers.

What is Dedekind's achievement? Irrational numbers had been known for a long time. Pythagoras allegedly discovered that the diagonal of a unit square is irrational, and Euclid's Book X is an immense collection of propositions devoted to incommensurable lines (which are the geometric equivalent or irrational numbers). What was lacking in all the earlier discussions of irrationals was a clear understanding of their nature. The early followers of Pythagoras were so puzzled by the character of irrationals that they thought there was something mystical about them. And indeed, an irrational number *is* strange: No common measure can be found—no matter how small—for the unit (that is, the number 1) and the irrational number. For if there were a common measure, it would go a certain number of times into the so-called irrational number, and another number of times into the unit. But this would make a rational fraction of the irrational. For let the irrational be called z. Then if there is some very small measure of both z and 1, it would go, say, 876 times into z, and 438 times into 1. But in that case, $z/1 = 876/438$, and this, of course is a rational fraction. Hence there is no common measure—no matter how tiny—for the irrational and the unit. (This is why irrational numbers are also "incommensurable"; they are incommensurable with the unit, since they have no measure in common with it.)

All this, however, is not saying *what* irrational numbers are. It merely describes a property they have—that of not having a common measure with the unit. And this property leaves in doubt whether, first, there are such things, and second, if there are, whether they are properly called numbers. Dedekind's cut, however, assures us on both counts. All numbers are now defined in terms of *cuts*; that is, each number is defined as making a unique division in the system of infinite numbers. Rational numbers and irrational numbers differ in just one respect: the presence or absence of a least or greatest member of the cut.

This definition of numbers defines numbers in terms of each other, and therefore does not really say "what a number is." It defines a given number in the sense of *distinguishing* it from all other numbers, and it does so in terms of a certain operation—that of dividing the set of numbers. In the next chapter we shall encounter an attempt at really defining number —that is, saying what it is.

CHAPTER SIX

Russell—The Definition of Number

PART I

Very often the simplest questions are the hardest to answer.
This is due to the fact that simple questions, or at least questions about simple things, often go to the very heart of a
matter. The question "What is a number?" is that kind of
question; it goes to the very heart of the science of arithmetic.
Not many people dare ask such questions; fewer still know
to answer them. Bertrand Russell, in the selection now before
us, dares ask the question and then proceeds to answer it—
in a manner that has stood the test of time. His answer is still
accepted, and it reveals to us a great deal about the character
of numbers.

Bertrand Russell:
Introduction to Mathematical Philosophy*

Chapter 1

THE SERIES OF NATURAL NUMBERS

Mathematics is a study which, when we start from its most
familiar portions, may be pursued in either of two opposite
directions. The more familiar direction is constructive, towards

* From *Introduction to Mathematical Philosophy* (London: George
Allen & Unwin, Ltd., 1919), pp. 1-28. Reprinted by permission of George
Allen & Unwin, Ltd., and the Macmillan Company.

gradually increasing complexity: from integers to fractions, real numbers, complex numbers; from addition and multiplication to differentiation and integration, and on to higher mathematics. The other direction, which is less familiar, proceeds, by analysing, to greater and greater abstractness and logical simplicity; instead of asking what can be defined and deduced from what is assumed to begin with, we ask instead what more general ideas and principles can be found, in terms of which what was our starting-point can be defined or deduced. It is the fact of pursuing this opposite direction that characterises mathematical philosophy as opposed to ordinary mathematics. But it should be understood that the distinction is one, not in the subject matter, but in the state of mind of the investigator. Early Greek geometers, passing from the empirical rules of Egyptian land-surveying to the general propositions by which those rules were found to be justifiable, and thence to Euclid's axioms and postulates, were engaged in mathematical philosophy, according to the above definition; but when once the axioms and postulates had been reached, their deductive employment, as we find it in Euclid, belonged to mathematics in the ordinary sense. The distinction between mathematics and mathematical philosophy is one which depends upon the interest inspiring the research, and upon the stage which the research has reached; not upon the propositions with which the research is concerned.

We may state the same distinction in another way. The most obvious and easy things in mathematics are not those that come logically at the beginning; they are things that, from the point of view of logical deduction, come somewhere in the middle. Just as the easiest bodies to see are those that are neither very near nor very far, neither very small nor very great, so the easiest conceptions to grasp are those that are neither very complex nor very simple (using "simple" in a *logical* sense). And as we need two sorts of instruments, the telescope and the microscope, for the enlargement of our visual powers, so we need two sorts of instruments for the enlargement of our logical powers, one to take us forward to the higher mathematics, the other to take us backward to the logical foundations of the things that we are inclined to take for granted in mathematics. We shall find that by analysing our ordinary mathematical notions we acquire fresh insight, new powers, and the means of reaching whole new mathematical subjects by adopting fresh lines of advance after our backward journey. It is the purpose of this book to explain mathematical philosophy simply and untechnically, without enlarging upon those portions which are so doubtful or difficult that an elementary treatment is scarcely possible. A full treatment will be found in *Principia Mathematica*;* the treatment in the present volume is intended merely as an introduction.

To the average educated person of the present day, the obvious starting-point of mathematics would be the series of whole numbers,

$$1, 2, 3, 4, \ldots \text{etc.}$$

Probably only a person with some mathematical knowledge would think of beginning with 0 instead of 1, but we will presume this degree of knowledge; we will take as our starting-point the series:

$$0, 1, 2, 3, \ldots n, n + 1, \ldots$$

and it is this series that we shall mean when we speak of the "series of natural numbers."

It is only at a high stage of civilisation that we could take this series as our starting-point. It must have required many ages to discover that a brace of pheasants and a couple of days were both instances of the number 2: the degree of abstraction involved is far from easy. And the discovery that 1 is a number must have been difficult. As for 0, it is a very recent addition; the Greeks and Romans had no such digit. If we had been embarking upon mathematical philosophy in earlier days, we should have had to start with something less abstract than the series of natural numbers, which we should reach as a stage on our backward journey. When the logical foundations of mathematics have grown more familiar, we shall be able to start further back, at what is now a late stage in our analysis. But for the moment the natural numbers seem to represent what is easiest and most familiar in mathematics.

But though familiar, they are not understood. Very few people are prepared with a definition of what is meant by "number," or "0" or "1." It is not very difficult to see that, starting from 0, any other of the natural numbers can be reached by repeated additions of 1, but we shall have to define what we mean by "adding 1," and what we mean by "repeated." These questions are by no means easy. It was believed until recently that some, at least, of these first notions of arithmetic must be accepted as too simple and primitive to be defined. Since all terms that are defined are defined by means of other terms, it is clear that human knowledge must always be

---

* Cambridge University Press, vol. i., 1910; vol. ii, 1911; vol. iii., 1913. By Whitehead and Russell.

content to accept some terms as intelligible without definition, in order to have a starting-point for its definitions. It is not clear that there must be terms which are *incapable* of definition: it is possible that, however far back we go in defining, we always *might* go further still. On the other hand, it is also possible that, when analysis has been pushed far enough, we can reach terms that really are simple, and therefore logically incapable of the sort of definition that consists in analysing. This is a question which it is not necessary for us to decide; for our purposes it is sufficient to observe that, since human powers are finite, the definitions known to us must always begin somewhere, with terms undefined for the moment, though perhaps not permanently.

All traditional pure mathematics, including analytical geometry, may be regarded as consisting wholly of propositions about the natural numbers. That is to say, the terms which occur can be defined by means of the natural numbers, and the propositions can be deduced from the properties of the natural numbers—with the addition, in each case, of the ideas and propositions of pure logic.

That all traditional pure mathematics can be derived from the natural numbers is a fairly recent discovery, though it had long been suspected. Pythagoras, who believed that not only mathematics, but everything else could be deduced from numbers, was the discoverer of the most serious obstacle in the way of what is called the "arithmetising" of mathematics. It was Pythagoras who discovered the existence of incommensurables, and, in particular, the incommensurability of the side of a square and the diagonal. If the length of the side is 1 inch, the number of inches in the diagonal is the square root of 2, which appeared not to be a number at all. The problem thus raised was solved only in our own day, and was only solved *completely* by the help of the reduction of arithmetic to logic, which will be explained in following chapters. For the present, we shall take for granted the arithmetisation of mathematics, though this was a feat of the very greatest importance.

Having reduced all traditional pure mathematics to the theory of the natural numbers, the next step in logical analysis was to reduce this theory itself to the smallest set of premisses and undefined terms from which it could be derived. This work was accomplished by Peano. He showed that the entire theory of the natural numbers could be derived from three primitive ideas and five primitive propositions in addition to those of pure logic. These three ideas and five propositions thus became, as it were, hostages for the whole of traditional pure mathematics. If they could be defined and proved in terms of others, so could all pure mathematics. Their logical "weight," if one may use such an expression, is equal to that of the whole series of sciences that have been deduced from the theory of the natural numbers; the truth of this whole series is assured if the truth of the five primitive propositions is guaranteed, provided, of course, that there is nothing erroneous in the purely logical apparatus which is also involved. The work of analysing mathematics is extraordinarily facilitated by this work of Peano's.

The three primitive ideas in Peano's arithmetic are:

0, number, successor.

By "successor" he means the next number in the natural order. That is to say, the successor of 0 is 1, the successor of 1 is 2, and so on. By "number" he means, in this connection, the class of the natural numbers.[1] He is not assuming that we know all the members of this class, but only that we know what we mean when we say that this or that is a number, just as we know what we mean when we say "Jones is a man," though we do not know all men individually.

The five primitive propositions which Peano assumes are:

(1) 0 is a number.
(2) The successor of any number is a number.
(3) No two numbers have the same successor.
(4) 0 is not the successor of any number.
(5) Any property which belongs to 0, and also to the successor of every number which has the property, belongs to all numbers.

The last of these is the principle of mathematical induction. We shall have much to say concerning mathematical induction in the sequel; for the present, we are concerned with it only as it occurs in Peano's analysis of arithmetic.

Let us consider briefly the kind of way in which the theory of the natural numbers results from these three ideas and five propositions. To begin with, we define 1 as "the successor of 0," 2 as "the successor of 1," and so on. We can obviously go on as long as we like with these definitions, since, in virtue of (2), every number that we reach will have a successor, and, in virtue of (3), this cannot be any of the numbers already defined, because, if it were, two different numbers would have the same successor; and in virtue of (4) none of the numbers we reach in the series of successors can be 0. Thus the series

---

[1] We shall use "number" in this sense in the present chapter. Afterwards the word will be used in a more general sense.

of successors gives us an endless series of continually new numbers. In virtue of (5) all numbers come in this series, which begins with 0 and travels on through successive successors: for (a) 0 belongs to this series, and (b) if a number n belongs to it, so does its successor, whence, by mathematical induction, every member belongs to the series.

Suppose we wish to define the sum of two numbers. Taking any number m, we define $m+0$ as m, and $m+(n+1)$ as the successor of $m+n$. In virtue of (5) this gives a definition of the sum of m and n, whatever number n may be. Similarly we can define the product of any two numbers. The reader can easily convince himself that any ordinary elementary proposition of arithmetic can be proved by means of our five premises, and if he has any difficulty he can find the proof in Peano.

It is time now to turn to the considerations which make it necessary to advance beyond the standpoint of Peano, who represents the last perfection of the "arithmetisation" of mathematics, to that of Frege, who first succeeded in "logicising" mathematics, *i.e.* in reducing to logic the arithmetical notions which his predecessors had shown to be sufficient for mathematics. We shall not, in this chapter, actually give Frege's definition of number and of particular numbers, but we shall give some of the reasons why Peano's treatment is less final than it appears to be.

In the first place, Peano's three primitive ideas—namely, "0," "number," and "successor"—are capable of an infinite number of different interpretations, all of which will satisfy the five primitive propositions. We will give some examples.

(1) Let "0" be taken to mean 100, and let "number" be taken to mean the numbers from 100 onward in the series of natural numbers. Then all our primitive propositions are satisfied, even the fourth, for, though 100 is the successor of 99, 99 is not a "number" in the sense which we are now giving the word "number." It is obvious that any number may be substituted for 100 in this example.

(2) Let "0" have its usual meaning, but let "number" mean what we usually call "even numbers," and let the "successor" of a number be what results from adding two to it. Then "1" will stand for the number two, "2" will stand for the number four, and so on; the series of "numbers" now will be.

0, two, four, six, eight . . .

All Peano's five premisses are satisfied still.

(3) Let "0" mean the number one, let "number" mean the set

$$1, \tfrac{1}{2}, \tfrac{1}{4}, \tfrac{1}{8}, \tfrac{1}{16}, \ldots$$

and let "successor" mean "half." Then all Peano's five axioms will be true of this set.

It is clear that such examples might be multiplied indefinitely. In fact, given any series

$$x_0, x_1, x_2, x_3, \ldots x_n, \ldots$$

which is endless, contains no repetitions, has a beginning, and has no terms that cannot be reached from the beginning in a finite number of steps, we have a set of terms verifying Peano's axioms. This is easily seen, though the formal proof is somewhat long. Let "0" mean x_0, let "number" mean the whole set of terms, and let the "successor" of x_n mean x_{n+1}. Then

(1) "0 is a number," *i.e.* x_0 is a member of the set.

(2) "The successor of any number is a number," *i.e.* taking any term x_n in the set, x_{n+1} is also in the set.

(3) "No two numbers have the same successor," *i.e.* if x_m and x_n are two different members of the set, x_{m+1} and x_{n+1} are different; this results from the fact that (by hypothesis) there are no repetitions in the set.

(4) "0 is not the successor of any number," *i.e.* no term in the set comes before x_0.

(5) This becomes: Any property which belongs to x_0, and belongs to x_{n+1} provided it belongs to x_n, belongs to all the x's.

This follows from the corresponding property for numbers.

A series of the form

$$x_0, x_1, x_2, \ldots x_n, \ldots$$

in which there is a first term, a successor to each term (so that there is no last term), no repetitions, and every term can be reached from the start in a finite number of steps, is called a *progression*. Progressions are of great importance in the principles of mathematics. As we have just seen, every progression verifies Peano's five axioms. It can be proved, conversely, that every series which verifies Peano's five axioms is a progression. Hence these five axioms may be used to define the class of progressions: "progressions" are "those series which verify these five axioms." Any progression may be taken as the basis of pure mathematics: we may give the name "0" to its first term, the name "number" to the whole set of its terms, and the name "successor" to the next in the progression. The progression need not be composed of numbers: it may be composed of points in space, or moments of time, or any other terms of which there is an infinite supply. Each different progression will give rise to a different interpretation of all the propositions of traditional pure mathematics; all these possible interpretations will be equally true.

In Peano's system there is nothing to enable us to distinguish between these different interpretations of his primitive ideas. It is assumed that we know what is meant by "0," and that we shall not suppose that this symbol means 100 or Cleopatra's Needle or any of the other things that it might mean.

This point, that "0" and "number" and "successor" cannot be defined by means of Peano's five axioms, but must be independently understood, is important. We want our numbers not merely to verify mathematical formulæ, but to apply in the right way to common objects. We want to have ten fingers and two eyes and one nose. A system in which "1" meant 100, and "2" meant 101, and so on, might be all right for pure mathematics, but would not suit daily life. We want "0" and "number" and "successor" to have meanings which will give us the right allowance of fingers and eyes and noses. We have already some knowledge (though not sufficiently articulate or analytic) of what we mean by "1" and "2" and so on, and our use of numbers in arithmetic must conform to this knowledge. We cannot secure that this shall be the case by Peano's method; all that we can do if we adopt his method, is to say "we know what we mean by '0' and 'number' and 'successor,' though we cannot explain what we mean in terms of other simpler concepts." It is quite legitimate to say this when we must, and at *some* point we all must; but it is the object of mathematical philosophy to put off saying it as long as possible. By the logical theory of arithmetic we are able to put it off for a very long time.

It might be suggested that, instead of setting up "0" and "number" and "successor" as terms of which we know the meaning although we cannot define them, we might let them stand for *any* three terms that verify Peano's five axioms. They will then no longer be terms which have a meaning that is definite though undefined: they will be "variables," terms concerning which we make certain hypotheses, namely, those stated in the five axioms, but which are otherwise undetermined. If we adopt this plan, our theorems will not be proved concerning an ascertained set of terms called "the natural numbers," but concerning all sets of terms having certain properties. Such a procedure is not fallacious; indeed for certain purposes it represents a valuable generalisation. But from two points of view it fails to give an adequate basis for arithmetic. In the first place, it does not enable us to know whether there are any sets of terms verifying Peano's axioms; it does not even give the faintest suggestion of any way of discovering whether there are such sets. In the second place, as already observed, we want our numbers to be such as can be used for counting common objects, and this requires that our numbers should have a *definite* meaning, not merely that they should have certain formal properties. This definite meaning is defined by the logical theory of arithmetic.

Chapter II

DEFINITION OF NUMBER

The question "What is a number?" is one which has been often asked, but has only been correctly answered in our own time. The answer was given by Frege in 1884, in his *Grundlagen der Arithmetik*.* Although this book is quite short, not difficult, and of the very highest importance, it attracted almost no attention, and the definition of number which it contains remained practically unknown until it was rediscovered by the present author in 1901.

In seeking a definition of number, the first thing to be clear about is what we may call the grammar of our inquiry. Many philosophers, when attempting to define number, are really setting to work to define plurality, which is quite a different thing. *Number* is what is characteristic of numbers, as *man* is what is characteristic of men. A plurality is not an instance of number, but of some particular number. A trio of men, for example, is an instance of the number 3, and the number 3 is an instance of number; but the trio is not an instance of number. This point may seem elementary and scarcely worth mentioning; yet it has proved too subtle for the philosophers, with few exceptions.

A particular number is not identical with any collection of terms having that number: the number 3 is not identical with the trio consisting of Brown, Jones, and Robinson. The number 3 is something which all trios have in common, and which distinguishes them from other collections. A number is something that characterises certain collections, namely, those that have that number.

* The same answer is given more fully and with more development in his *Grundgesetze der Arithmetik*, vol. i., 1893.

Instead of speaking of a "collection," we shall as a rule speak of a "class," or sometimes a "set." Other words used in mathematics for the same thing are "aggregate" and "manifold." We shall have much to say later on about classes. For the present, we will say as little as possible. But there are some remarks that must be made immediately.

A class or collection may be defined in two ways that at first sight seem quite distinct. We may enumerate its members, as when we say, "The collection I mean is Brown, Jones, and Robinson." Or we may mention a defining property, as when we speak of "mankind" or "the inhabitants of London." The definition which enumerates is called a definition by "extension," and the one which mentions a defining property is called a definition by "intension." Of these two kinds of definition, the one by intension is logically more fundamental. This is shown by two considerations: (1) that the extensional definition can always be reduced to an intensional one; (2) that the intensional one often cannot even theoretically be reduced to the extensional one. Each of these points needs a word of explanation.

(1) Brown, Jones and Robinson all of them possess a certain property which is possessed by nothing else in the whole universe, namely, the property of being either Brown or Jones or Robinson. This property can be used to give a definition by intension of the class consisting of Brown and Jones and Robinson. Consider such a formula as "x is Brown or x is Jones or x is Robinson." This formula will be true for just three x's, namely, Brown and Jones and Robinson. In this respect it resembles a cubic equation with its three roots. It may be taken as assigning a property common to the members of the class consisting of these three men, and peculiar to them. A similar treatment can obviously be applied to any other class given in extension.

(2) It is obvious that in practice we can often know a great deal about a class without being able to enumerate its members. No one man could actually enumerate all men, or even all the inhabitants of London, yet a great deal is known about each of these classes. This is enough to show that definition by extension is not *necessary* to knowledge about a class. But when we come to consider infinite classes, we find that enumeration is not even theoretically possible for beings who only live for a finite time. We cannot enumerate all the natural numbers: they are 0, 1, 2, 3, *and so on*. At some point we must content ourselves with "and so on." We cannot enumerate all fractions

or all irrational numbers, or all of any other infinite collection. Thus our knowledge in regard to all such collections can only be derived from a definition by intension.

These remarks are relevant, when we are seeking the definition of number, in three different ways. In the first place, numbers themselves form an infinite collection, and cannot therefore be defined by enumeration. In the second place, the collections having a given number of terms themselves presumably form an infinite collection: it is to be presumed, for example, that there are an infinite collection of trios in the world, for if this were not the case the total number of things in the world would be finite, which, though possible, seems unlikely. In the third place, we wish to define "number" in such a way that infinite numbers may be possible; thus we must be able to speak of the number of terms in an infinite collection, and such a collection must be defined by intension, *i.e.* by a property common to all its members and peculiar to them.

For many purposes, a class and a defining characteristic of it are practically interchangeable. The vital difference between the two consists in the fact that there is only one class having a given set of members, whereas there are always many different characteristics by which a given class may be defined. Men may be defined as featherless bipeds, or as rational animals, or (more correctly) by the traits by which Swift delineates the Yahoos. It is this fact that a defining characteristic is never unique which makes classes useful; otherwise we could be content with the properties common and peculiar to their members.* Any one of these properties can be used in place of the class whenever uniqueness is not important.

Returning now to the definition of number, it is clear that number is a way of bringing together certain collections, namely, those that have a given number of terms. We can suppose all couples in one bundle, all trios in another, and so on. In this way we obtain various bundles of collections, each bundle consisting of all the collections that have a certain number of terms. Each bundle is a class whose members are collections, *i.e.* classes; thus each is a class of classes. The bundle consisting of all couples, for example, is a class of classes: each couple is a class with two members, and the whole bundle of couples is a class with an infinite number of members, each of which is a class of two members.

* As will be explained later, classes may be regarded as logical fictions, manufactured out of defining characteristics. But for the present it will simplify our exposition to treat classes as if they were real.

How shall we decide whether two collections are to belong to the same bundle? The answer that suggests itself is: "Find out how many members each has, and put them in the same bundle if they have the same number of members." But this presupposes that we have defined numbers, and that we know how to discover how many terms a collection has. We are so used to the operation of counting that such a presupposition might easily pass unnoticed. In fact, however, counting, though familiar, is logically a very complex operation; moreover it is only available, as a means of discovering how many terms a collection has, when the collection is finite. Our definition of number must not assume in advance that all numbers are finite; and we cannot in any case, without a vicious circle, use counting to define numbers, because numbers are used in counting. We need, therefore, some other method of deciding when two collections have the same number of terms.

In actual fact, it is simpler logically to find out whether two collections have the same number of terms than it is to define what that number is. An illustration will make this clear. If there were no polygamy or polyandry anywhere in the world, it is clear that the number of husbands living at any moment would be exactly the same as the number of wives. We do not need a census to assure use of this, nor do we need to know what is the actual number of husbands and of wives. We know the number must be the same in both collections, because each husband has one wife and each wife has one husband. The relation of husband and wife is what is called "one-one."

A relation is said to be "one-one" when, if *x* has the relation in question to *y*, no other term *x'* has the same relation to *y*, and *x* does not have the same relation to any term *y'* other than *y*. When only the first of these two conditions is fulfilled. the relation is called "one-many"; when only the second is fulfilled, it is called "many-one." It should be observed that the number 1 is not used in these definitions.

In Christian countries, the relation of husband to wife is one-one; in Mohammedan countries it is one-many; in Tibet it is many-one. The relation of father to son is one-many; that of son to father is many-one, but that of eldest son to father is one-one. If n is any number, the relation of n to $n + 1$ is one-one; so is the relation of n to $2n$ or to $3n$. When we are considering only positive numbers, the relation of n to n^2 is one-one; but when negative numbers are admitted, it becomes two-one, since n *and* $-n$ have the same square. These instances should suffice to make clear the notions of one-one, one-many, and many-one relations, which play a great part in the principles of mathematics, not only in relation to the definition of numbers, but in many other connections.

Two classes are said to be "similar" when there is a one-one relation which correlates the terms of the one class each with one term of the other class, in the same manner in which the relation of marriage correlates husbands with wives. A few preliminary definitions will help us to state this definition more precisely. The class of those terms that have a given relation to something or other is called the *domain* of that relation: thus fathers are the domain of the relation of father to child, husbands are the domain of the relation of husband to wife, wives are the domain of the relation of wife to husband, and husbands and wives together are the domain of the relation of marriage. The relation of wife to husband is called the *converse* of the relation of husband to wife. Similarly *less* is the converse of *greater*, *later* is the converse of *earlier*, and so on. Generally, the converse of a given relation is that relation which holds between y and x whenever the given relation holds between x and y. The *converse domain* of a relation is the domain of its converse: thus the class of wives is the converse domain of the relation of husband to wife. We may now state our definition of similarity as follows:—

One class is said to be "similar" to another when there is a one-one relation of which the one class is the domain, while the other is the converse domain.

It is easy to prove (1) that every class is similar to itself, (2) that if a class a is similar to a class β, then β is similar to a, (3) that if a is similar to β and β to γ, then a is similar to γ. A relation is said to be *reflexive* when it possesses the first of these properties, *symmetrical* when it possesses the second, and *transitive* when it possesses the third. It is obvious that a relation which is symmetrical and transitive must be reflexive throughout its domain. Relations which possess these properties are an important kind, and it is worth while to note that similarity is one of this kind of relations.

It is obvious to common sense that two finite classes have the same number of terms if they are similar, but not otherwise. The act of counting consists in establishing a one-one correlation between the set of objects counted and the natural numbers (excluding 0) that are used up in the process. Accordingly common sense concludes that there are as many objects in the set to be counted as there are numbers up to the last number used in the counting. And we also know that, so long as we confine ourselves to finite numbers, there are just *n* numbers from 1 up to *n*. Hence it follows that the last number used in counting a collection is the number of terms in the collection, provided the collection is finite. But this result, besides being only applicable to finite collections, depends upon and assumes the fact that two classes which are similar have the same number of terms; for what we do when we count (say) 10 objects is to show that the set of these objects is similar to the set of numbers 1 to 10. The notion of similarity is logically presupposed in the operation of counting, and is logically simpler though less familiar. In counting, it is necessary to take the objects counted in a certain order, at first, second, third, etc., but order is not of the essence of number: it is an irrelevant addition, an unnecessary complication from the logical point of view. The notion of similarity does not demand an order: for example, we saw that the number of husbands is the same as the number of wives, without having to establish an order of precedence among them. The notion of similarity also does not require that the classes which are similar should be finite. Take, for example, the natural numbers (excluding 0) on the one hand, and the fractions which have 1 for their numerator on the other hand: it is obvious that we can correlate 2 with ½, 3 with ⅓, and so on, thus proving that the two classes are similar.

We may thus use the notion of "similarity" to decide when two collections are to belong to the same bundle, in the sense in which we were asking this question earlier in this chapter. We want to make one bundle containing the class that has no members: this will be for the number 0. Then we want a bundle of all the classes that have one member: this will be for the number 1. Then, for the number 2, we want a bundle consisting of all couples; then one of all trios; and so on. Given any collection, we can define the bundle it is to belong to as being the class of all those collections that are "similar" to it. It is very easy to see that if (for example) a collection has three members, the class of all those collections that are similar to it will be the class of trios. And whatever number of terms a collection may have, those collections that are "similar" to it will have the same number of terms. We may take this as a *definition* of "having the same number of terms." It is obvious that it gives results conformable to usage so long as we confine ourselves to finite collections.

So far we have not suggested anything in the slightest degree paradoxical. But when we come to the actual definition of numbers we cannot avoid what must at first sight seem a paradox, though this impression will soon wear off. We naturally think that the class of couples (for example) is something different from the number 2. But there is no doubt about the class of couples: it is indubitable and not difficult to define, whereas the number 2, in any other sense, is a metaphysical entity about which we can never feel that it exists or that we have tracked it down. It is therefore more prudent to content ourselves with the class of couples, which we are sure of, than to hunt for a problematical number 2 which must always remain elusive. Accordingly we set up the following definition:—

The number of a class is the class of all those classes that are similar to it.

Thus the number of a couple will be the class of all couples. In fact, the class of all couples will *be* the number 2, according to our definition. At the expense of a little oddity, this definition secures definiteness and indubitableness; and it is not difficult to prove that numbers so defined have all the properties that we expect numbers to have.

We may now go on to define numbers in general as any one of the bundles into which similarity collects classes. A number will be a set of classes such as that any two are similar to each other, and none outside the set are similar to any inside the set. In other words, a number (in general) is any collection which is the number of one of its members; or, more simply still:

A number is anything which is the number of some class.

Such a definition has a verbal appearance of being circular, but in fact it is not. We define "the number of a given class" without using the notion of number in general; therefore we may define number in general in terms of "the number of a given class" without committing any logical error.

Definitions of this sort are in fact very common. The class of fathers, for example, would have to be defined by first defining what it is to be the father of somebody; then the class of fathers will be all those who are somebody's father. Similarly if we want to define square numbers (say), we must first define what we mean by saying that one number is the square of another, and then define square numbers as those that are the squares of other numbers. This kind of procedure is very common, and it is important to realise that it is legitimate and even often necessary.

We have now given a definition of numbers which will serve for finite collections. It remains to be seen how it will serve for infinite collections. But first we must decide what we mean by "finite" and "infinite," which cannot be done within the limits of the present chapter.

Chapter III

FINITUDE AND MATHEMATICAL INDUCTION

The series of natural numbers, as we saw in Chapter I., can all be defined if we know what we mean by the three terms "0," "number," and "successor." But we may go a step farther: we can define all the natural numbers if we know what we mean by "0" and "successor." It will help us to understand the difference between finite and infinite to see how this can be done, and why the method by which it is done cannot be extended beyond the finite. We will not yet consider how "0" and "successor" are to be defined: we will for the moment assume that we know what these terms mean, and show how thence all other natural numbers can be obtained.

It is easy to see that we can reach any assigned number, say 30,000. We first define "1" as "the successor of "0," then we define "2" as "the successor of 1," and so on. In the case of an assigned number, such as 30,000, the proof that we can reach it by proceeding step by step in this fashion may be made, if we have the patience, by actual experiment: we can go on until we actually arrive at 30,000. But although the method of experiment is available for each particular natural number, it is not available for proving the general proposition that *all* such numbers can be reached in this way, *i.e.* by proceeding from 0 step by step from each number to its successor. Is there any other way by which this can be proved?

Let us consider the question the other way around. What are the numbers that can be reached, given the terms "0" and "successor"? Is there any way by which we can define the whole class of such numbers? We reach 1, as the successor of 0; 2, as the successor of 1; 3, as the successor of 2; and so on. It is this "and so on" that we wish to replace by something less vague and indefinite. We might be tempted to say that "and so on" means that the process of proceeding to the successor may be repeated *any finite number* of times; but the problem upon which we are engaged is the problem of defining "finite number," and therefore we must not use this notion in our definition. Our definition must not assume that we know what a finite number is.

The key to our problem lies in *mathematical induction*. It will be remembered that, in Chapter I., this was the fifth of the five primitive propositions which we laid down about the natural numbers. It stated that any property which belongs to 0, and to the successor of any number which has the property, belongs to all the natural numbers. This was then presented as a principle, but we shall now adopt it as a definition. It is not difficult to see that the terms obeying it are the same as the numbers that can be reached from 0 by successive steps from next to next, but as the point is important we will set forth the matter in some detail.

We shall do well to begin with some definitions, which will be useful in other connections also.

A property is said to be "hereditary" in the natural-number series if, whenever it belongs to a number n, it also belongs to $n + 1$, the successor of n. Similarly a class is said to be "hereditary" if, whenever n is a member of the class, so is $n + 1$. It is easy to *see*, though we are not yet supposed to know, that to say a property is hereditary is equivalent to saying that it belongs to all the natural numbers not less than some one of them, *e.g.* it must belong to all that are not less than 100, or all that are not less than 1000, or it may be that it belongs to all that are not less than 0, *i.e.* to all without exception.

A property is said to be "inductive" when it is a hereditary property which belongs to 0. Similarly a class is "inductive" when it is a hereditary class of which 0 is a member.

Given a hereditary class of which 0 is a member, it follows that 1 is a member of it, because a hereditary class contains the successors of its members, and 1 is the successor of 0. Similarly, given a hereditary class of which 1 is a member, it follows that 2 is a member of it; and so on. Thus we can prove by a step-by-step procedure that any assigned natural number, say 30,000, is a member of every inductive class.

We will define the "posterity" of a given natural number with respect to the relation "immediate predecessor" (which is the converse of "successor") as all those terms that belong to every hereditary class to which the given number belongs. It is again easy to *see* that the posterity of a natural number consists of itself and all greater natural numbers; but this also we do not yet officially know.

By the above definitions, the posterity of 0 will consist of those terms which belong to every inductive class.

It is now not difficult to make it obvious that the posterity of 0 is the same set as those terms that can be reached from 0 by successive steps from next to next. For, in the first place, 0 belongs to both these sets (in the sense in which we have defined our terms); in the second place, if n belongs to both sets, so does $n + 1$. It is to be observed that we are dealing here with the kind of matter that does not admit of precise proof, namely, the comparison of a relatively vague idea with a relatively precise one. The notion of "those terms that can be reached from 0 by successive steps from next to next" is vague, though it *seems* as if it conveyed a definite meaning; on the other hand, "the posterity of 0" is precise and explicit just where the other idea is hazy. It may be taken as giving what we *meant* to mean when we spoke of the terms that can be reached from 0 by successive steps.

We now lay down the following definition:—

The "natural numbers" are the posterity of 0 with respect to the relation "immediate predecessor" (which is the converse of "successor").

We have thus arrived at a definition of one of Peano's three primitive ideas in terms of the other two. As a result of this definition, two of his primitive propositions—namely, the one asserting that 0 is a number and the one asserting mathematical induction—become unnecessary, since they result from the definition. The one asserting that the successor of a natural number is a natural number is only needed in the weakened form "every natural number has a successor."

We can, of course, easily define "0" and "successor" by means of the definition of number in general which we arrived at in Chapter II. The number 0 is the number of terms in a class which has no members, *i.e.* in the class which is called the "null-class." By the general definition of number, the number of terms in the null-class is the set of all classes similar to the null-class, *i.e.* (as is easily proved) the set consisting of the null-class all alone, *i.e.* the class whose only member is the null-class. (This is not identical with the null-class: it has one member, namely, the null-class, whereas the null-class itself has no members. A class which has one member is never identical with that one member, as we shall explain when we come to the theory of classes.) Thus we have the following purely logical definition:— 0 *is the class whose only member is the null-class.*

It remains to define "successor." Given any number n, let a be a class which has n members, and let x be a term which

is not a member of a. Then the class consisting of a with x
added on will have $n + 1$ members. Thus we have the following definition:—

*The successor of the number of terms in the class a is the
number of terms in the class consisting of a together with* x,
where x *is any term not belonging to the class.*

Certain niceties are required to make this definition perfect,
but they need not concern us.* It will be remembered that we
have already given (in Chapter II) a logical definition of the
number of terms in a class, namely, we defined it as the set of
all classes that are similar to the given class.

We have thus reduced Peano's three primitive ideas to ideas
of logic: we have given definitions of them which make them
definite, no longer capable of an infinity of different meanings,
as they were when they were only determinate to the extent of
obeying Peano's five axioms. We have removed them from the
fundamental apparatus of terms that must be merely apprehended, and have thus increased the deductive articulation of
mathematics.

As regards the five primitive propositions, we have already
succeeded in making two of them demonstrable by our definition of "natural number." How stands it with the remaining
three? It is very easy to prove that 0 is not the successor of any
number, and that the successor of any number is a number. But
there is a difficulty about the remaining primitive proposition,
namely, "no two numbers have the same successor." The difficulty does not arise unless the total number of individuals in
the universe is finite; for given two numbers m and n, neither of
which is the total number of individuals in the universe, it is
easy to prove that we cannot have $m+1 = n+1$ unless we have
$m = n$. But let us suppose that the total number of individuals
in the universe were (say) 10; then there would be no class of
11 individuals, and the number 11 would be the null-class. So
would the number 12. Thus we should have $11 = 12$; therefore
the successor of 10 would be the same as the successor of 11,
although 10 would not be the same as 11. Thus we should have
two different numbers with the same successor. This failure of
the third axiom cannot arise, however, if the number of individuals in the world is not finite. We shall return to this topic
at a later stage.

Assuming that the number of individuals in the universe is
not finite, we have now succeeded not only in defining Peano's
three primitive ideas, but in seeing how to prove his five primi-

* See *Principia Mathematica*, vol. ii. • 110.

tive propositions, by means of primitive ideas and propositions belonging to logic. It follows that all pure mathematics, in so far as it is deducible from the theory of the natural numbers, is only a prolongation of logic. The extension of this result to those modern branches of mathematics which are not deducible from the theory of the natural numbers offers no difficulty of principle, as we have shown elsewhere.*

The process of mathematical induction, by means of which we defined the natural numbers, is capable of generalisation. We defined the natural numbers as the "posterity" of 0 with respect to the relation of a number to its immediate successor. If we call this relation N, any number m will have this relation to $m + 1$. A property is "hereditary with respect to N," or simply "N-hereditary," if, whenever the property belongs to a number m, it also belongs to $m + 1$, *i.e.* to the number to which m has the relation N. And a number n will be said to belong to the "posterity" of m with respect to the relation N if n has every N-hereditary property belonging to m. These definitions can all be applied to any other relation just as well as to N. Thus if R is any relation whatever, we can lay down the following definitions:†

A property is called "R-hereditary" when, if it belongs to a term x, and x has the relation R to y, then it belongs to y.

A class is R-hereditary when its defining property is R-hereditary.

A term x is said to be an "R-ancestor" of the term y if y has every R-hereditary property that x has, provided x is a term which has the relation R to something or to which something has the relation R. (This is only to exclude trivial cases.)

The "R-posterity" of x is all the terms of which x is an R-ancestor.

We have framed the above definitions so that if a term is the ancestor of anything it is its own ancestor and belongs to its own posterity. This is merely for convenience.

It will be observed that if we take for R the relation "parent," "ancestor" and "posterity" will have the usual meanings, except that a person will be included among his own ancestors and posterity. It is, of course, obvious at once that "ancestor"

---

* For geometry, in so far as it is not purely analytical, see *Principles of Mathematics*, part vi.; for rational dynamics, *ibid,* part vii.

† These definitions, and the generalised theory of induction, are due to Frege, and were published so long ago as 1879 in his *Begriffsschrift.* In spite of the great value of this work, I was, I believe, the first person who ever read it—more than twenty years after its publication.

must be capable of definition in terms of "parent," but until Frege developed his generalised theory of induction, no one could have defined "ancestor" precisely in terms of "parent." A brief consideration of this point will serve to show the importance of the theory. A person confronted for the first time with the problem of defining "ancestor" in terms of "parent" would naturally say that A is an ancestor of Z if, between A and Z, there are a certain number of people, B, C, . . . , of whom B is a child of A, each is a parent of the next, until the last, who is a parent of Z. But this definition is not adequate unless we add that the number of intermediate terms is to be finite. Take, for example, such a series as the following:—

$$-1, \ -\tfrac{1}{2}, \ -\tfrac{1}{4}, \ -\tfrac{1}{8}, \ \ldots \ \tfrac{1}{8}, \ \tfrac{1}{4}, \ \tfrac{1}{2}, \ 1.$$

Here we have first a series of negative fractions with no end, and then a series of positive fractions with no beginning. Shall we say that, in this series, $-\tfrac{1}{8}$ is an ancestor of $\tfrac{1}{8}$? It will be so according to the beginner's definition suggested above, but it will not be so according to any definition which will give the kind of idea that we wish to define. For this purpose, it is essential that the number of intermediaries should be finite. But, as we saw, "finite" is to be defined by means of mathematical induction, and it is simpler to define the ancestral relation generally at once than to define it first only for the case of the relation of n to $n+1$, and then extend it to other cases. Here, as constantly elsewhere, generality from the first, though it may require more thought at the start, will be found in the long run to economise thought and increase logical power.

The use of mathematical induction in demonstrations was, in the past, something of a mystery. There seemed no reasonable doubt that it was a valid method of proof, but no one quite knew why it was valid. Some believed it to be really a case of induction, in the sense in which that word is used in logic. Poincaré* considered it to be a principle of the utmost importance, by means of which an infinite number of syllogisms could be condensed into one argument. We now know that all such views are mistaken, and that mathematical induction is a definition, not a principle. There are some numbers to which it can be applied, and there are others (as we shall see in Chapter VIII) to which it cannot be applied. We *define* the "natural numbers" as those to which proofs by mathematical induction can be applied, *i.e.* as those that possess all inductive properties. It follows that such proofs can be applied to the natural numbers, not in virtue of any mysterious intuition or axiom or

* *Science and Method*, chap. iv.

principle, but as a purely verbal proposition. If "quadrupeds" are defined as animals having four legs, it will follow that animals that have four legs are quadrupeds; and the case of numbers that obey mathematical induction is exactly similar.

We shall use the phrase "inductive numbers" to mean the same set as we have hitherto spoken of as the "natural numbers." The phrase "inductive numbers" is preferable as affording a reminder that the definition of this set of numbers is obtained from mathematical induction.

Mathematical induction affords, more than anything else, the essential characteristic by which the finite is distinguished from the infinite. The principle of mathematical induction might be stated popularly in some such form as "what can be inferred from next to next can be inferred from first to last." This is true when the number of intermediate steps between first and last is finite, not otherwise. Anyone who has ever watched a goods train beginning to move will have noticed how the impulse is communicated with a jerk from each truck to the next, until at last even the hindmost truck is in motion. When the train is very long, it is a very long time before the last truck moves. If the train were infinitely long, there would be an infinite succession of jerks, and the time would never come when the whole train would be in motion. Nevertheless, if there were a series of trucks no longer than the series of inductive numbers (which, as we shall see, is an instance of the smallest of infinites), every truck would begin to move sooner or later if the engine persevered, though there would always be other trucks further back which had not yet begun to move. This image will help to elucidate the argument from next to next, and its connection with finitude. When we came to infinite numbers, where arguments from mathematical induction will be no longer valid, the properties of such numbers will help to make clear, by contrast, the almost unconscious use that is made of mathematical induction where finite numbers are concerned.

PART II

In the previous chapter we saw how the system of "natural numbers" is gradually enlarged, for the sake of making the various arithmetical operations possible under all conditions; thus there are added to it, first, the negative whole numbers, and then, the fractions resulting from division. The resulting system of positive and negative integers together with fractions is called the system of rational numbers. Dedekind then showed that each rational number can be defined as a certain cut in this system; furthermore, he showed that there exists an infinite number of cuts in the rational number system not made by rational numbers. These cuts, therefore, are made by a different type of number, called irrational. The system of rational and irrational numbers together contains all the *real* numbers.

This entire development of the number system begins with the concept of *natural number*. It is entirely appropriate, therefore, that we should take up in this chapter the question, What is a natural number? For an answer we turn to Bertrand Russell's *Introduction to Mathematical Philosophy*.

This book, which appeared in 1919, was written while the author was in prison. In a way this fact is symbolic of much of Russell's life: his main interests are mathematics, philosophy, and a social doctrine directed toward liberty and peace. Because of his social and political views, Russell has been troubling, and been troubled by, governments and authorities all his life. In 1918, when he was forty-six years of age, his pacifist views brought about his imprisonment; in 1962, at the age of ninety, he was imprisoned again, because of civil disobedience while advocating nuclear disarmament. Controversy has surrounded Russell all his life, and he has seemed to thrive on it.

Bertrand Russell (he became Earl Russell in 1931) was born in 1872. He studied at Cambridge and soon became interested in philosophy. His gift for mathematics caused him to study for a while with the Italian mathematician Giuseppe Peano in Paris (whom he mentions in our excerpt from the *Introduction to Mathematical Philosophy*). Peano's work led

Russell to investigate the logical foundations of mathematics, together with Alfred North Whitehead (1861–1947). Together they produced the monumental *Principia Mathematica*, whose three volumes appeared in 1910, 1912, and 1913.

Russell's output of books has been prodigious. In *The Philosophy of Bertrand Russell* (ed. Paul A. Schilpp, third edition, New York, 1951: Tudor Publishing Co.), the bibliography of his writings takes fifty-six pages, and he has been by no means idle since then. In philosophy his main interest has been the theory of knowledge; some of his major works in this field are *Our Knowledge of the External World; The Analysis of Mind; The Analysis of Matter; An Inquiry into the Meaning of Truth; Human Knowledge: Its Scope and Limits*. He has also written a history of philosophy. He is the author of many other books on logic and mathematics besides the ones we have mentioned, as well as of scores of articles. In the field of social theory he has written innumerable articles, essays, and pamphlets, as well as books. In 1950 he was awarded the Nobel Prize for Literature.

Let us begin our study of the *Introduction to Mathematical Philosophy* by examining Chapter 2, because this is where Russell discusses the concept of number.

We start by looking back at Euclid's simple way of dealing with these matters, "A unit," he says, "is that in virtue of which each of the things that exist is called one." Number, then, is very straightforwardly defined as "a multitude composed of units." Is anything wrong with these definitions? We might feel just a little uncomfortable with this definition of "unit." It hardly seems very practical; there is an air of the obscure and metaphysical about it. This is not to say that the definition is false—definitions are never false as long as they are internally consistent. But this definition may be more suitable for the man who discusses metaphysical problems of the oneness or manyness of things than the mathematician who is only concerned to perform operations with numbers. The objection then, to Euclid's definition of "unit" would be that it appears to suffer from inutility.

The objection to his definition of "number" would be that while it may be correct, it nevertheless is unilluminating. What does it mean to call a number a multitude of units except that a number consists of a number of units? Obviously the number 5 is a multitude consisting of 5 units. But can we say more precisely what the number 5 is, and then, what number in general is? This is what Russell sets out to do: first to tell us what characterizes a given multitude (or, as he calls it, plurality) such as 5, or 7, etc., and then to go to the more abstract concept of number in general.

First, Russell notes that a particular number, such as 3, is not identical with all those collections (or sets) consisting of 3 members. Rather, the number 3 is something which all sets of 3 members have in common. Hence it is entirely reasonable to expect that the number 3 will and should be defined in terms of the sets consisting of 3 members.

Russell proceeds as follows: Collect for example, all the

Bundle of couples

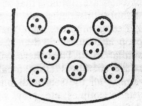

Bundle of trios

sets consisting of two members. Put all these sets into one "bundle." Then collect all the sets consisting of three members, and put them into another bundle. Do this for all sets, so that we end up with an (infinite) number of bundles, where each bundle contains all the sets with a given number of members. Each bundle will, of course, contain an infinite number of sets. Then we will try to define the number 2 in terms of the "bundle" containing all the sets of two members, the number 3 in terms of all the sets of three members, and so on.

An immediate difficulty presents itself. In advance of having defined "2," how can we know whether a given set belongs to the "bundle" of sets of two members? Our definition of "2" should not be dependent on prior knowledge of what "2" is. This matter can be dealt with rather neatly, however. Consider the infinite number of sets which are to be distributed over the various "bundles." Put into the same bundle, says Russell, all those sets which are *similar*. Similar sets are those whose members can be put into one-to-one correspondence with one another. This can be done without any actual counting; I can know, for example, that two sets are similar, without knowing how many members each of them has.

Thus, says Russell, barring the existence of polygamy or polyandry in the world, we can know that the number of living husbands is exactly the same as the number of living wives, for these two sets can be put in one-to-one correspondence—that is, each husband to his wife. Nor is it necessary that two sets be finite in order for us to know that they can be put in one-to-one correspondence. For example, it is perfectly obvious that the set of natural numbers can be put in one-to-one correspondence with the set of fractions $\frac{1}{1}$, $\frac{1}{2}$, $\frac{1}{3}$, and so on. In fact, putting any collection into one-to-one correspondence with the set of natural numbers is what *counting* is. What concerns us here, however, is that it is possible to decide whether two sets are similar (that is, belong to the same bundle of sets), without this decision's involving the concept of number.

Let us suppose, then, that all sets have been collected in appropriate bundles—that is, each set with all those sets that are similar to it. Thus there will be a "bundle" containing the set of no members (the so-called null set), then a bundle containing all the sets with one member, then a bundle with the sets of couples, etc. Now we—or rather Russell—are ready to define "number."

Here it is well to remind ourselves that a definition is something arbitrary. However, while any (consistent) definition of "number" would in one way be acceptable, there is another criterion. That is utility. A mathematician, whether Euclid or Russell, is at liberty to begin his work with his own definitions; nobody can deny him the right to define things and assign names as he pleases. If, however, the mathematician wants to be of use to his reader, he will be careful to define his elements in such a way that the reader will recognize the things being defined—will, in other words, be able to make use of the definitions. With this caution, let us look at Russell's definition:

The number of a class is the class of all those classes that are similar to it (p. 175).

Before discussing the definition, let us translate it. Suppose there is a set containing a certain number of members, say five. How are we going to define the number 5? What are we going to say is the number 5? Russell answers: "Five" is the class of all those classes containing five members.

Russell recognizes that his definition of number will seem strange at first. "We naturally think," he writes, "that the class of couples (for example) is something different from the num-

ber 2." In defense of his definition he does not attempt to
show that our common-sense impression is wrong. He does
not try to convince us that the class of couples *is* the number
2, if we would only try to understand more deeply what "number" or "the number 2" is. Russell's defense is much more
pragmatic:

> There is no doubt about the class of couples: it is indubi-
> table and not difficult to define, whereas the number 2,
> in any other sense, is a metaphysical entity about which
> we can never feel sure that it exists or that we have
> tracked it down.

And so he concludes:

> It is therefore more prudent to content ourselves with
> the class of couples, which we are sure of, than to hunt
> for a problematical number 2, which must always re-
> main elusive (p. 175).

Since Russell claims only pragmatic justification for his definition, we cannot attack it on the grounds that it is not what
we had expected, that it is too different from Euclid's definition, or that it does not really tell us what the essence of
number is, etc. We can, however, quite legitimately withhold
judgment until we have seen whether the definition works—
that is, until it has been established whether in fact this definition of "number" is useful. Since Russell bases his entire
justification for the definition on this level, we are entitled to
judge it on that level also. Euclid's definition, on the other
hand, should be judged on different grounds, since it in fact
attempts to tell us what a number is. Which kind of definition
is better is a matter to be decided by the theory of definitions,
a branch of the science of logic.

But to return to Russell's definition of "number": The number 2 is the class of all those classes which have two members;
the number 5 is the class of all those classes which have 5
members—but can we generalize these definitions? Yes, a
number obviously will be "a set of classes such that any two
are similar to each other, and none outside the set are similar
to any inside the set." Or, to generalize still further, since we
have defined what "number of a class" means, we can now
say (following Russell) that anything which is the number of
a class is a number simply. A little more elegantly, we say:

A number is anything which is the number of some class (p. 175).

Russell briefly considers the charge that this definition of number is circular, since it appears to define "number" in terms of "number." He dismisses this charge easily, however, because "number" is here defined in terms of "number of a class." And "number of a class" has been defined by him earlier in terms that do not involve the concept of number, but only the concepts of "class" and "similar classes." There is an appearance of circularity because of the occurrence of the word "number" among the words used to define "number." But Russell points out that this quite frequently happens in valid definitions. For example, the father of a person might be defined as that person's immediate male progenitor. "Father," in general, then would be defined as he who is some person's father.

This is exactly the sort of thing that we do in the definition of number. However, if we wish to avoid even the appearance of circularity, we can easily do it by substituting for "number of a class" *its* definition. Then we can say:

A number is anything which is a set of similar classes.

The definition of "number" which Russell develops in Chapter 2 is, as Russell points out, due to the German mathematician Gottlob Frege (1848–1925). Frege's endeavor—and Russell's after him—was to reduce mathematics to non-mathematical terms. The definition of "number" is a good instance of this. It involves no purely mathematical or arithmetical terms; the concepts used in it are taken from the science of logic. Basically, the concepts used are two: that of *class* (which in turn involves such concepts as "membership in a class" or "belonging to a class"), and that of *similarity* of a class. Number, an arithmetical concept as we ordinarily think of it, emerges from these purely logical concepts. Whenever there are classes that are similar to one another, there is a class of all these similar classes. That class is a number.

Russell's definition of "number" is an instance, therefore, of *reduction*, of reducing one science at least partly to another. By defining "number" in purely logical terms, we reduce, to that extent, arithmetic to a part of logic. But Russell is interested in much more extensive reductions. In Chapter 1 he mentions (but does not prove) that all of mathematics can be reduced to arithmetic, or more precisely to the science of natural numbers. We can believe this quite easily; we have already seen in Chapter 3 that geometry can be reduced to algebra, and we have just learned in the previous chapter how irrational numbers can be defined in terms of rational numbers, so that the entire theory of irrational numbers is reduced to that of natural numbers. This arithmetization of mathematics reached its climax in the work of the Italian mathematician Guiseppe Peano (1858–1932).

Peano undertook the next logical step in this progressive arithmetization. That step consisted in reducing arithmetic itself—or better, the theory of natural numbers—to the smallest possible number of primitive, undefined terms and primitive, unproved propositions. The three undefined terms are "0," "number," "successor." It is clear what Peano means by "0"; by "number" he means the class of natural numbers (including 0); by "successor" he means the successor of a natural number, or the next number in the natural order.

There is no need for us here to repeat the five primitive propositions; Russell lists them on page 000. By means of the three primitive terms and the five primitive propositions, all the ordinary propositions of arithmetic can be proved. It is quite obvious that this is precisely the sort of thing which Euclid did in geometry: the three primitive terms correspond to the terms in the Definitions (remember, we noted at the time that some of them might better have been left undefined); the five primitive propositions correspond to Euclid's postulates.

Russell notes, however, that it is necessary to go beyond Peano's work. One reason for this is that the primitive undefined terms of Peano's system are capable of an infinite number of interpretations. We gave the terms their "ordinary" interpretation above. That is, we interpreted "0" as meaning "zero" in the ordinary sense, "number" as meaning "the class of natural numbers," and "successor" as meaning "next natural number." It is important to realize that this was an interpretation—that is, an attachment of meaning to those three terms made by us—because that meaning is not contained in those terms as such. Russell points out various other possible interpretations for these three terms; they are just as valid as the first interpretation, even though they may seem a little strange and unfamiliar.

Faced with a number of undefined terms capable of a variety of interpretations, we have a choice of two courses of action. First, we could leave them undefined and uninterpreted, simply noting that these terms are variables, the only restriction on these variables being that they must fit the five primitive propositions. Such a course of action is logically permissible, but of course the result will be that our "arithmetical" results (the propositions proved by means of the primitive propositions about the primitive terms) will not really be arithmetical. The propositions will be exercises in logic; we will not know to what these propositions apply, or even whether there are any things in reality to which they apply.

The second course, and the one which Russell follows, is to give a definite interpretation to these primitive terms. This interpretation is of course, the "ordinary" one—that is, one which interprets "number" to mean "the class of natural numbers," and so forth. But where can we turn for the means of making such an interpretation? Russell's answer is *logic*.

In Chapter 3 of the *Introduction to Mathematical Philosophy* Russell turns to the task of giving interpretations to the primitive terms and primitive propositions in Peano's theory by the use of logical terms. When he has finished his task, Russell has therefore succeeded in *logicizing* arithmetic. Since all arithmetical terms and propositions will have been reduced to logical terms and propositions, arithmetic will cease to exist as a separate science and will from now on be understood as merely a part of the science of logic.

Peano's three primitive terms were "0," "number," "successor." The first thing which Russell proposes to do is to define "number" in terms of "0" and "successor." These last two terms are, for the time being, still considered as undefined and not in need of definition. We must note one important difference between the task which Russell solved in Chapter 2 and the task which he sets himself here in Chapter 3. In the earlier chapter, Russell gave a definition in logical terms, of any number, or "number" in general. Here in Chapter 3, Russell searches for a definition, in terms of "0" and "successor," of "the class of natural numbers." Whereas the definition developed in Chapter 2 seeks only to say what any natural number is, the definition looked for here is that of the entire class of natural numbers in terms of one natural number, namely 0. The definition developed here will, therefore, be a genetic definition; that is, it will tell us how the class of natural numbers comes to be, starting with the first natural number, 0.

We can assume that the natural number series starts with 0, and that each natural number has a successor (that is, there is a next one after it). This of course also means that every natural number has an immediate predecessor, except 0. For if a number m has the successor n, then n has the immediate predecessor m.

Now the natural numbers have a great many different properties. Some properties are such that if they belong to a number, then they belong also to the successor of that number. Russell calls such properties "hereditary." Most properties are not of this kind; for example, the property of being even is not hereditary. If a number is even, then its successor is *not* even.

Consider the property "being a member of a class A"; suppose this property is hereditary. This means that if a number belongs to class A, then its successor also belongs to class A. Since the property of being a member in this class A is hereditary, we call the class A also hereditary.

If a property is hereditary and belongs to the number 0, then the property is called *inductive*. Similarly, if the property "being a member of class A" is hereditary and 0 is a member of class A, then A is said to be an inductive class. Let us note the obvious: the four statements concerning hereditary properties, hereditary classes, inductive properties, and inductive class are all definitions; as such they are arbitrary, not subject to dispute, and simply laid down by Russell for convenience and clarity.

It follows from the definition of "inductive class" that any natural number is a member of every inductive class. For 0 is a member of any inductive class (by definition); and if 0 is a member of an inductive class, then 1 is also a member of it; if 1 is a member of it, then 2 is, and so forth until we reach the given natural number.

Russell needs to make one more definition in order to accomplish his task. Let us state once more what that task is, so that we can be sure to understand in what sense he accomplishes what he sets out to do. Russell's aim is to replace the vague, intuitive understanding of the class of natural numbers with a precise definition, where that definition is to involve only the terms "0" and "successor" from the field of number theory (the definition may and will of course involve other general logical terms). The vague intuitive understanding of the class of natural numbers states that each number is reached step by step as the successor of a number; or to put it the other way around, each number is the predecessor of another number.

Since this is vague and unclear, Russell proposes to clarify it. What do we mean, he asks, when we say that all numbers after a given number arise from it, step by step, because each number, beginning with the given number, is the predecessor of another number? Or, what do we mean when we consider all numbers after a given number as the "posterity" of that number, arising from the relation of "immediate predecessor"? In our restatement of Russell's task, we have placed first the vague and intuitive statements which all of us bring to the study of numbers; and we have indicated that it is his task to clarify these vague statements. Actually, Russell approaches the matter in a slightly different way. He first gives a *precise* (though unusual) definition of the class of natural numbers, and then he indicates that this is what we meant all along by our vague statements concerning the class of natural numbers.

The one added definition which, we noted above, Russell needs is that of *posterity*. Our common sense tells us that posterity is that which comes after, but we need to be more precise. A person or a thing has different posterities with respect to different relations. To take the most obvious example first: A man's posterity, with respect to fatherhood, consists of his children, and his children's children, and so forth. If I ask what a man's posterity is with respect to the relation of being the father of sons, then it will be all his male children, and their male children, and so forth. (It may happen, of course, that with respect to this relationship a man has no posterity at all.) Similarly, too, we might define a relation of authorship so that an author's posterity would consist of all those persons who read his books, and then of all those who read books written by the first generation of readers, and so on.

What Russell sets out to define, then, is the posterity of a number with respect to the relation "immediate predecessor." To put what Russell is looking for in plainer terms, he wants to define what all those numbers are which follow a given number, as a result of the fact that the given number is the immediate predecessor of a number, while this second number is again the immediate predecessor of another number. The posterity of a given number, in other words, consists of all those numbers which arise from it, step by step. This, we recall, was the intuitive and vague understanding of the class of numbers. Now let us look at Russell's definition, which makes it precise. He defines the posterity of a given number (with respect to the relation of "immediate predecessor"— that is, arising from the fact that every number is the immediate predecessor of another number) as "all those terms that belong to every hereditary class to which the given number belongs." Or, to put it in less precise but plainer words, the posterity of a given number consists of all those numbers that are connected with it by a hereditary property. If the given number is 0, then for "hereditary" class we substitute "inductive" class, and we will find that the posterity of 0, with respect to the relation "immediate predecessor," is all those terms which belong to every inductive class. (Or, again, the posterity of 0 is all those numbers that are connected with it by some inductive property.) Having defined the posterity of 0, Russell now turns around and defines the class of natural numbers as follows:

> The "natural numbers" are the posterity of 0 with respect
> to the relation "immediate predecessor" (which is the
> converse of "successor") (p. 178).

What has this definition accomplished? First, it states precisely what we mean by the vague expression "each number comes from its predecessor, step by step." Secondly, this definition has accomplished this task using only two of Peano's undefined terms. Russell immediately proceeds to show that the other two undefined primitive terms can also be replaced by expressions involving only logical and no arithmetical terms. Thus 0, in accord with the work done in Chapter II, is defined as the class of all the classes having no members. Since there is only one class that has no members—the so-called null class —0 can be defined as the class that has only one member, namely the null class. Then Russell also defines "successor" in strictly logical terms—that is, using such terms as "class," "member," etc.

Thus arithmetic is left with no primitive undefined terms. (The only undefined terms are those that are undefined in logic; arithmetic has no undefined terms of its own.) Furthermore, Russell shows, arithmetic also does not have any unproved, primitive propositions. We will not repeat Russell's reasoning here, except with respect to Peano's axiom 5, the one dealing with matematical induction. That particular axiom (see p. 165) stated this:

> Any property which belongs to 0, and also to the successor of every number which has the property, belongs to all numbers.

This seems like a fairly complicated and lengthy axiom, and

consequently one might wish that it would not be necessary to accept it without proof. (This, of course, was precisely the kind of objection urged against Euclid's fifth postulate.) Peano's fifth axiom is no longer necessary, however, if we define "natural numbers" as Russell does. For that definition includes the property of "inductiveness." In other words, the class of natural numbers is defined in such a way that mathematical induction must necessarily hold. For the natural numbers are said to be the posterity of 0, and the posterity of 0 is defined as all those numbers connected with 0 by the inductive property. To see this, it is merely necessary to go back to the definition of "posterity"; it involves the definition of hereditariness, and this in turn means "inductiveness." Thus, mathematical induction, far from being a problem for the arithmetician, becomes in fact the defining property of natural numbers. We can even say that Russell defines natural numbers as all those, starting from 0, for which mathematical induction holds.

> The use of mathematical induction in demonstrations was, in the past, something of a mystery. There seemed no reasonable doubt that it was a valid method of proof, but no one quite knew why it was valid. ... We now know that ... mathematical induction is a definition, not a principle. There are some numbers to which it can be applied, and there are others ... to which it cannot be applied. We *define* the "natural numbers" as those to which proofs by mathematical induction can be applied, *i.e.* as those that possess all inductive properties (p. 181).

What finally, is the result of Russell's work as far as we have read it? He himself sums it up quite clearly, on p. 179:

> We have now succeeded not only in defining Peano's three primitive ideas, but in seeing how to prove his five primitive propositions, by means of primitive ideas and propositions belonging to logic. It follows that all pure mathematics, in so far as it is deducible from the theory of natural numbers, is only a prolongation of logic.

III

advanced topics

CHAPTER SEVEN

Euler—A New Branch of Mathematics: Topology

PART I

Most of us tacitly assume that mathematics is a science dealing with the measurement of quantities. Indeed, the word "geometry," which is sometimes used synonymously with "mathematics," means "measurement of the earth." In the selection before us now, however, we see that mathematics includes a great deal more than measurement. Leonhard Euler, an eighteenth-century mathematician, shows us that "position" or "relative position" is a property that can be treated mathematically. Not only such questions as "are these two triangles of the same shape?" or "Is this number a factor of that number?" but also a question like "Is this point inside or outside of that figure?" are all mathematically significant.

If it seems strange that "relative position" should be a part of mathematics, a look at Euler's treatment will dispel any doubt. These "topological" matters are treated deductively and just as rigorously as matters of size and shape are treated by Euclid.

Leonhard Euler:
Solution of a Problem Belonging to the "Geometry of Position"*

1. Beside that part of geometry which deals with quantities and which always is studied with the greatest care, Leibniz makes mention of another part. He was the first to do so, al-

---

* A new translation by Peter Wolff. Copyright © 1963 by Peter Wolff.

though it is almost unknown, and he called it *geometria situs* (geometry of position). This part of geometry was stated by him to deal only with the determination of location and with eliciting the properties of location. In this business no regard is had to quantities nor is there any need for calculating quantities. However, this does not sufficiently define the sort of problems that belong to this geometry of position, nor what method is to be used in solving them. Therefore, since recently there has been made mention of a certain problem, which seems to pertain to geometry, but which is so constituted that it requires neither quantitative determination nor admits of quantitative solution through calculation, I have not had any doubt at all to refer it to the geometry of position, especially because in its solution only position comes under consideration, while calculation is of no use. Hence I have determined here to exhibit my method, which I have invented for solving problems of this kind, as an example of the geometry of position.

2. The problem, then, which I was told is quite well enough known, was the following: In Königsberg in Prussia there is an island A, called the Kneipfhof, encircled by a river which divides into two arms, as can be seen from the figure: the branches are furnished with seven bridges, *a*, *b*, *c*, *d*, *e*, *f*, and *g*. Now the following question is asked concerning these bridges: Could someone follow a course so that he crosses each bridge once, and none more than once? I was told that some deny altogether that this is possible while others doubt it, but nobody asserts that it is possible. I formulated for myself the following general problem from this: whatever be the shape of the river and the distribution of its branches and whatever be the number of bridges, to find whether it is possible to cross all bridges once only, or not.

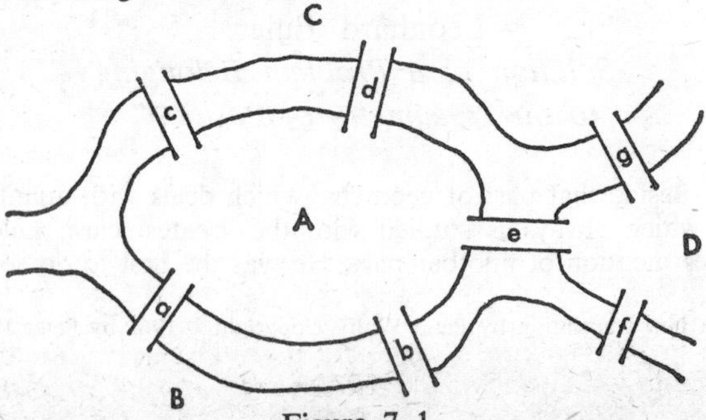

Figure 7–1

3. But since the problem of Königsberg pertains to seven bridges, it could be solved by a complete enumeration of all the routes which can be taken; from this it would become clear whether some route satisfies the problem or not. But because of the great number of combinations this mode of solution is both too difficult and laborious and in other problems of more bridges cannot be employed at all. If this kind of method should be pursued to the end, many answers will be found to questions that were not asked; in this without doubt consists the cause of great difficulty. Wherefore having dismissed this method I have searched for another one which would not do anything more than show whether such a route can be found or not; for I suspected that such a method would be much simpler.

4. Now my whole method rests on a suitable way of designating each single crossing of the bridges; for this I use the capital letters *A, B, C, D* which describe each of the regions that are separated by the river. Thus, if someone goes from region *A* to region *B,* by either the bridge *a* or the bridge *b,* I denote this crossing by the letters *AB.* The first of these shows the region from which the traveler came, and the second gives the region into which he goes after crossing the bridge. Again, if a traveler should go from region *B* to region *D* by bridge *f,* this crossing is represented by the letters *BD.* Two successive crossings *AB* and *BD* I then denote by the three letters *ABD,* because the middle letter *B* designates both the region which he reached by the first crossing and the region which he left by the second crossing.

5. Similarly, if the traveler should go on from region *D* to region *C* by the way of bridge *g,* I denote these three successive crossings by the four letters *ABDC.* From these four letters *ABDC* it will be understood that the traveler was first in region *A* and crossed into region *B,* that from here he went on to region *D* and that from here he finally proceeded to *C.* Since, however, these regions are separated from each other by the river, it is necessary that the walker crossed three bridges. Thus crossings that are undertaken by way of four successive bridges are denoted by five letters; and if the walker crosses any number of bridges the number of letters denoting his route will be one greater than the number of bridges. Thus a crossing by seven bridges requires eight letters for its designation.

6. In this manner of denoting the crossings, I pay no attention to which bridges are used, but if the same crossing can

be made from one region into another by several bridges, then it is just the same, whichever bridge be crossed, as long as the traveler reaches the designated region. From this it is clear that if the path over the seven bridges of the figure can be traced in such fashion that it crosses over each one once but over none twice, then this path can be represented by eight letters and these letters must be disposed in such fashion that the letters A and B occur directly next to each other twice, because there are two bridges a and b joining regions A and B; similarly, the two letters A and C also should occur twice in immediate succession in this series of eight letters; then the sequence of letters A and D should occur once, and similarly the sequence of letters B and D and C and D must occur once.

7. The question is reduced to this, then, that from the four letters A, B, C, and D a series of eight letters must be formed, in which all the sequences occur just as many times as we have indicated. However, before beginning work to find such an arrangement, it is convenient to show whether these letters can be disposed in this manner or not. For if it can be demonstrated that such an arrangement can by no means be made, all labor would be useless which was directed toward bringing this about. Wherefore I have searched for a rule, by means of which it could easily be ascertained—both for this question and for all similar ones—whether such an arrangement of letters can exist.

8. In order to find this rule I consider the single region A, into which any number of bridges a, b, c, d, etc. lead (Figure 7–2). Of all these bridges, I first pay attention to the single one a, which leads to the region A. If now the traveler crosses by way of this bridge, he necessarily must either have been in region A before he crosses, or must reach region A after the crossing. Therefore, according to the way of naming the crossing that I established above, it is necessary that the letter A occur once. If three bridges, say a, b, c, lead to region A and the traveler crosses over all three, then in naming his travel the letter A will occur twice, whether or not he started his course from A. Similarly, if five bridges lead to A, then in naming crossings by way of all five, the letter A must occur three times. And if the number of bridges be any odd number whatever, if we add one to this number and take half of it, this will give the number of times that letter A must occur.

9. To turn now to the case of the bridges that are to be crossed in Königsberg. Because five bridges a, b, c, d, e lead to the island A, the letter A must occur three times in naming

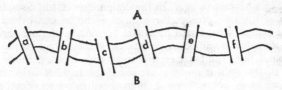

Figure 7–2

the crossings over these bridges. Because three bridges lead to the region B, the letter B must occur twice, and similarly the letter D and the letter C must each occur twice. Hence in the series of eight letters, by which the crossing of seven bridges must be designated, the letter A should occur three times, and the letters B, C, and D each twice. But in a series of eight letters this can in no way be accomplished. From this it is clear that the required crossing over the seven bridges of Königsberg cannot be done.

10. In similar fashion we can decide in any other case of bridges, if only the number which lead to any region is odd, whether each single bridge can be crossed just once. If it happens that the sum of all the times that each single letter should occur is equal to the number of all the bridges plus one, then such a crossing can be made. But if, as happened in our example, the sum of all the times should be greater than the number of bridges plus one, then such a crossing cannot be accomplished. The rule which I have given for finding the number of times of the letter A from the number of bridges leading into the region A, is equally valid whether all bridges come from one region B, as is the case in Figure 7–2, or whether they come from different regions; for I only consider the region A and inquire, how many times the letter A ought to occur.

11. If, however, the number of bridges leading to region A is even, then it must be known, in the matter of crossing each single bridge, whether the traveler began his course in A or not. For if two bridges lead to A and the traveler begins his course in A, then the letter A must occur twice; for it must once be present in order to denote the exit from A by one bridge, and once more in order to designate the re-entry into A by way of the other bridge. But if the traveler begins his course in some other region, then the letter A will occur only once; for being written once it will denote both the arrival at A and the exit from A, in my manner of denoting such a course.

12. Now let four bridges lead into region A and let the trav-

eler begin his course in A. In the designation of this course the letter A must be present three times, if he crosses over each single bridge once. But if he begins to walk in another region, then the letter A will occur only twice. If six bridges lead to the region A, then the letter A will occur four times, if the beginning of the walk is made at A; but if the traveler does not at the beginning come from A, then it will have to occur only three times. Generally therefore, if the number of bridges is even, one half of that number gives the number of times which the letter A must occur, if the beginning of the route is not in the region A; one half of the number of bridges plus one will give the number of times that the letter A must occur, if the beginning of the route is made in A itself.

13. But because in such a course the beginning can only be made in one region, I determine the number of times that the letter designating each region must occur from the number of bridges leading into the region, as half the sum of all the bridges plus one, if the number of bridges is odd; but as the half of the number of bridges themselves, if it is even. Then if the number of all the letter occurrences equals the number of the bridges plus one, the desired course can successfully be traversed; but the beginning must be made from a region into which an odd number of bridges leads. If, however, the number of letter occurrences should happen to be less by one than that of the bridges plus one, then the course can successfully be traversed by beginning in a region into which an even number of bridges leads, because in this way the number of letter occurrences is increased by one.

14. Suppose then that any configuration whatever of water and bridges is given and that it is to be investigated whether it is possible to cross over each bridge once; I go about it in the following fashion: *First*, I name all regions that are separated by water from each other by the letters A, B, C, etc. *Second*, I take the number of all the bridges, add one to it, and place this number at the head of the succeeding calculation. *Third*, after the letters A, B, C, etc., written below one another, I write the number of bridges leading into the region. *Fourth*, I mark with an asterisk those letters that have even numbers after them. *Fifth*, I write half of the even number next to each of the even numbers, and I write a number equal to half of each odd number plus one next to each odd number. *Sixth*, I add together the numbers written in the last column. If this sum is equal to, or less by one than the number of bridges plus one—then I conclude that the desired cross-

ing can be made. But it must be noted that, if the sum is one less than the number placed above, then the beginning of the route must be made in a region marked with an asterisk; on the other hand, from a region not so marked, if the sum is equal to the number in question. Thus in the case of Königsberg I make the following calculations:

Number of bridges 7; key number, 8

Bridges

A	5	3
B	3	2
C	3	2
D	3	2

Because this calculation results in a sum greater than 8, a crossing of this kind cannot be made in any way.

15. Let there be two islands *A* and *B*, surrounded by water, and let this water be connected with four rivers, as the figure (Figure 7–3) shows. So that the island can be reached let there be 15 bridges *a, b, c, d,* etc. across the water surrounding the islands and the rivers. The question is whether some course can

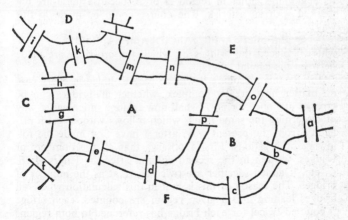

Figure 7–3

be found so that each of the bridges is crossed, but none more than once. First, therefore, I name all the regions which are separated by water from one another, by the letters *A, B, C, D, E, F;* there are six of these regions. Then I add one to the

number 15 of the bridges, and place the sum 16 at the head
of the following calculation:

Key number = 16

A*	8	4
B*	4	2
C*	4	2
D	3	2
E	5	3
F*	6	3
		16

Third, I write the letters A, B, C, etc. under one another and
with each I place the number of bridges that lead into this
region, as 8 bridges lead to A, and four to B, etc. Fourth, those
letters which have even numbers attached I mark with an
asterisk. Fifth, in the third column I write half of the even
numbers, but to the odd numbers I add one and write half of
that. Sixth, I add the numbers of the third column to one another and obtain the sum 16. Since this is equal to the number 16 placed above the calculation, it follows that the crossing can be made in the desired fashion, if the course takes
its beginnings either in region D or E, because these are not
marked with an asterisk. The course could be made in this
way:

EaFbBcFdAeFfCgAhCiDkAmEnApBoElD,

where I placed the bridges by which the crossings are made
between the capital letters.

16. By this reasoning it will be easy to judge in every case
no matter how greatly complex, whether all bridges can be
crossed just once, or not. I shall now relate a much easier way
of discerning the same thing, which follows without great difficulty from the present way, after I have first made the following observations. First I observe that all the numbers of
bridges, written in the second column after the letters $A, B,$
C, etc. if added together are twice as great as the number of
bridges. The reason of this is that in this calculation where all
bridges leading into a given region are counted, each bridge
is counted twice; for each bridge has reference to both regions
which it joins.

17. From this observation it follows therefore that the sum
of all the bridges which lead into each region is an even number, because its half is equal to the number of bridges. Hence
it cannot happen that among the numbers of bridges leading
into the several regions there is just one that is uneven; nor
that three be uneven, nor five, etc. Hence if any of the numbers

signifying the bridges, attached to the letters A, B, C, etc. are uneven, it is necessary that the number of these numbers be even. Thus in the example of Königsberg there were four numbers of bridges that were odd, attached to the letters of the regions A, B, C, D, as can be seen from section 14. And in the preceding example, in section 15, there are only two odd numbers, attached to the letters D and E.

18. Since the sum of all the numbers attached to the letters A, B, C, etc. equals twice the number of bridges, it is apparent that if two be added to this sum and the result divided by 2, then this must give the number placed at the head of the calculation. If, therefore, all the numbers attached to the letters A, B, C, D, etc. are even and in order to obtain the numbers of the third column half of each of them is taken, their sum will be less by one than the key number at the top. Therefore in such cases a crossing over the bridges can always be made. For in whatever region the course begins, it has bridges even in number leading to it, as is required. Thus in the Königsberg case it would be possible for someone to cross over each bridge twice; each bridge could be, as it were, divided in two, and then the number of bridges leading into each region will be even.

19. Furthermore, if only two of the numbers attached to the letters A, B, C, etc. are odd, but all the others are even, then the desired crossing can always be successfully made, as long as the beginning of the course is in a region with which an odd number of bridges connect. For if the even numbers are halved as well as the odd numbers plus one, according to the rule, the sum of all these halves will be greater by one than the number of bridges and therefore equal to the key number at the head.

From this it will then be seen that, if there are four or six or eight, etc. odd numbers in the second column, then the sum of the numbers in the third column will be greater than the key number at the head and will exceed it by one or two or three etc. and hence the crossing cannot be made.

20. Hence if any case whatsoever be given, it can now very easily be recognized whether a crossing over all bridges once can be made or not, with the help of this rule:

If there are more than two regions which have an odd number of bridges leading to them, then it can with certainty be affirmed that such a crossing cannot be made.

If, however, there are two regions which have an odd number of bridges leading to them, then the crossing can be made, if the course begins in one of these regions.

If, finally, there are no regions which have odd numbers of bridges leading to them, then the desired crossing can be made, no matter in which region the beginning of the walk is made.

This rules therefore fully solves the given problem.

21. But when it has been found that such a crossing can be made, the question still remains, how the course is to be found. For this I use the following rule: Let pairs of bridges which lead from one region to another, be eliminated in thought, as many times as it can be done. In this way, the number of bridges will be radically and quickly diminished. Then the desired course over the remaining bridges which can easily be done is looked for. When this has been found, it will at once be clear to anyone who attends to it that the bridges eliminated in thought will not disturb this course: and I judge it is not necessary for me to teach more about the finding of the course.

PART II

Leonhard Euler lived from 1707-1783, during the period that is often called "the age of reason" or "the enlightenment." The French encyclopedists (men like Diderot and d'Alembert) worked to publish the first encyclopedia; Voltaire, living sometimes in France, sometimes in Germany, wrote novels, satires, and a philosophical dictionary; in Great Britain, George Berkeley and David Hume published important treatises on the theory of knowledge, while Edward Gibbon labored for twenty years on *The Decline and Fall of the Roman Empire*. Europe was in broad intellectual ferment, with all the arts and sciences flourishing.

This favorable environment for intellectual pursuits resulted in the establishment of royal academies in many European countries. These were centers of learning, supported financially by the rulers of their countries, in which research of the most diverse kind was carried on under the patronage of the king. Many of the most important achievements of the eighteenth century are recorded in the annals of proceedings of one or another of these academies. Many scholars were able to pursue their studies only because of the support of these institutions.

Euler, who was Swiss (he was born at Basel) spent almost his entire life at the royal academies in St. Petersburg and Berlin. Originally destined for the ministry, his brilliance as a mathematician soon became apparent. He studied geometry under Jean Bernoulli, and later went to St. Petersburg with Daniel Bernoulli. In 1730, when Daniel Bernoulli left, Euler became professor of mathematics at the academy. In 1741 Euler went to Berlin as a member of the Prussian academy, but in 1766 he returned to St. Petersburg.

Euler's output of work was tremendous in quantity, a fact all the more astonishing because he lost the sight first of one eye and then of the other. For the last seventeen years of his life he was blind, but continued to work at a prodigious rate, thanks to his fantastic memory.

His work covered almost the entire range of mathematics, as well as many related sciences. He made contributions of the highest importance to algebra, the theory of equations, the study of infinite series, the theory of surfaces, and many other branches of mathematics. Euler worked out mathematical principles in the sciences of astronomy, hydrodynamics, optics, and acoustics. His collected works comprise a vast number of large volumes.

The little work we have translated here by itself is only of minor importance, but it is worth examining because it affords a very easy introduction to the branch of mathematics called topology. It also shows forth, in very exemplary fashion, Euler's ability in analysis and his almost instinctive habit of generalizing any problem in such a way that the general principles of the solution, as well as the particular solution, become apparent. It is this desire and ability to see the general principles which are the mark of a true mathematician.

We have said that this is a work in *topology*. Let us postpone a definition of "topology" and instead rest content with the statement that it treats problems like this one, of the seven bridges in Königsberg. After we have examined the problem and Euler's treatment of it, we can make an attempt to indicate just what branch of geometry this is.

The question which, according to Euler, had been of long standing, was whether a certain course could be followed without any retracing of steps. Starting from any point in the city of Königsberg, we are to cross over each one of seven bridges that lead across the river Pregel. As Figure 7–1 shows, the river

splits into two branches, forming an island (the Kneipfhof),
and then continues in two branches. The city of Königsberg
is located on both sides of the river and on the island, and the
bridges are arranged accordingly.

This problem is one of a more general kind, which is probably familiar to the reader. That is, it belongs to the class of
problems in which we are given a certain figure and we are
asked to trace this figure in "one stroke"—that is, without repeating or retracing any part of the diagram. Euler's problem
has a certain added charm because of the geographical details, but they are of no importance to the character of the
problem. Euler gives us a method for solving not only the
Königsberg problem, but all other problems of a similar sort
as well.

An important part of Euler's scheme of solving problems
of this kind consists in the proper labeling of the figure. He
gives capital letters to each of the regions that are completely
separated from each other by the river; there are four of them:
A, B, C, D. (It is clear that in order for these four regions to
be truly separated, we must conceive the river to go on indefinitely to the left; similarly, each of the two branches of the
river on the right must continue indefinitely.) Then Euler
designates the various bridges by small letters, a, b, c, d, e, f, g.

Next, he denotes the crossing from A to B by way of bridge
a by the sequence of letters AaB, or, if no attention is paid to
which bridge is used, the crossing from A to B is simply denoted by AB. Similarly going from B to D would be denoted by
BfD, if we want to call attention to the bridge used, or simply
by BD, if we do not. In the same fashion, going from A first
to B and then to D is denoted by ABD. (Since no small letters
are used, we do not know whether the crossing from A to B
was by way of bridge a or b). Crossing over *one* bridge takes
us from one region to a second one; and conversely, going
from one region to a second one and from the second one to
a third involves two bridges. In general, it is easy to see, the
number of regions (that is, the number of capital letters) in
a given course must be greater by one than the number of
bridges crossed. In the Königsberg problem, therefore, we
know that if the required course can be traced, over seven
bridges, it must be designated by eight letters.

Furthermore, since there are two bridges from A to B, the
letters A and B must appear next to each other (either as AB
or BA) twice in the sequence of eight letters; similarly, the
letters A and C also must appear next to each other twice,

while the letters *AD* (or *DA*), *BD* (or *DB*), and *CD* (or *DC*) must each occur once. The question then is, Can a sequence of eight letters be formed in which this arrangement of letters holds? The whole rest of the paper is devoted to the problem of investigating the possibility of this letter sequence (or generally, other letter sequences of similar sort).

Euler reasons as follows. (The problem is made a little easier, as we shall see, because each of the four regions *A*, *B*, *C*, *D*, has an odd number of bridges leading to it.) If a region has just one bridge leading to it, then the letter (say, *A*) of the region must occur just once, namely as either the starting point or the arrival point for a crossing. Suppose there are three bridges leading to the region *A*. Then the letter *A* must occur twice, whether the traveler starts in *A* or not. (See Figures 7–4a and 7–4b). And again, if there are five bridges lead-

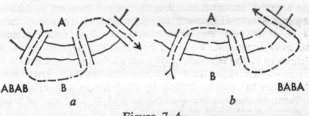

ABAB   B   BABA

a   *b*

Figure 7–4

ing to region *A*, then the letter *A* must occur three times. Generally, if there is an odd number of bridges leading to a region, the number of times which that letter must occur is equal to the number of bridges plus 1, divided by 2.

This immediately answers the question about the Königsberg problem. Since five bridges lead to *A*, the letter *A* must occur three times. Since three bridges lead to *B*, the letter *B* must occur twice. Since three bridges lead to *C*, the letter *C* must occur twice. Finally, since three bridges lead to *D*, the letter *D* must occur twice. Thus the total sequence of letters must contain 3 *A*'s, 2 *B*'s, 2 *C*'s, and 2 *D*'s. But that is a total of 9 letters; yet the total sequence of letters is only supposed to consist of 8 letters (since each bridge is to be crossed just once.) Hence the problem is insoluble, since two incompatible conditions must be met: When we consider the problem as a whole, we find that just 8 letters must describe the series of crossings. When we consider the problem region by region, we find that a total of 9 letters is needed to describe the crossings. Thus Euler has proved what, he tells us, had always been suspected but had never been demonstrated—that the required course over the seven bridges cannot be traced.

Euler immediately sets out to generalize his solution. He begins by investigating the situation when an even number of bridges leads to a region. Let us say that two bridges lead to region A. It immediately becomes apparent that it makes a difference whether the course begin at A or not. If two bridges lead to A, and the beginning of the course is in A, then the letter A will occur twice. (See Figure 7–5a.)

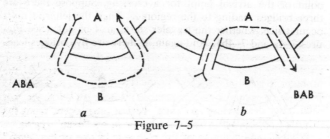

Figure 7–5

But if two bridges lead to A, and the beginning of the course is not in A, then the letter A will occur only once. (See Figure 7–5b.)

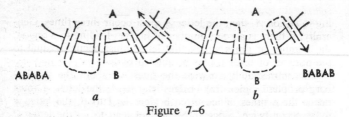

Figure 7–6

Similarly, consider the case of four bridges leading to A. If the beginning of the course is at A, then the letter A must occur three times, but if the beginning of the course is not a A, then the letter A must occur just twice. (See Figures 7–6a and 7–6b). And the general rule is that if n is an even number of bridges leading to a region, then the number of times which the letter A must occur is equal to $\frac{n}{2}$, if the beginning of the course is not in A. But if the beginning of the course is in A, then the number of times which the letter A must occur is given by $\frac{n}{2} + 1$.

Suppose, then, that we have a problem where there are a number of regions, and where some of the regions have odd numbers of bridges leading to them, while others have even numbers of bridges leading to them. How can we determine how many times each letter must occur (when we consider the problem region by region)? Euler's reasoning goes like this: Let us assume that the beginning of the course is in some region that has an odd number of bridges leading to it. Then the problem becomes perfectly determinate. For in the case of regions with odd numbers of bridges, it makes no difference where the course starts; consequently, I can determine the number of times that each letter designating an "odd" region must occur from the number of bridges. Now the rest of the problem is also determinate. For if the course starts in one of the "odd" regions, I can determine the number of times that each letter designating an "even" region must occur from the rule that applies when the start is *not* in an "even" region.

What if the beginning of the course is in one of the "even" regions? This means that for one region, *but only one region*, the number of times that the letter designating that region occurs must be increased by one. None of the other letter occurrences need to be changed, because as far as the other even regions go, the beginning of the course is still in a region other than themselves. And, of course, as far as the "odd" regions are concerned, the numbers of times that the letters designating them occur are not at all affected by where the beginning is made. So the rule for finding the number of times that the letters designating the various regions occur is very simple: For the "odd" regions take half of the sum obtained by adding one to the number of bridges; for the "even" regions take half of the number of bridges. This will give the number of letter occurrences, if the start of the course is in an "odd" region. If the start is in an "even" region, simply add one to the previous sum. If the sum is equal to the number of letter occurrences in the problem as a whole, it is soluble.

This solves the general problem, but Euler is still not satisfied. The general solution is too complicated for easy application, since we must consider each region separately and calculate the number of times that the letter of that region will occur from the number of bridges leading into it. Next, therefore, Euler derives a method that enables us to determine with hardly any calculation at all whether a crossing of the required kind can be made.

First, Euler notes that if we consider for each region how many bridges lead into it, and then add up these numbers, the resulting sum will be double the total number of bridges in the problem. For in the calculation region by region, each bridge is counted twice: The bridge connecting A and B is counted once as leading into A, and once as leading into B. This in turn means that the total number of bridges, when we count them region by region, must be an even number (for twice any number is an even number).

From this Euler concludes that there cannot be just one region that has an odd number of bridges leading into it (for then the sum of all bridges considered region by region would be odd); nor can there be three regions with odd numbers of bridges, for the same reason. In general, the number of "odd" regions cannot be odd but must be even.

What can we say about the number of times that each letter must occur? Suppose all the regions are "even"; then for each region the number of letter occurrences is equal to half of the bridges, except for one region. This one region—whichever it may be—is the one where the course starts; for this region the number of letter occurrences will be one greater than half of the bridges leading into it. If we, then, add up all the numbers of letter occurrences, we get this result: it would be equal exactly to the number of bridges; for the number of letter occurrences is equal to half the bridges, but the bridges are counted twice, when we go region by region. However, because we have to start in some one region, one more letter occurrence must be added. So, if all regions are "even," the letter occurrences are exactly equal to the number of bridges plus one. And that is how many times we saw the letters must occur when we consider the path as a whole. Euler concludes, therefore, that if all the regions are "even," the problem can always be solved.

If there are just two "odd" regions, the result will be the same, provided we start in an odd region. Each of the "even" regions now will give us letter occurrences equal to half the bridges. The two "odd" regions will each give us letter occurrences equal to one-half more than half the number of bridges. When we add up all the letter occurrences, therefore, we will find (since each bridge is considered twice), that we have a number equal to the number of bridges plus one. (But we must be sure to start the course in an "odd" region; otherwise, one more will be added from the fact that one of the "even" regions contains the start.)

If there are more than two "odd" regions, either four, or six, or more, the problem will not have a solution. Each two "odd" regions will add one to the number of letter occurrences above the number of bridges, and the result will be a number too large for the solution to be possible. (This is what happens in the Königsberg problem.)

And so, as the result of Euler's analysis, we can say that "bridge" problems similar to the Königsberg problem can be solved, provided all the regions are "even" or no more than two regions are "odd." If we have two "odd" regions, then we must start the course in one of the odd regions.

Now let us make a slight switch on Euler's problem. Let us replace the picture of river, island, and bridges with a different diagram. Let each of the four regions A, B, C, D be replaced by a point. Let each of the seven bridges a, b, c, d, e, f, g be replaced by a line joining two of the points. The Königsberg diagram will then become like Figure 7–7.

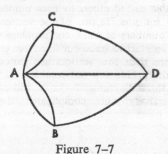

Figure 7–7

Why is it legitimate to replace entire "regions" by points? For the purposes of Euler's problem, there is no real difference between his regions and points. The basic and essential fact about the four regions is that they must be totally unconnected except by bridges. And this is exactly the case with four points located in space. They have no connection until we draw lines joining them (corresponding to the bridges). It is also apparent that there are any number of equivalent diagrams that I could draw for the Königsberg problem. For example, consider Figures 7–8a, b, and c. Each one of them is the "same" as the Königsberg diagram.

Euler's general problem may now be stated as follows: Given any figure consisting only of lines joining a number of vertices, can we determine whether such a figure can be traced

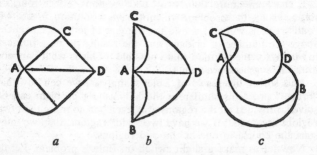

Figure 7–8

by a continuous line, without any part of the line being retraced? and the answer which Euler has found is this: Consider each vertex. Count the lines joining this vertex. If all the vertices are joined to others by even numbers of lines, the problem has a solution. If two of the vertices are joined to others by odd numbers of lines, the problem still has a solution, but we must start to trace our line from one of the "odd" vertices. If more than two vertices are joined by odd numbers of lines, the problem is not soluble.

Look at the three diagrams, 7—9a, b, and c. Although they become progressively more complicated, the simplest one

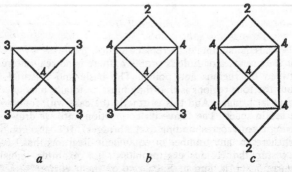

Figure 7–9

cannot be traced in one continuous line, because it has four "odd" vertices (that is, four vertices where three lines come together). The figure in 7–9b can be drawn in one continuous line, provided we start at one of the two vertices marked "3," while the figure in 7–9c can be drawn no matter where we start.

Now we can look back and indicate in a general sort of way what topology is. It is obviously a branch of geometry, in that it deals with points and lines. However, it does not treat these elements in any metric way; that is, it is not interested in size relationships. It is interested only in relative position. That is why Leibniz, as Euler tells us at the beginning of his little piece, called this branch of geometry "geometry of position." It is also sometimes called "analysis situs," which is merely a Latin way of saying that it analyzes position. (These names have an advantage over topology in that the latter name is nowadays used in a wider sense.) In general, geometry of position deals with properties that remain constant (invariant) when size and distance relationships are distorted.

If you look again at the three diagrams in Figure 7–8, you can see how uninterested topology is in absolute size, of lines, angles, etc., and even in whether a line is straight or curved. From the topological point of view, all three figures are exactly the same. Similarly, a triangle, a square, and a circle are exactly the same from the point of view of topology, because each of these figures divides the plane into two parts, one "inside" the figure, the other one "outside" it. Furthermore, it is of no importance how big the closed figure is; topologically the situation is exactly the same.

Euler's problem, it is apparent, has nothing to do with measurement. The only question is this: Can a continuous line be drawn, through the four points, A, B, C, D, connecting A and B twice, A and C twice, A and D once, B and C not at all, B and D once, C and D once, with the continuous line crossing itself only at the four points A, B, C, D? The answer, we have just learned, is No.

Another typical topological problem is that of determining the inside and outside for a given figure. This may seem like no problem at all. In a triangle, for example, it is obvious what is inside the figure and what is outside. But there are other figures for which this determination is a problem. Consider the famous Moebius strip (named after its discoverer). We obtain this strip by taking a long, thin rectangle and bending it so as to connect one end with the other. However, before making the final connection (by pasting or in some other way) we twist the rectangle so as to place C on A and D on B. (See Figure 7–10.)

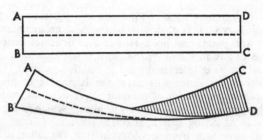

Figure 7–10

The resulting figure is the Moebius strip. (See Figure 7–11.)

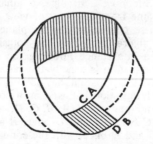

Figure 7–11

If we trace a line parallel to the two long sides of the rectangle (such as the dotted line in the figure), we find that although we start on the "outside" of the strip, pretty soon we are on the "inside" of it. If you puncture the strip somewhere along the dotted line and then make a cut following that line, all the way around, you will find that the strip has not been separated in two parts. It is still one whole!

The coloring of maps gives rise to a fascinating puzzle that belongs to topology: We wish to color a map in such a fashion that the same color shall not appear on both sides of a boundary between two countries. (If several countries come together at only one point, then the same color may be used.) The problem is: If the map is drawn on a plane surface, what is the least number of colors that have to be used? This is one of those problems, like the one of the Königsberg bridges, where everyone is pretty sure of the answer, but no one has been able to prove that the answer is correct. You will lose no money if you bet that four colors are sufficient, but mathematically speaking, the problem is still unsolved. Incidentally, it *has* been proved that at most five colors need to be used for a map on a plane surface.

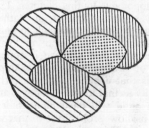

Figure 7–12

CHAPTER EIGHT

Laplace—The Theory of Probability

PART I

In the previous chapter, Euler introduced us to a new branch of mathematics, topology. In this chapter, Laplace makes us acquainted with yet another branch of mathematics, the calculus of probability. It is not so difficult to understand that the treatment of probabilities belongs to mathematics; but it is important to remember that Laplace is concerned only with the mathematics of probabilities. For example, if we know how probable it is that a baby will be a girl (it is not quite the same probability as that it will be a boy), and how probable it is that a given child will have blond hair, then Laplace's calculus can tell us how probable it is that a newborn baby will be a blond girl. This calculus cannot, however, tell us anything about the probability of a baby being a girl: this is a matter for medicine and statistics to determine.

Just as geometry and calculus cannot tell us anything about the motions of the planets and yet are used in the calculations which astronomers make about these motions, so the calculus of probabilities is a tool that is used in many different sciences, without itself giving us information about the content of these sciences.

Pierre Simon de Laplace:
A Philosophical Essay on Probabilities*

Chapter I

INTRODUCTION

This philosophical essay is the development of a lecture on probabilities which I delivered in 1795 to the normal schools whither I had been called, by a decree of the national convention, as professor of mathematics with Lagrange. I have recently published upon the same subject a work entitled *The Analytical Theory of Probabilities*. I present here without the aid of analysis the principles and general results of this theory, applying them to the most important questions of life, which are indeed for the most part only problems of probability. Strictly speaking it may even be said that nearly all our knowledge is problematical; and in the small number of things which we are able to know with certainty, even in the mathematical sciences themselves, the principal means for ascertaining truth —induction and analogy—are based on probabilities; so that the entire system of human knowledge is connected with the theory set forth in this essay. Doubtless it will be seen here with interest that in considering, even in the eternal principles of reason, justice, and humanity, only the favorable chances which are constantly attached to them, there is a great advantage in following these principles and serious inconvenience in departing from them: their chances, like those favorable to lotteries, always end by prevailing in the midst of the vacillations of hazard. I hope that the reflections given in this essay may merit the attention of philosophers and direct it to a subject so worthy of engaging their minds.

* From *A Philosophical Essay on Probabilities*, trans. by F. W. Truscott and F. L. Emory (New York: Dover Publications, Inc., 1951), pp. 1-19.

Chapter II

CONCERNING PROBABILITY

All events, even those which on account of their insignificance do not seem to follow the great laws of nature, are a result of it just as necessarily as the revolutions of the sun. In ignorance of the ties which unite such events to the entire system of the universe, they have been made to depend upon final causes or upon hazard, according as they occur and are repeated with regularity, or appear without regard to order; but these imaginary causes have gradually receded with the widening bounds of knowledge and disappear entirely before sound philosophy, which sees in them only the expression of our ignorance of the true causes.

Present events are connected with preceding ones by a tie based upon the evident principle that a thing cannot occur without a cause which produces it. This axiom, known by the name of *the principle of sufficient reason,* extends even to actions which are considered indifferent; the freest will is unable without a determinative motive to give them birth; if we assume two positions with exactly similar circumstances and find that the will is active in the one and inactive in the other, we say that its choice is an effect without a cause. It is then, says Leibniz, the blind chance of the Epicureans. The contrary opinion is an illusion of the mind, which, losing sight of the evasive reasons of the choice of the will in different things, believes that choice is determined of itself and without motives.

We ought then to regard the present state of the universe as the effect of its anterior state and as the cause of the one which is to follow. Given for one instant an intelligence which could comprehend all the forces by which nature is animated and the respective situation of the beings who compose it— an intelligence sufficiently vast to submit these data to analysis —it would embrace in the same formula the movements of the greatest bodies of the universe and those of the lightest atom; for it, nothing would be uncertain and the future, as the past, would be present to its eyes. The human mind offers, in the perfection which it has been able to give to astronomy, a feeble idea of this intelligence. Its discoveries in mechanics and geometry, added to that of universal gravity, have enabled it to comprehend in the same analytical expressions the past and future states of the system of the world. Applying the same method to some other objects of its knowledge, it has succeeded in referring to general laws observed phenomena and in foreseeing those which given circumstances ought to produce. All these efforts in the search for truth tend to lead it back continually to the vast intelligence which we have just mentioned, but from which it will always remain infinitely removed. This tendency, peculiar to the human race, is that which renders it superior to animals; and their progress in this respect distinguishes nations and ages and constitutes their true glory.

Let us recall that formerly, and at no remote epoch, an unusual rain or an extreme drought, a comet having in train a very long tail, the eclipses, the aurora borealis, and in general all the unusual phenomena were regarded as so many signs of celestial wrath. Heaven was invoked in order to avert their baneful influence. No one prayed to have the planets and the sun arrested in their courses: observation had soon made apparent the futility of such prayers. But as these phenomena, occurring and disappearing at long intervals, seemed to oppose the order of nature, it was supposed that Heaven, irritated by the crimes of the earth, had created them to announce its vengeance. Thus the long tail of the comet of 1456 spread terror through Europe, already thrown into consternation by the rapid successes of the Turks, who had just overthrown the Lower Empire. This star after four revolutions has excited among us a very different interest. The knowledge of the laws of the system of the world acquired in the interval had dissipated the fears begotten by the ignorance of the true relationship of man to the universe; and Halley, having recognized the identity of this comet with those of the years 1531, 1607, and 1682, announced its next return for the end of the year 1758 or the beginning of the year 1759. The learned world awaited with impatience this return which was to confirm one of the greatest discoveries that have been made in the sciences, and fulfill the prediction of Seneca when he said, in speaking of the revolutions of those stars which fall from an enormous height: "The day will come when, by study pursued through several ages, the things now concealed will appear with evidence; and posterity will be astonished that truths so clear had escaped us." Clairaut then undertook to submit to analysis the perturbations which the comet had experienced by the action of the two great planets, Jupiter and Saturn;

after immense calculations he fixed its next passage at the perihelion toward the beginning of April, 1759, which was actually verified by observation. The regularity which astronomy shows us in the movements of the comets doubtless exists also in all phenomena.

The curve described by a simple molecule of air or vapor is regulated in a manner just as certain as the planetary orbits; the only difference between them is that which comes from our ignorance.

Probability is relative, in part to this ignorance, in part to our knowledge. We know that of three or a greater number of events a single one ought to occur; but nothing induces us to believe that one of them will occur rather than the others. In this state of indecision it is impossible for us to announce their occurrence with certainty. It is, however, probable that one of these events, chosen at will, will not occur because we see several cases equally possible which exclude its occurrence, while only a single one favors it.

The theory of chance consists in reducing all the events of the same kind to a certain number of cases equally possible, that is to say, to such as we may be equally undecided about in regard to their existence, and in determining the number of cases favorable to the event whose probability is sought. The ratio of this number to that of all the cases possible is the measure of this probability, which is thus simply a fraction whose numerator is the number of favorable cases and whose denominator is the number of all the cases possible.

The preceding notion of probability supposes that, in increasing in the same ratio the number of favorable cases and that of all the cases possible, the probability remains the same. In order to convince ourselves let us take two urns, A and B, the first containing four white and two black balls, and the second containing only two white balls and one black one. We may imagine the two black balls of the first urn attached by a thread which breaks at the moment when one of them is seized in order to be drawn out, and the four white balls thus forming two similar systems. All the chances which will favor the seizure of one of the balls of the black system will lead to a black ball. If we conceive now that the threads which unite the balls do not break at all, it is clear that the number of possible chances will not change any more than that of the chances favorable to the extraction of the black balls; but two balls will be drawn from the urn at the same time; the probability of drawing a black ball from the urn A will then be the same as at first. But then we have obviously the case of urn B with the single difference that the three balls of this last urn would be replaced by three systems of two balls invariably connected.

When all the cases are favorable to an event the probability changes to certainty and its expression becomes equal to unity. Upon this condition, certainty and probability are comparable, although there may be an essential difference between the two states of the mind when a truth is rigorously demonstrated to it, or when it still perceives a small source of error.

In things which are only probable the difference of the data, which each man has in regard to them, is one of the principal causes of the diversity of opinions which prevail in regard to the same objects. Let us suppose, for example, that we have three urns, A, B, C, one of which contains only black balls while the two others contain only white balls; a ball is to be drawn from the urn C and the probability is demanded that this ball will be black. If we do not know which of the three urns contains black balls only, so that there is no reason to believe that it is C rather than B or A, these three hypotheses will appear equally possible, and since a black ball can be drawn only in the first hypothesis, the probability of drawing it is equal to one third. If it is known that the urn A contains white balls only, the indecision then extends only to the urns B and C, and the probability that the ball drawn from the urn C will be black is one half. Finally this probability changes to certainty if we are assured that the urns A and B contain white balls only.

It is thus that an incident related to a numerous assembly finds various degrees of credence, according to the extent of knowledge of the auditors. If the man who reports it is fully convinced of it and if, by his position and character, he inspires great confidence, his statement, however extraordinary it may be, will have for the auditors who lack information the same degree of probability as an ordinary statement made by the same man, and they will have entire faith in it. But if some one of them knows that the same incident is rejected by other equally trustworthy men, he will be in doubt and the incident will be discredited by the enlightened auditors, who will reject it whether it be in regard to facts well averred or the immutable laws of nature.

It is to the influence of the opinion of those whom the multitude judges best informed and to whom it has been accustomed to give its confidence in regard to the most important matters of life that the propagation of those errors is due which in times of ignorance have covered the face of the earth. Magic and astrology offer us two great examples. These errors inculcated in infancy, adopted without examination, and having for a basis only universal credence, have maintained themselves during a very long time; but at last the progress of science has destroyed them in the minds of enlightened men, whose opinion consequently has caused them to disappear even among the common people, through the power of imitation and habit which had so generally spread them abroad. This power, the richest resource of the moral world, establishes and conserves in a whole nation ideas entirely contrary to those which it upholds elsewhere with the same authority. What indulgence ought we not then to have for opinions different from ours, when this difference often depends only upon the various points of view where circumstances have placed us! Let us enlighten those whom we judge insufficiently instructed; but first let us examine critically our own opinions and weigh with impartiality their respective probabilities.

The difference of opinions depends, however, upon the manner in which the influence of known data is determined. The theory of probabilities holds to considerations so delicate that it is not surprising that with the same data two persons arrive at different results, especially in very complicated questions. Let us examine now the general principles of this theory.

Chapter III

THE GENERAL PRINCIPLES OF THE CALCULUS OF PROBABILITIES

First Principle.—The first of these principles is the definition itself of probability, which, as has been seen, is the ratio of the number of favorable cases to that of all the cases possible.

Second Principle. — But that supposes the various cases equally possible. If they are not so, we will determine first their respective possibilities, whose exact appreciation is one of the most delicate points of the theory of chance. Then the probability will be the sum of the possibilities of each favorable case. Let us illustrate this principle by an example.

Let us suppose that we throw into the air a large and very thin coin whose two large opposite faces, which we will call heads and tails, are perfectly similar. Let us find the probability of throwing heads at least one time in two throws. It is clear that four equally possible cases may arise, namely, heads at the first and at the second throw; heads at the first throw and tails at the second; tails at the first throw and heads at the second; finally, tails at both throws. The first three cases are favorable to the event whose probability is sought; consequently this probability is equal to ¾; so that it is a bet of three to one that heads will be thrown at least once in two throws.

We can count at this game only three different cases, namely, heads at the first throw, which dispenses with throwing a second time; tails at the first throw and heads at the second; finally, tails at the first and at the second throw. This would reduce the probability to ⅔ if we should consider with d'Alembert these three cases as equally possible. But it is apparent that the probability of throwing heads at the first throw is ½, while that of the other two cases is ¼, the first case being a simple event which corresponds to two events combined: heads at the first and at the second throw, and heads at the first throw, tails at the second. If we then, conforming to the second principle, add the possibility ½ of heads at the first throw to the possibility ¼ of tails at the first throw and heads at the second, we shall have ¾ for the probability sought, which agrees with what is found in the supposition when we play the two throws. This supposition does not change at all the chance of that one who bets on this event; it simply serves to reduce the various cases to the cases equally possible.

Third Principle.—One of the most important points of the theory of probabilities and that which lends the most to illusions is the manner in which these probabilities increase or diminish by their mutual combination. If the events are independent of one another, the probability of their combined existence is the product of their respective probabilities. Thus the probability of throwing one ace with a single die is ⅙; that of throwing two aces in throwing two dice at the same time is ⅟₃₆. Each face of the one being able to combine with the six faces of the other, there are in fact thirty-six equally possible cases, among which one single case gives two aces. Generally the probability that a simple event in the same circumstances will occur consecutively a given number of times is equal to the probability of this simple event raised to the power indicated by this number. Having thus the successive powers of a fraction less than unity diminishing, without ceasing, an event which depends upon a series of very great probabilities may become extremely improbable. Suppose then an incident be transmitted to us by twenty witnesses in such manner that the first has transmitted it to the second, the second to the third, and so on. Suppose again that the probability of each testimony be equal to the fraction $9/10$; that of the incident resulting from the testimonies will be less than $1/8$. We cannot better compare this diminution of the probability than with the extinction of the light of objects by the interposition of several pieces of glass. A relatively small number of pieces suffices to take away the view of an object that a single piece allows us to perceive in a distinct manner. The historians do not appear to have paid sufficient attention to this degradation of the probability of events when seen across a great number of successive generations; many historical events reputed as certain would be at least doubtful if they were submitted to this test.

In the purely mathematical sciences the most distant consequences participate in the certainty of the principle from which they are derived. In the applications of analysis to physics the results have all the certainty of facts or experiences. But in the moral sciences, where each inference is deduced from that which precedes it only in a probable manner, however probable these deductions may be, the chance of error increases with their number and ultimately surpasses the chance of truth in the consequences very remote from the principle.

Fourth Principle. — When two events depend upon each other, the probability of the compound event is the product of the probability of the first event and the probability that, this event having occurred, the second will occur. Thus in the preceding case of the three urns A, B, C, of which two contain only white balls and one contains only black balls, the probability of drawing a white ball from the urn C is $2/3$, since of the three urns only two contain balls of that color. But when a white ball has been drawn from the urn C, the indecision relative to that one of the urns which contain only black balls extends only to the urns A and B; the probability of drawing a white ball from the urn B is $1/2$; the product of $2/3$ by $1/2$, or $1/3$, is then the probability of drawing two white balls at one time from the urns B and C.

We see by this example the influence of past events upon the probability of future events. For the probability of drawing a white ball from the urn B, which primarily is $2/3$, becomes $1/2$ when a white ball has been drawn from the urn C; it would change to certainty if a black ball had been drawn from the same urn. We will determine this influence by means of the following principle, which is a corollary of the preceding one.

Fifth Principle.—If we calculate *a priori* the probability of the occurred event and the probability of an event composed of that one and a second one which is expected, the second probability divided by the first will be the probability of the event expected, drawn from the observed event.

Here is presented the question raised by some philosophers touching the influence of the past upon the probability of the future. Let us suppose at the play of heads and tails that heads has occurred oftener than tails. By this alone we shall be led to believe that in the constitution of the coin there is a secret cause which favors it. Thus in the conduct of life constant happiness is a proof of competency which should induce us to employ preferably happy persons. But if by the unreliability of circumstances we are constantly brought back to a state of absolute indecision, if, for example, we change the coin at each throw at the play of heads and tails, the past can shed no light upon the future and it would be absurd to take account of it.

Sixth Principle.—Each of the causes to which an observed event may be attributed is indicated with just as much likelihood as there is probability that the event will take place, supposing the event to be constant. The probability of the existence of any one of these causes is then a fraction whose numerator is the probability of the event resulting from this cause and whose denominator is the sum of the similar probabilities relative to all the causes; if these various causes, considered *a priori*, are unequally probable, it is necessary, in place of the probability of the event resulting from each cause, to employ the product of this probability by the possibility of the cause itself. This is the fundamental principle of this branch of the analysis of chances which consists in passing from events to causes.

This principle gives the reason why we attribute regular events to a particular cause. Some philosophers have thought that these events are less possible than others and that at the play of heads and tails, for example, the combination in which heads occurs twenty successive times is less easy in its nature than those where heads and tails are mixed in an irregular manner. But this opinion supposes that past events have an influence on the possibility of future events, which is not at all admissible. The regular combinations occur more rarely only because they are less numerous. If we seek a cause wherever we perceive symmetry, it is not that we regard a symmetrical event as less possible than the others, but, since this event ought to be the effect of a regular cause or that of chance, the first of these suppositions is more probable than the second. On a table we see letters arranged in this order, *C o n s t a n t i n o p l e*, and we judge that this arrangement is not the result of chance, not because it is less possible than the others, for if this word were not employed in any language we should not suspect it came from any particular cause, but this word being in use among us, it is incomparably more probable that some person has thus arranged the aforesaid letters than that this arrangement is due to chance.

This is the place to define the word *extraordinary*. We arrange in our thought all possible events in various classes; and we regard as *extraordinary* those classes which include a very small number. Thus at the play of heads and tails the occurrence of heads a hundred successive times appears to us as extraordinary because of the almost infinite number of combinations which may occur in a hundred throws; and if we divide the combinations into regular series containing an order easy to comprehend, and into irregular series, the latter are incomparably more numerous. The drawing of a white ball from an urn which among a million balls contains only one of this color, the others being black, would appear to us likewise extraordinary, because we form only two classes of events relative to the two colors. But the drawing of the number 475813, for example, from an urn that contains a million numbers seems to us an ordinary event; because, comparing individually the numbers with one another without dividing them into classes, we have no reason to believe that one of them will appear sooner than the others.

From what precedes, we ought generally to conclude that the more extraordinary the event, the greater the need of its being supported by strong proofs. For, those who attest it being able to deceive or to have been deceived, these two causes are as much more probable as the reality of the event is less. We shall see this particularly when we come to speak of the probability of testimony.

Seventh Principle.—The probability of a future event is the sum of the products of the probability of each cause, drawn from the event observed, by the probability that, this cause existing, the future event will occur. The following example will illustrate this principle.

Let us imagine an urn which contains only two balls, each

of which may be either white or black. One of these balls is drawn and is put back into the urn before proceeding to a new draw. Suppose that in the first two draws white balls have been drawn; the probability of again drawing a white ball at the third draw is required.

Only two hypotheses can be made here: either one of the balls is white and the other black, or both are white. In the first hypothesis the probability of the event observed is ¼; it is unity or certainty in the second. Thus in regarding these hypotheses as so many causes, we shall have for the sixth principle ⅕ and ⅘ for their respective probabilities. But if the first hypothesis occurs, the probability of drawing a white ball at the third draw is ½; it is equal to certainty in the second hypothesis; multiplying then the last probabilities by those of the corresponding hypotheses, the sum of the products, or 9/10, will be the probability of drawing a white ball at the third draw.

When the probability of a single event is unknown we may suppose it equal to any value from zero to unity. The probability of each of these hypotheses, drawn from the event observed, is, by the sixth principle, a fraction whose numerator is the probability of the event in this hypothesis and whose denominator is the sum of the similar probabilities relative to all the hypotheses. Thus the probability that the possibility of the event is comprised within given limits is the sum of the fractions comprised within these limits. Now if we multiply each fraction by the probability of the future event, determined in the corresponding hypothesis, the sum of the products relative to all the hypotheses will be, by the seventh principle, the probability of the future event drawn from the event observed. Thus we find that an event having occurred successively any number of times, the probability that it will happen again the next time is equal to this number increased by unity divided by the same number, increased by two units. Placing the most ancient epoch of history at five thousand years ago, or at 1,826,213 days, and the sun having risen constantly in the interval at each revolution of twenty-four hours, it is a bet of 1,826,214 to one that it will rise again tomorrow. But this number is incomparably greater for him who, recognizing in the totality of phenomena the principal regulator of days and seasons, sees that nothing at the present moment can arrest the course of it.

Buffon in his *Political Arithmetic* calculates differently the preceding probability. He supposes that it differs from unity only by a fraction whose numerator is unity and whose denominator is the number 2 raised to a power equal to the number of days which have elapsed since the epoch. But the true manner of relating past events with the probability of causes and of future events was unknown to this illustrious writer.

PART II

In the preceding chapter we saw how Euler's life was spent under the patronage of the Russian and Prussian courts. His fortunes rose and sank with the shifting political winds of St. Petersburg and at Berlin. Pierre Simon de Laplace had to cope with the changing political fortunes of his native France—but cope he did, very successfully, although his lifetime (1749–1827) overlapped the reigns of Louis XVI, the French Revolution, Napoleon Bonaparte, and Louis XVIII. Laplace held several high governmental offices under Napolean, was awarded numerous decorations, and achieved the title of Marquis.

Almost all of Laplace's creative life was spent in work on his masterpiece, the *Mécanique Céleste*. Its five volumes were published over a period of twenty-six years. In this work Laplace attempted—and to a great extent succeeded—to explain all the various motions of all the bodies in the solar system by means of Newton's law of universal gravitation. Laplace's work on probability, of which we here have a small part, was inspired by his astronomical work, for its need arose there.

The concept of a probable event is a very tricky one. It is very difficult to state what it means without contradiction. Let us begin by noting an obvious puzzle: What need was there for probability theory in planetary theory based on Newton's laws? Without going into details about those laws, it is well known that Newton's laws of motion, and his law of universal gravitation, *determine* in a precise way all the motions of all bodies. Is it only probable that the earth revolves around the sun in an ellipse, or is it certainly so? Does the relative position of the sun and moon precisely or only probably determine the tides? According to the Newtonian theory, or any other deterministic account of the universe, these results are certain and true, not merely probable. And Laplace himself must have thought so, otherwise he would hardly have attempted his *Mécanique Céleste.* The reason why such an ambitious project seemed possible was precisely that it appeared that with the help of Newton's laws all the motions of the planetary bodies would be determined and therefore could be calculated.

In the preceding paragraph we have employed three related concepts—namely "true," "certain," and "probable." Only if these three concepts are clearly distinguished from one another can we hope to understand the nature of probable knowledge. The important point to realize is that "probable" is not opposed to "true," but to "certain." The opposite of "true" is "false." Thus we have two pairs of terms: true–false and probable–certain.

A proposition is either true or false, and this is quite independent of whether anybody knows the truth or falsity of the proposition. A proposition which is true may to a given person, however, be only probable. The reason for this would be that the person under consideration has insufficient evidence on which to base anything except the judgment "This proposition is probable" (he may also be able to say how probable). This explains the role of probability in science: although any given event is determined, and although all the propositions of the science are true, we may not have—at least initially—sufficient evidence to know the truth of the propositions and may have to rest content with probability.

Let us take a trivial example of probability: Suppose a baseball broadcast is put on tape and the broadcast begins an hour later than the game itself. Now let us assume that someone listens to the broadcast, who has no idea of the outcome of the game and who does not, in fact, realize that the broadcast is delayed. In the eighth inning, the listener hears that team A is ahead 7–2. At this time, A actually has already won the game. Our listener, however, does not know this; and so all he can say at this point is that in the light of his evidence it is probable that A is going to win. He cannot claim that it is certain that team A is going to win, nor can he maintain that he knows that A is going to win (although it is in fact true).

An interesting corollary of this is that a proposition which is false can also be probable to a given person. To return to our baseball example: Let's imagine another game, in which team

A leads 7–2 in the eighth inning. In the ninth inning, however, B makes a tremendous comeback and wins the game 9–7. Again, the listener in the eighth inning, unapprised of the final score, would be justified in saying, "It is probable that A is going to win." This would be a perfectly reasonable statement. It would of course be false, but it would nevertheless be probable.

Probability, in other words, is always relative to a given amount of evidence. We can never simply say, "This proposition is probable to such an extent"; we must always use some expression like, "This proposition, on the basis of this evidence, has such and such probability." It is clear, therefore, that the probability of a given proposition can change—if, namely, the available evidence changes. What may seem like an astonishing—that is, very improbable—proposition to someone when he is first told about it without any (or hardly any) evidence, may turn out to be quite probable to him when he sees what the evidence for the proposition is.

Another way of stating what probability is consists in calling it a "reasonable degree of belief." On the basis of such and such evidence, it is reasonable to believe that the proposition under consideration has this amount of probability. By speaking of *reasonable* belief, we call attention to the fact that the belief must be based on the available evidence, not on "hunches," or on no evidence at all, or on blind faith. To go back to our baseball game example once more: If team A leads by 7–2 in the eighth inning, then it is reasonable to believe that A will go on to win the game. There may, however, be a devoted fan of team B who in the face of adversity still claims, "I just know that B is going to pull this game out of the fire and win it." Now this would not be a reasonable belief on the basis of the evidence, or at least—to put the matter more accurately—it would not be as reasonable as the belief that A is going to win. The fact that B does go on to victory in no way affects the judgment of the reasonableness (or probability) of the earlier beliefs, based on the incomplete evidence at that time.

What are the kinds of things that constitute evidence for the probability of a proposition? There is quite a bit of controversy here. However, we shall not try to make any determinations of what is and is not correct, since this would involve us in discussions of induction and similar topics that go beyond the mathematical theory of probability. Let us note only one way in which evidence for a proposition may be accumulated. Suppose we are given a die and are asked what the probability is that the number 5 will come up. We might then ask: What has been the past experience with this particular die? If we are told that in 100 throws of the die, it came up "1" 10 times, "2" 20 times, "3" 10 times, "4" 10 times, "5" 40 times, and "6" 10 times, we might conclude on the basis of this evidence that *first,* the die is loaded, and *second,* there is forty per cent probability (or a probability of 0.4) that number 5 will come up in the next throw.

In this example, we have inferred the probability of a future event from past events. Thus, the evidence for the 0.4 probability is arrived at empirically or *a posteriori* (together with some fancy reasoning, which we are purposely ignoring, about the future being like the past, or nature being uniform, etc.). There might seem to be another, *a priori,* way of judging probability: Confronted with a die we might say that, in the absence of any information about previous throws with this die, each number should come up as frequently as the others. Consequently, the probability that one number, 5, will come up is ⅙ or 0.167.

This last line of reasoning is often attacked, because it is an argument from ignorance. That is, it makes sense only because we say that we have no information about previous throws. But can knowledge be based on ignorance? This seems like a weighty objection to the *a priori* argument; still, there are also some powerful defenses for it. For example, on what are we to base a probability judgment in the case where there is no past experience? Or must we say that the next throw has no probability whatever? (The answer here would be that, since probability is related to evidence and here there is no evidence, it is meaningless to speak of a probability judgment.) Furthermore, when we did have evidence and found that 40 per cent of the throws came up "5," we added, apparently very reasonably, that the die was loaded. Now what does this mean except that *a priori*—that is, before being informed of past throws—we would not have expected so high a percentage of 5's? The fact that 40 per cent rather than 16.67 per cent of the throws were 5's is contrary to our initial expectation.

Let us stop here and not pursue this topic further, although it is important and very interesting in its own right. However, it is not a topic which Laplace pursues in the present essay. This little treatise is merely concerned with the *mathematical* theory of probability, not with the problem of how probabilities are determined. In fact, more correctly, Laplace in these chapters is interested in a calculus of probabilities, not in probability as such. To the extent that Laplace has to make a commitment, however, he seems to favor the *a priori* school, which derives probability from ignorance. "The theory of chance," he writes,

> consists in reducing all the events of the same kind to a certain number of cases equally possible, that is to say, to such as we may be equally undecided about in regard to their existence, and in determining the number of cases favorable to the event whose probability is sought.

On the basis of this, Laplace gives his definition of the probability of an event:

> The ratio of this number to that of all the cases possible is the measure of this probability, which is thus simply a fraction whose numerator is the number of favorable cases and whose denominator is the number of all the cases possible.

The real difficulty, of course, comes in determining what are equally possible cases, and this cannot be decided *a priori*. In the case of a die, it may seem as though we know *a priori* that there are six equally possible cases, but this is not true. The six possible cases are equally possible only if we know that the die is not loaded, and this fact can be determined only by experience. In other words, we know that all six cases are equally possible only if we have thrown the die a great many times and have found empirically that all six cases come up the same, or almost the same, number of times.

However it be determined, probability is expressed by a fraction, always less than 1 and more than 0. To say that a proposition is to be believed with probability 1 would mean that the proposition is certainly known to be true, whereas if its probability is 0, it would be certainly false.

In Chapter 3 of his essay, Laplace outlines the principles of the calculus of probabilities. Here he states the *rules* which must be employed in performing operations with probabilities. Just as there are rules for arithmetic (the calculus of numbers), such as $a + b = b + a$, so there are certain rules about how we must combine probabilities. This calculus is a branch of pure mathematics; that is, it has nothing to do with how we determine probabilities in practice, nor does it in any way depend on our definition of probability. This calculus simply assumes that there are things called probabilities, and that certain things can be done with them. The calculus begins where the empirical determination of probabilities leaves off.

Laplace's *first principle* is the definition of probability as "the ratio of the number of favorable cases to that of all the cases possible." We have already seen that in practice there is considerable difficulty in knowing what the number of all possible cases is.

This definition of probability assumes that all the possible cases are equi-possible cases. (The probability of throwing a 4 with a die is ⅙, because there are 6 equally possible cases, and only one of them is favorable, namely, when the 4 comes up.) In the *second principle* Laplace tells us what to do if the possible cases are not all equal. We must then divide the unequally possible cases until we have only equally possible cases. Let us look at his example.

Given a coin that is perfectly balanced and that is to be thrown twice, what is the probability of throwing heads at least once—that is, either once or twice? Before solving the problem, we should note that it perfectly exemplifies the non-empirical character of Laplace's procedure. When Laplace writes that the "opposite faces which we will call heads and tails, are perfectly similar" he means to tell us that the probability of throwing heads in one throw is exactly ½. This is the meaning of the expression "perfectly similar." The problem may therefore be stated as follows: Given a coin, which is such that the probability of throwing heads in any given throw is ½, what is the probability of throwing heads at least once in two throws? From one given probability (that of throwing heads in one throw) another probability is to be derived (that of throwing heads once in two throws). Nothing is said about how the given probability is determined, although we may infer from Laplace's way of stating things that it is an *a priori* determination.

In this example, there are four equally possible cases. Let us list them in a table.

	First throw	Second throw
1st case:	Heads	Heads
2nd case:	Heads	Tails
3rd case:	Tails	Heads
4th case:	Tails	Tails

Of these four cases, the first three are favorable to the event in question (throwing at least one heads); hence the probability of this event is ¾. There is another, but erroneous, way of looking at this problem. According to this second way, there are only three cases:

1st case: Heads in first throw. A second throw is then un-necessary, because we have "won."

2nd case: Tails in first throw. This is unfavorable, but we get another chance and make another throw. This time heads comes up and we still "win."

3rd case: Tails in first throw. We throw again, but tails comes up a second time. We "lose."

Of these three cases, the first two are favorable to the event in question, and so the probability would seem to be ⅔. But this analysis is incorrect, because the three cases are not equally possible. The first case actually is twice as "possible"—that is, twice as likely to come up as either of the second two. For the first case contains in itself two cases; that of heads first and heads second, and that of heads first and tails second. If we insist on only considering three cases, we must therefore as-cribe to the first case (heads at the first throw) the probability of ½, while the other favorable case (heads at the second throw, after the first throw has been tails) has the probability of ¼. The probability of all the favorable cases is then the sum of ½ and ¼, or ¾. It is probably easier, however, simply to disallow the analysis into three cases and insist that the cor-rect analysis takes account of all four cases.

The *third principle* is a most important one. It concerns the probability of two events both happening, when we know the probability of the first event, the probability of the second event, and also that the two events are independent of one another. This last stricture is most important. If the fact that event a has happened influences the probability that b will hap-pen, then the probability that a and b will both happen is ob-viously quite different from what it would be if the fact that a has happened has no influence on the probability of b happen-ing. In the former case, a and b are not independent events, but in the latter case they are.

Now if the two events a and b are independent, and if the probability that a will happen is p and the probability that b will happen is q, then the probability that a and b will both happen is $p \cdot q$. The example which Laplace uses is that of two dice being thrown. We wish to know the probability that both dice will come up with an ace. Considering only one die, the probability of 1 coming up is ⅙; considering only the second die, the probability that 1 will come up is also ⅙; the probability that both dice will come up with a 1 is, therefore, ⅙ · ⅙, or ⅟₃₆. To see that this is correct, we need only realize that for two dice there are all together 36 different cases that may arise, namely the following:

1–1	2–1	3–1	4–1	5–1	6–1
1–2	2–2	3–2	4–2	5–2	6–2
1–3	2–3	3–3	4–3	5–3	6–3
1–4	2–4	3–4	4–4	5–4	6–4
1–5	2–5	3–5	4–5	5–5	6–5
1–6	2–6	3–6	4–6	5–6	6–6

Of all these 36 cases, only one is favorable, namely the 1–1 case. And so its probability is ⅟₃₆. Of course, the probability of any other specified combination of faces coming up is exactly the same; for instance, the probability of getting a 4 with the first die and getting a 5 with the second is also ⅟₃₆.

Let us try to give another example, but one which is not so artificial as one involving dice. What is the probability that a given automobile in the United States is (1) made by manufacturer X, and (2) registered in the state of Y? We must find out what the probability of any cars being made by X is; let it be 0.5. Then we must find out what the probability of any car's being registered in state Y is; let it be 0.2. We must make certain of one another condition: that these two events are independent of one another. In practice, they probably are not quite independent. It may well be that manufacturer X sells more cars in one state than in another; that would make the two events to a certain degree dependent on one another. For if Y happens to be a state in which X sells more cars than it does in Z, then the occurrence of the first favorable event (the car being manufactured by X) influences the occurrence of the second event favorably (the car's being registered in the state of Y). But if we assume that X sells exactly the same percentage of cars in every state, then the probability of the two events both occurring would be 0.5, 0.2 or 0.01.

The *fourth principle* considers what we are to do when the two events whose combined probability we wish to find are not independent of one another. The answer is simple, though again in practice not always easy to apply. Suppose the probability of a's occurring is p, and suppose that the probability of b's occurring *if a has occurred* is r. Then the probability of a and b both occurring is $p \cdot r$. The difficulty, of course, is in determining the value of r. In order to find it, we must be able to state what the influence of a's occurrence on b is.

Laplace's example for this case involves three urns, A, B, C. All that is known of these three urns is that two of them contain only white balls, while one contains only black balls. A ball is drawn from urn C. What is the probability of its being white? There are three possible cases, two of which are favorable to the drawn ball being white, as follows:

1st case:	A—white balls	B—white balls	C—black balls
2nd case:	A—white balls	B—black balls	C—white balls
3rd case:	A—black balls	B—white balls	C—white balls

Suppose now that a white ball has been drawn from urn C, and that we draw another ball from urn B. What is the probability of this ball's being white? Since the ball drawn from C was white, only two cases are now left as possibilities (the two marked "2nd" and "3rd" in the table above). Hence, on the assumption of C's containing white balls, the probability of drawing a white ball from B is ½. Consequently, the probability of drawing white balls from both C and B is equal to ⅔ · ½ = ²⁄₆ or ⅓.

Thus the occurrence or nonoccurrence of past events can influence the probability of future events. In the case of the three urns, the probability of drawing a white ball from urn B is ⅔ (if nothing is known about past drawings). If, however, a ball is first drawn from urn C and is white, then the probability of drawing a white ball from B becomes, as we saw, ½. On the other hand, if a ball is first drawn from C and is black, then the probability of drawing a white ball from B becomes 1 or certainty (since there is only one urn with black balls).

Laplace formalizes this as the *fifth principle*. Let an event have occurred, such as drawing a white ball from urn C. Calculate the probability of this event. It is ⅔. Now calculate the probability of another event combined of the occurred event and another one (drawing a white ball from both C and B); this we saw was ⅓. If we take the last probability (that of the combined event) and divide it by the first probability (that of the event which actually occurred), the result will give us the probability of the second event(drawing a white ball from B) on the basis of C containing white balls. In our example, ⅓ divided by ⅔ = ½.

This is the place at which to discuss the so-called "gambler's fallacy." It is based on an incorrect analysis of how the past influences the future. In its broadest terms, this fallacy is the following: Suppose a coin, assumed to be perfectly balanced, is thrown a number of times. The probability of either heads or tails coming up in any given throw is ½. Consequently, if we make a very large number of throws, we should expect that half of them would be heads and half tails. Suppose, however, that we have made 50 throws, and that of these 35 were heads and 15 tails. Now let us make ten more throws; all ten come up heads, so that we have a total of 45 heads and 15 tails in 60 throws. The "gambler's fallacy" consists in concluding that therefore there is a probability of more than ½ that the next throw will be tails. The fallacious reasoning is that the number of heads and tails has to "even out"; this is incorrect. We assumed, in stating this problem, that the coin was perfectly balanced. The probability that the sixty-first throw will come up tails is, therefore, exactly ½; no more and no less. (The coin, after all, does not know that the past throws have been heavily in favor of heads.) The reason why the probability is unchanged is that there is no dependence of the latter events on the former (the way there was in the case of the three urns).

Only one other possibility need be considered: we may have been incorrect in our initial statement that the coin was perfectly balanced. If this is so—if the coin is weighted in such a fashion as to favor heads—then, of course, the gambler is all the more foolish to judge that tails are more likely to come up in the sixty-first throw than before. On the contrary, on this assumption, the gambler will do well to judge that he is faced with a coin so weighted that the probability of heads coming up is ¾, while that of tails coming up is only ¼.

In the *sixth principle* Laplace goes from events to causes. (This is what we did in discussing the gambler's fallacy.) Suppose that there is a probability of ½ that event a will occur, as the result of either cause g, cause h, or cause k. Let us further assume that the three causes g, h, k are equally probable. Then there is a ⅓ probability that if a occurs, it will be due to g; there is a ⅓ probability that if it occurs, it will be due to h; and there is also a ⅓ probability that if it occurs it will be due to k. Since the probability that the event will occur at all is equal to ½, the probability of g existing will be ⅓ multiplied by ½, or ⅙. Similarly for the other two causes.

Usually, of course, we will not know, independently of considering the causes, that the probability of an event a is ½ or any other figure. Instead, we usually work the other way around: We may know that the probability of event a due to *g* is one thing; that the probability of *a* due to *h* is something else, while the probability of *a* due to *k* is yet a third value. Then we calculate the probability of *g* or *h* or *k* being the actually existing cause on the basis of these figures.

In his discussion of the *seventh principle* Laplace gives an example which illustrates this. He imagines that there is an urn which contains two balls. Each ball may be either black or white. We do not know what the colors are before we begin to draw the balls out. One ball is drawn and found to be white. It is replaced in the urn. Another ball is now drawn and replaced. It, too, is found to be white. The "event" corresponding to *a* above is that of drawing two successive white balls. The "causes" which bring this about are different possible contents of the urn. We know right away that it is impossible for both balls to be black. Only two "causes" remain which could have caused the event of drawing a white ball each time. Either one of the two balls is white and the other black, or both balls are white. On the assumption of the first "cause," the probability of drawing two white balls in succession is ¼. On the assumption of the second "cause," the probability is 1. Then, by the sixth principle, we calculate the probability of either of the two causes existing as follows: Form a fraction whose denominator is the sum of the probabilities of the event occurring due to all the causes. In our case, this is ¼ + 1, or 5/4. The probability of the first cause existing, is then ¼ divided by 5/4, while the probability of the second cause existing is 1 divided by 5/4. The resulting probabilities are 1/5 and 4/5.

But the seventh principle does more than merely illustrate the sixth one. There is an additional problem which Laplace investigates: In the same example as above (that is, one urn with two balls in it, their color unknown before we start drawing out balls and replacing them), we want to know what the probability is that the third time we draw a ball it will be white, on the assumption that the first two times the ball drawn was white.

We know, from the sixth principle, that there is a 1/5 probability that one ball is black and one is white, while there is a 4/5 probability that both balls are white. If the first hypothesis (one white, one black) is correct, then there is a ½ probability that the third ball drawn will be white; if the second hypothesis (two white balls) is correct, there is a probability of 1 (that is, certainty) that the third ball will be white. Hence the probability of drawing a white ball will be 1/5 · ½ on the basis of the first hypothesis; and it will be 4/5 · 1 on the basis of the second hypothesis. The probability therefore of drawing a white ball (when the first two draws have shown white balls) is $\frac{1}{10} + \frac{4}{5} = \frac{9}{10}$. This last fraction is pretty close to unity or certainty. That is as it should be, for if we already have drawn two white balls, it is pretty likely, according to common sense, that both balls are white and that the third and all succeeding drawings will result in white balls. The seventh principle of Laplace tells us just *how* likely it is.

CHAPTER NINE

Boole—Algebra and Logic Joined

PART I

George Boole, in his *Laws of Thought*, shows us that there is yet another branch of learning which is part of mathematics. Here we have logic being treated as a part of mathematics. To be sure, it is strange mathematics, with strange laws and strange propositions.

Later developments have shown that Boole was on the right track. At present, it is a question whether logic ought to be considered a branch of mathematics, or mathematics a branch of logic. Indeed, the best way to solve this problem may be to say that logic and mathematics are one.

How important Boole's work has been to modern science and technology can be seen when we recall such expressions as "mechanical brains" or "thinking machines" for the modern computer. What these expressions signify, of course, is that these machines can perform certain mathematical operations which have a logical counterpart. If the machine is properly set up ("programmed"), and if the various operations are correctly interpreted, then the computer can be used to perform in a few minutes logical and mathematical calculations that it would take a human being weeks or months to perform. It is all based on Boole's insight that logical and mathematical operations are, to a certain extent, interchangeable!

George Boole:
*The Laws of Thought**

Chapter II

OF SIGNS IN GENERAL, AND OF THE SIGNS
APPROPRIATE TO THE SCIENCE OF LOGIC IN
PARTICULAR; ALSO OF THE LAWS TO WHICH
THAT CLASS OF SIGNS ARE SUBJECT

1. That Language is an instrument of human reason, and
not merely a medium for the expression of thought, is a truth
generally admitted. It is proposed in this chapter to inquire
what it is that renders Language thus subservient to the most
important of our intellectual faculties. In the various steps of
this inquiry we shall be led to consider the constitution of
Language, considered as a system adapted to an end or purpose; to investigate its elements; to seek to determine their
mutual relation and dependence; and to inquire in what manner they contribute to the attainment of the end to which, as
co-ordinate parts of a system, they have respect.

In proceeding to these inquiries, it will not be necessary to
enter into the discussion of that famous question of the schools,
whether Language is to be regarded as an *essential* instrument
of reasoning, or whether, on the other hand, it is possible for
us to reason without its aid. I suppose this question to be beside the design of the present treatise, for the following reason,
viz., that it is the business of Science to investigate laws; and
that, whether we regard signs as the representatives of things
and of their relations, or as the representatives of the conceptions and operations of the human intellect, in studying the
laws of signs, we are in effect studying the manifested laws
of reasoning. If there exists a difference between the two inquiries, it is one which does not affect the scientific expressions
of formal law, which are the object of investigation in the

* From *George Boole's Collected Logical Works* (Cambridge: Macmillan and Co., 1854), Vol. II, *An Investigation of the Laws of Thought*,
pp. 26-56.

present stage of this work, but relates only to the mode in which those results are presented to the mental regard. For though in investigating the laws of signs, *a posteriori*, the immediate subject of examination is Language, with the rules which govern its use; while in making the internal processes of thought the direct object of inquiry, we appeal in a more immediate way to our personal consciousness, — it will be found that in both cases the results obtained are formally equivalent. Nor could we easily conceive, that the unnumbered tongues and dialects of the earth should have preserved through a long succession of ages so much that is common and universal, were we not assured of the existence of some deep foundation of their agreement in the laws of the mind itself.

2. The elements of which all language consists are signs or symbols. Words are signs. Sometimes they are said to represent things; sometimes the operations by which the mind combines together the simple notions of things into complex conceptions; sometimes they express the relations of action, passion, or mere quality, which we perceive to exist among the objects of our experience; sometimes the emotions of the perceiving mind. But words, although in this and in other ways they fulfill the office of signs, or representative symbols, are not the only signs which we are capable of employing. Arbitrary marks, which speak only to the eye, and arbitrary sounds or actions, which address themselves to some other sense, are equally of the nature of signs, provided that their representative office is defined and understood. In the mathematical sciences, letters, and the symbols $+$, $-$, $=$, &c., are used as signs, although the term "sign" is applied to the latter class of symbols, which represent operations or relations, rather than to the former, which represent the elements of number and quantity. As the real import of a sign does not in any way depend upon its particular form or expression, so neither do the laws which determine its use. In the present treatise, however, it is with written signs that we have to do, and it is with reference to these exclusively that the term "sign" will be employed. The essential properties of signs are enumerated in the following definition.

Definition.—A sign is an arbitrary mark, having a fixed interpretation, and susceptible of combination which other signs in subjection to fixed laws dependent upon their mutual interpretation.

3. Let us consider the particulars involved in the above definition separately.

(1.) In the first place, a sign is an *arbitrary* mark. It is clearly indifferent what particular word or token we associate with a given idea, provided that the association once made is permanent. The Romans expressed by the word "civitas" what we designate by the word "state." But both they and we might equally well have employed any other word to represent the same conception. Nothing, indeed, in the nature of Language would prevent us from using a mere letter in the same sense. Were this done, the laws according to which that letter would require to be used would be essentially the same with the laws which govern the use of "civitas" in the Latin, and of "state" in the English language, so far at least as the use of those words is regulated by any general principles common to all languages alike.

(2.) In the second place, it is necessary that each sign should possess, within the limits of the same discourse or process of reasoning, a fixed interpretation. The necessity of this condition is obvious, and seems to be founded in the very nature of the subject. There exists, however, a dispute as to the precise nature of the representative office of words or symbols used as names in the processes of reasoning. By some it is maintained, that they represent the conceptions of the mind alone; by others, that they represent things. The question is not of great importance here, as its decision cannot affect the laws according to which signs are employed. I apprehend, however, that the general answer to this and such like questions is, that in the processes of reasoning, signs stand in the place and fulfill the office of the conceptions and operations of the mind; but that as those conceptions and operations represent things, and the connexions and relations of things, so signs represent things with their connexions and relations; and lastly, that as signs stand in the place of the conceptions and operations of the mind, they are subject to the laws of those conceptions and operations. This view will be more fully elucidated in the next chapter; but it here serves to explain the third of those particulars involved in the definition of a sign, viz., its subjection to fixed laws of combination depending upon the nature of its interpretation.

4. The analysis and classification of those signs by which the operations of reasoning are conducted will be considered in the following Proposition:

Proposition I

All the operations of Language, as an instrument of reasoning, may be conducted by a system of signs composed of the following elements, viz.:

1st. Literal symbols, as x, y, &c., representing things as subjects of our conceptions.

2nd. Signs of operation, as +, −, ×, standing for those operations of the mind by which the conceptions of things are combined or resolved so as to form new conceptions involving the same elements.

3rd. The sign of identity, =.

And these symbols of Logic are in their use subject to definite laws, partly agreeing with and partly differing from the laws of the corresponding symbols in the science of Algebra.

Let it be assumed as a criterion of the true elements of rational discourse, that they should be susceptible of combination in the simplest forms and by the simplest laws, and thus combining should generate all other known and conceivable forms of language; and adopting this principle, let the following classification be considered.

CLASS I

5. Appellative or descriptive signs, expressing either the name of a thing, or some quality or circumstance belonging to it.

To this class we may obviously refer the substantive proper or common, and the adjective. These may indeed be regarded as differing only in this respect, that the former expresses the substantive existence of the individual thing or things to which it refers; the latter implies that existence. If we attach to the adjective the universally understood subject 'being" or 'thing," it becomes virtually a substantive, and may for all the essential purposes of reasoning be replaced by the substantive. Whether or not, in every particular of the mental regard, it is the same thing to say, "Water is a fluid thing," as to say, "Water is fluid"; it is at least equivalent in the expression of the processes of reasoning.

It is clear also, that to the above class we must refer any sign which may conventionally be used to express some circumstances or relation, the detailed exposition of which would involve the use of many signs. The epithets of poetic diction are very frequently of this kind. They are usually compounded adjectives, singly fulfilling the office of a many-worded description. Homer's "deep-eddying ocean" embodies a virtual description in the single word $\beta\alpha\theta\upsilon\delta\iota\nu\eta s$. And conventionally any other description addressed either to the imagination or to the intellect might equally be represented by a single sign, the use of which would in all essential points be subject to the same laws as the use of the adjective "good" or "great." Combined with the subject "thing," such a sign would virtually become a substantive; and by a single substantive the combined meaning both of thing and quality might be expressed.

6. Now, as it has been defined that a sign is an arbitrary mark, it is permissible to replace all signs of the species above described by letters. Let us then agree to represent the class of individuals to which a particular name or description is applicable, by a single letter, as x. If the name is "men," for instance, let x represent "all men," or the class "men." By a class is usually meant a collection of individuals, to each of which a particular name or description may be applied; but in this work the meaning of the term will be extended so as to include the case in which but a single individual exists, answering to the required name or description, as well as the cases denoted by the terms "nothing" and "universe," which as "classes" should be understood to comprise respectively "no beings," "all beings." Again, if an adjective, as "good," is employed as a term of description, let us represent by a letter, as y, all things to which the description "good" is applicable, *i.e.* "all good things," or the class "good things." Let it further be agreed, that by the combination xy shall be represented that class of things to which the names or descriptions represented by x and y are simultaneously applicable. Thus, if x alone stands for "white things," and y for "sheep," let xy stand for "white sheep"; and in like manner, if z stand for "horned things," and x and y retain their previous interpretations, let zxy represent "horned white sheep," *i.e.* that collection of things to which the name "sheep," and the descriptions "white" and "horned" are together applicable.

Let us now consider the laws to which the symbols x, y, &c., used in the above sense, are subject.

7. First, it is evident, that according to the above combinations, the order in which two symbols are written is indifferent. The expressions xy and yx equally represent that class of things

to the several members of which the names or descriptions x and y are together applicable. Hence we have,

$$xy = yx. \tag{1}$$

In the case of x representing white things, and y sheep, either of the members of this equation will represent the class of "white sheep." There may be a difference as to the order in which the conception is formed, but there is none as to the individual things which are comprehended under it. In like manner, if x represent "estuaries," and y "rivers," the expressions xy and yx will indifferently represent "rivers that are estuaries," or "estuaries that are rivers," the combination in this case being in ordinary language that of two substantives, instead of that of a substantive and an adjective as in the previous instance. Let there be a third symbol, as z, representing that class of things to which the term "navigable" is applicable, and any one of the following expressions,

$$zxy, \ zyx, \ xyz, \ \&c.,$$

will represent the class of "navigable rivers that are estuaries."

If one of the descriptive terms should have some implied reference to another, it is only necessary to include that reference expressly in its stated meaning, in order to render the above remarks still applicable. Thus, if x represent "wise" and y "counsellor," we shall have to define whether x implies wisdom in the absolute sense, or only the wisdom of counsel. With such definition the law $xy = yx$ continues to be valid.

We are permitted, therefore, to employ the symbols x, y, z, &c., in the place of the substantives, adjectives, and descriptive phrases subject to the rule of interpretation, that any expression in which several of these symbols are written together shall represent all the objects or individuals to which their several meanings are together applicable, and to the law that the order in which the symbols succeed each other is indifferent.

As the rule of interpretation has been sufficiently exemplified, I shall deem it unnecessary always to express the subject "things" in defining the interpretation of a symbol used for an adjective. When I say, let x represent "good," it will be understood that x only represents "good" when a subject for that quality is supplied by another symbol, and that, used alone, its interpretation will be "good things."

8. Concerning the law above determined, the following observations, which will also be more or less appropriate to certain other laws to be deduced hereafter, may be added.

First, I would remark, that this law is a law of thought, and not, properly speaking, a law of things. Difference in the order of the qualities or attributes of an object, apart from all questions of causation, is a difference in conception merely. The law (1) expresses as a general truth, that the same thing may be conceived in different ways, and states the nature of that difference; and it does no more than this.

Secondly, as a law of thought, it is actually developed in a law of Language, the product and the instrument of thought. Though the tendency of prose writing is toward uniformity, yet even there the order of sequence of adjectives, absolute in their meaning, and applied to the same subject, is indifferent but poetic diction borrows much of its rich diversity from the extension of the same lawful freedom to the substantive also. The language of Milton is peculiarly distinguished by this species of variety. Not only does the substantive often precede the adjectives by which it is qualified, but it is frequently placed in their midst. In the first few lines of the invocation to Light, we meet with such examples as the following:

"Offspring of heaven first-born."
"The rising world of *waters dark and deep.*"
"Bright effluence of *bright essence increate.*"

Now these inverted forms are not simply the fruits of a poetic license. They are the natural expressions of a freedom sanctioned by the intimate laws of thought, but for reasons of convenience not exercised in the ordinary use of language.

Thirdly, the law expressed by (1) may be characterized by saying that the literal symbols x, y, z, are *commutative, like the symbols of Algebra.* In saying this, it is not affirmed that the process of multiplication in Algebra, of which the fundamental law is expressed by the equation

$$xy = yx,$$

possesses in itself any analogy with that process of logical combination which xy has been made to represent above; but only that if the arithmetical and the logical process are expressed in the same manner, their symbolical expressions will be subject to the same formal law. The evidence of that subjection is in the two cases quite distinct.

9. As the combination of two literal symbols in the form xy expresses the whole of that class of objects to which the names or qualities represented by x and y are together applicable, it follows that if the two symbols have exactly the same signification, their combination expresses no more than either

of the symbols taken alone would do. In such case we should therefore have

$$xy = x.$$

As y is, however, supposed to have the same meaning as x, we may replace it in the above equation by x, and we thus get

$$xx = x.$$

Now in common Algebra the combination xx is more briefly represented by x^2. Let us adopt the same principle of notation here; for the mode of expressing a particular succession of mental operations is a thing in itself quite as arbitrary as the mode of expressing a single idea or operation (II. 3). In accordance with this notation, then, the above equation assumes the form

$$x^2 = x, \tag{2}$$

and is, in fact the expression of a second general law of those symbols by which names, qualities, or description, are symbolically represented.

The reader must bear in mind that although the symbols x and y in the examples previously formed received significations distinct from each other, nothing prevents us from attributing to them precisely the same signification. It is evident that the more nearly their actual significations approach to each other, the more nearly does the class of things denoted by the combination xy approach to identity with the class denoted by x, as well as with that denoted by y. The case supposed in the demonstration of the equation (2) is that of *absolute* identity of meaning. The law which it expresses is practically exemplified in language. To say "good, good," in relation to any subject, though a cumbrous and useless pleonasm, is the same as to say "good." Thus "good, good" men, is equivalent to "good" men. Such repetitions of words are indeed sometimes employed to heighten a quality or strengthen an affirmation. But this effect is merely secondary and conventional; it is not founded in the intrinsic relations of language and thought. Most of the operations which we observe in nature, or perform ourselves, are of such a kind that their effect is augmented by repetition, and this circumstance prepares us to expect the same thing in language, and even to use repetition when we design to speak with emphasis. But neither in strict reasoning nor in exact discourse is there any just ground for such a practice.

10. We pass now to the consideration of another class of the signs of speech, and of the laws connected with their use.

CLASS II

11. *Signs of those mental operations whereby we collect parts into a whole, or separate a whole into its parts.*

We are not only capable of entertaining the conceptions of objects, as characterized by names, qualities, or circumstances, applicable to each individual of the group under consideration, but also of forming the aggregate conception of a group of objects consisting of partial groups, each of which is separately named or described. For this purpose we use the conjunctions "and," "or," &c. "Trees and minerals," "barren mountains, or fertile vales," are examples of this kind. In strictness, the words "and," "or," interposed between the terms descriptive of two or more classes of objects, imply that those classes are quite distinct, so that no member of one is found in another. In this and in all other respects the words "and" "or" are analogous with the sign $+$ in algebra, and their laws are identical. Thus the expression "men and women" is, conventional meanings set aside, equivalent with the expression "women and men." Let x represent "men," y "women"; and let $+$ stand for " *and* " and "*or*," then we have

$$x + y = y + x, \tag{3}$$

an equation which would equally hold true if x and y represented *numbers*, and $+$ were the sign of arithmetical addition.

Let the symbol z stand for the adjective "European," then since it is, in effect, the same thing to say "European men and women," as to say "European men and European women," we have

$$z(x + y) = zx + zy. \tag{4}$$

And this equation also would be equally true were x, y, and z symbols of number, and were the juxtaposition of two literal symbols to represent their algebraic product, just as in the logical signification previously given, it represents the class of objects to which both the epithets conjoined belong.

The above are the laws which govern the use of the sign $+$, here used to denote the positive operation of aggregating parts into a whole. But the very idea of an operation effecting some positive change seems to suggest to us the idea of an opposite or negative operation, having the effect of undoing what the former one has done. Thus we cannot conceive it possible to collect parts into a whole, and not conceive it also possible to separate a part from a whole. This operation we express in common language by the sign *except*, as, "All men *except* Asiatics," "All states *except* those which are monarchical." Here it is implied that the things excepted form a part of the things from which they are excepted. As we have expressed the operation of aggregation by the sign +, so we may express the negative operation above described by − (minus). Thus if x be taken to represent men, and y, Asiatics, *i.e.* Asiatic men, then the conception of "All men except Asiatics" will be expressed by $x − y$. And if we represent by x, "states," and by y the descriptive property "having a monarchial form," then the conception of "All states except those which are monarchical" will be expressed by $x − xy$.

As it is indifferent for all the *essential* purposes of reasoning whether we express excepted cases first or last in the order of speech, it is also indifferent in what order we write any series of terms, some of which are affected by the sign −. Thus we have, as in the common algebra,

$$x − y = − y + x. \qquad (5)$$

Still representing by x the class "men," and by y "Asiatics," let z represent the adjective "white." Now to apply the adjective "white" to the collection of men expressed by the phrase "Men except Asiatics," is the same as to say, "White men, except white Asiatics." Hence we have

$$z(x − y) = zx − zy. \qquad (6)$$

This is also in accordance with the laws of ordinary algebra.

The equations (4) and (6) may be considered as exemplification of a single general law, which may be stated by saying, *that the literal symbols, x, y, z, &c. are distributive in their operation.* The general fact which that law expresses is this, viz.:—If any quality or circumstance is ascribed to all the members of a group, formed either by aggregation or exclusion of partial groups, the resulting conception is the same as if the quality or circumstance were first ascribed to each member of the partial groups, and the aggregation or exclusion effected afterwards. That which is ascribed to the members of the whole is ascribed to the members of all its parts, howsoever those parts are connected together.

CLASS III

12. *Signs by which relation is expressed, and by which we form propositions.*

Though all verbs may with propriety be referred to this

class, it is sufficient for the purposes of Logic to consider it as including only the substantive verb *is* or *are*, since every other verb may be resolved into this element, and one of the signs included under Class I. For as those signs are used to express quality or circumstance of every kind, they may be employed to express the active or passive relation of the subject of the verb, considered with reference either to past, to present, or to future time. Thus the Proposition, "Cæsar conquered the Gauls," may be resolved into "Cæsar is he who conquered the Gauls." The ground of this analysis I conceive to be the following:—Unless we understand what is meant by having conquered the Gauls, *i.e.* by the expression "One who conquered the Gauls," we cannot understand the sentence in question. It is, therefore, truly an element of that sentence; another element is "Cæsar," and there is yet another required, the copula *is*, to show the connexion of these two. I do not, however, affirm that there is no other mode than the above of contemplating the relation expressed by the proposition, "Cæsar conquered the Gauls,"; but only that the analysis here given is a correct one for the particular point of view which has been taken, and that it suffices for the purposes of logical deduction. It may be remarked that the passive and future participles of the Greek language imply the existence of the principle which has been asserted, viz.: that the sign *is* or *are* may be regarded as an element of every personal verb.

13. The above sign, *is* or *are*, may be expressed by the symbol $=$. The laws, or as would usually be said, the axioms which the symbol introduces, are next to be considered.

Let us take the Proposition, "The stars are the suns and the planets," and let us represent stars by x, suns by y, and planets by z; we have then

$$x = y + z. \qquad (7)$$

Now if it be true that the stars are the suns and the planets, it will follow that the stars, except the planets, are suns. This would give the equation

$$x - z = y, \qquad (8)$$

which must therefore be a deduction from (7). Thus a term z has been removed from one side of an equation to the other by changing its sign. This is in accordance with the algebraic rule of transposition.

But instead of dwelling upon particular cases, we may at once affirm the general axioms:—

1st. If equal things are added to equal things, the wholes are equal.

2nd. If equal things are taken from equal things, the re-mainders are equal.

And it hence appears that we may add or subtract equations, and employ the rule of transposition above given just as in common algebra.

Again: If two classes of things, x and y, be identical, that is, if all the members of the one are members of the other, then those members of the one class which possess a given property z will be identical with those members of the other which possess the same property z. Hence if we have the equation

$$x = y;$$

then whatever class or property z may represent, we have also

$$zx = zy.$$

This is formally the same as the algebraic law:—If both members of an equation are multiplied by the same quantity, the products are equal.

In like manner it may be shown that if the corresponding members of two equations are multiplied together, the resulting equation is true.

14. Here, however, the analogy of the present system with that of algebra, as commonly stated, appears to stop. Suppose it true that those members of a class x which possess a certain property z are identical with those members of a class y which possess the same property z, it does not follow that the members of the class x universally are identical with the members of the class y. Hence it cannot be inferred from the equation

$$zx = zy,$$

that the equation

$$x = y$$

is also true. In other words, the axiom of algebraists, that both sides of an equation may be divided by the same quantity, has no formal equivalent here. I say no *formal equivalent*, because, in accordance with the general spirit of these inquiries, it is not even sought to determine whether the mental operation which is represented by removing a logical symbol, z, from a combination zx, is in itself analogous with the operation of division in Arithmetic. That mental operation is indeed identical with what is commonly termed Abstraction, and it will hereafter appear that its laws are dependent upon the laws already deduced in this chapter. What has now been shown is, that there does not exist among those laws anything analogous in *form* with a commonly received axiom of Algebra.

But a little consideration will show that even in common

algebra that axiom does not possess the generality of those other axioms which have been considered. The deduction of the equation $x = y$ from the equation $zx = zy$ is only valid when it is known that z is not equal to 0. If then the value $z = 0$ is supposed to be admissible in the algebraic system, the axiom above stated ceases to be applicable, and the analogy before exemplified remains at least unbroken.

15. However, it is not with the symbols or quantity generally that it is of any importance, except as a matter of speculation, to trace such affinities. We have seen (II. 9) that the symbols of Logic are subject to the special law,

$$x^2 = x.$$

Now of the symbols of Number there are but two, viz. 0 and 1, which are subject to the same formal law. We know that $0^2 = 0$, and that $1^2 = 1$; and the equation $x^2 = x$, considered as algebraic, has no other roots than 0 and 1. Hence, instead of determining the measure of formal agreement of the symbols of Logic with those of Number generally, it is more immediately suggested to us to compare them with symbols of quantity *admitting only of the values* 0 *and* 1. Let us conceive, then, of an Algebra in which the symbols x, y, z, &c. admit indifferently of the values 0 and 1, and of these values alone. The laws, the axioms, and the processes of such an Algebra will be identical in their whole extent with the laws, the axioms, and the processes of an Algebra of Logic. Difference of interpretation will alone divide them. Upon this principle the method of the following work is established.

16. It now remains to show that those constituent parts of ordinary language which have not been considered in the previous sections of this chapter are either resolvable into the same elements as those which have been considered, or are subsidiary to those elements by contributing to their more precise definition.

The substantive, the adjective, and the verb, together with the particles *and, except,* we have already considered. The pronoun may be regarded as a particular form of the substantive or the adjective. The adverb modifies the meaning of the verb, but does not affect its nature. Prepositions contribute to the expression of circumstance or relation, and thus tend to give precision and detail to the meaning of the literal symbols. The conjunctions *if, either, or,* are used chiefly in the expression of relation among propositions, and it will hereafter be shown that the same relations can be completely expressed by elementary symbols analogous in interpretation, and identical in form and law with the symbols whose use and meaning have been explained in this Chapter. As to any remaining elements of speech, it will, upon examination, be found that they are used either to give a more definite significance to the terms of discourse, and thus enter into the interpretation of the literal symbols already considered, or to express some emotion or state of feeling accompanying the utterance of a proposition, and thus do not belong to the province of the understanding, with which alone our present concern lies. Experience of its use will testify to the sufficiency of the classification which has been adopted.

Chapter III

DERIVATION OF THE LAWS OF THE SYMBOLS OF LOGIC FROM THE LAWS OF THE OPERATIONS OF THE HUMAN MIND

1. The object of science, properly so called, is the knowledge of laws and relations. To be able to distinguish what is essential to this end, from what is only accidentally associated with it, is one of the most important conditions of scientific progress. I say, to *distinguish* between these elements, because a consistent devotion to science does not require that the attention should be altogether withdrawn from other speculations, often of a metaphysical nature, with which it is not unfrequently connected. Such questions, for instance, as the existence of a sustaining ground of phænomena, the reality of cause, the propriety of forms of speech implying that the successive states of things are connected by *operations*, and others of a like nature, may possess a deep interest and significance in relation to science, without being essentially scientific. It is indeed scarcely possible to express the conclusions of natural science without borrowing the language of these conceptions. Nor is there necessarily any practical inconvenience arising from this source. They who believe, and they who refuse to believe, that there is more in the relation of cause and effect than an invariable order of succession, agree in their interpretation of the conclusions of physical astronomy. But they only agree because they recognise a common element of scientific truth, which is independent of their particular views of the nature of causation.

2. If this distinction is important in physical science, much more does it deserve attention in connexion with the science of the intellectual powers. For the questions which this science presents become, in expression at least, almost necessarily mixed up with modes of thought and language, which betray a metaphysical origin. The idealist would give to the laws of reasoning one form of expression; the sceptic, if true to his principles, another. They who regard the phænomena with which we are concerned in this inquiry as the mere successive *states* of the thinking subject devoid of any causal connexion, and they who refer them to the *operations* of an active intelligence, would, if consistent, equally differ in their modes of statement. Like difference would also result from a difference of classification of the mental faculties. Now the principle which I would here assert, as affording us the only ground of confidence and stability amid so much of seeming and of real diversity, is the following, viz., that if the laws in question are really deduced from observation, they have a real existence as laws of the human mind, independently of any metaphysical theory which may seem to be involved in the mode of their statement. They contain an element of truth which no ulterior criticism upon the nature, or event upon the reality, of the mind's operations, can essentially affect. Let it even be granted that the mind is but a succession of states of consciousness, a series of fleeting impressions uncaused from without or from within, emerging out of nothing, and returning into nothing again,—the last refinement of the sceptic intellect,—still, as laws of succession, or at least of a past succession, the results to which observation had led would remain true. They would require to be intepreted into a language from whose vocabulary all such terms as cause and effect, operation and subject, substance and attribute, had been banished; but they would still be valid as scientific truths.

Moreover, as any statement of the laws of thought, founded upon actual observation, must thus contain scientific elements which are independent of metaphysical theories of the nature of the mind, the practical application of such elements to the construction of a system or method of reasoning must also be independent of metaphysical distinctions. For it is upon the scientific elements involved in the statement of the laws, that any practical application will rest, just as the practical conclusions of physical astronomy are independent of any theory of the cause of gravitation, but rest only on the knowledge of its phænomenal effects. And, therefore, as respects both the determination of the laws of thought, and the practical use of them when discovered, we are, for all really scientific ends, unconcerned with the truth or falsehood of any metaphysical speculations whatever.

3. The course which it appears to me to be expedient, under these circumstances, to adopt, is to avail myself as far as possible of the language of common discourse, without regard to any theory of the nature and powers of the mind which it may be thought to embody. For instance, it is agreeable to common usage to say that we converse with each other by the communication of ideas, or conceptions, such communication being the office of words; and that with reference to any particular ideas or conceptions presented to it, the mind possesses certain powers or faculties by which the mental regard may be fixed upon some ideas, to the exclusion of others, or by which the given conceptions or ideas may, in various ways, be combined together. To those faculties or powers different names, as Attention, Simple Apprehension, Conception or Imagination, Abstraction, &c., have been given,—names which have not only furnished the titles of distinct divisions of the philosophy of the human mind, but passed into the common language of men. Whenever, then, occasion shall occur to use these terms, I shall do so without implying thereby that I accept the theory that the mind possesses such and such powers and faculties as distinct elements of its activity. Nor is it indeed necessary to inquire whether such powers or the understanding have a distinct existence or not. We may merge these different titles under the one generic name of *Operations* of the human mind, define these operations so far as is necessary for the purposes of this work, and then seek to express their ultimate laws. Such will be the general order of the course which I shall pursue, though reference will occasionally be made to the names which common agreement has assigned to the particular states or operations of the mind which may fall under our notice.

It will be most convenient to distribute the more definite results of the following investigation into distinct Propositions.

PROPOSITION I

4. *To deduce the laws of the symbols of Logic from a consideration of those operations of the mind which are implied in the strict use of language as an instrument of reasoning.*

In every discourse, whether of the mind conversing with its own thoughts, or of the individual in his intercourse with others, there is an assumed or expressed limit within which the subjects of its operation are confined. The most unfettered discourse is that in which the words we use are understood in the widest possible application, and for them the limits of discourse are co-extensive with those of the universe itself. But more usually we confine ourselves to a less spacious field. Sometimes, in discoursing of men we imply (without expressing the limitation) that it is of men only under certain circumstances and conditions that we speak, as of civilized men, or of men in the vigour of life, or of men under some other condition or relation. Now, whatever may be the extent of the field within which all the objects of our discourse are found, that field may properly be termed the universe of discourse.

5. Furthermore, this universe of discourse is in the strictest sense the ultimate *subject* of the discourse. The office of any name or descriptive term employed under the limitations supposed is not to raise in the mind the conception of all the beings or objects to which that name or description is applicable, but only of those which exist within the supposed universe of discourse. If that universe of discourse is the actual universe of things, which it always is when our words are taken in their real and literal sense, then by men we mean *all men that exist*; but if the universe of discourse is limited by any antecedent implied understanding, then it is of men under the limitation thus introduced that we speak. It is in both cases the business of the word *men* to direct a certain operation of the mind, by which, from the proper universe of discourse, we select or fix upon the individuals signified.

6. Exactly of the same kind is the mental operation implied by the use of an adjective. Let, for instance, the universe of discourse be the actual Universe. Then, as the word *men* directs us to select mentally from that Universe all the beings to which the term "men" is applicable; so the adjective "good," in the combination "good men," directs us still further to select mentally from the class of *men* all those who possess the further quality "good"; and if another adjective were prefixed to the combination "good men," it would direct a further operation of the same nature, having reference to that further quality which it might be chosen to express.

It is important to notice carefully the real nature of the operation here described, for it is conceivable, that it might have been different from what it is. Were the adjective simply *attributive* in its character, it would seem, that when a particular set of beings is designated by *men,* the prefixing of the adjective *good* would direct us to attach mentally to all those beings the quality of goodness. But this is not the real office of the adjective. The operation which we really perform is one of *selection according to a prescribed principle or idea.* To what faculties of mind such an operation would be referred, according to the received classification of its powers, it is not important to inquire, but I suppose that it would be considered as dependent upon the two faculties of Conception or Imagination, and Attention. To the one of these faculties might be referred the formation of the general conception; to the other the fixing of the mental regard upon those individuals within the prescribed universe of discourse which answer to the conception. If, however, as seems not improbable, the power of Attention is nothing more than the power of continuing the exercise of any other faculty of the mind, we might properly regard the whole of the mental process above described as referrible to the mental faculty of Imagination or Conception, the first step of the process being the conception of the Universe itself, and each succeeding step limiting in a definite manner the conception thus formed. Adopting this view, I shall describe each such step, or any definite combination of such steps, as a *definite act of conception.* And the use of this term I shall extend so as to include in its meaning not only the conception of classes of objects represented by particular names or simple attributes of quality, but also the combination of such conceptions in any manner consistent with the powers and limitations of the human mind; indeed, any intellectual operation short of that which is involved in the structure of a sentence or proposition. The general laws to which such operations of the mind are subject are now to be considered.

7. Now it will be shown that the laws which in the preceding chapter have been determined *a posteriori* from the constitution of language, for the use of the literal symbols of Logic, are in reality the laws of that definite mental operation which has just been described. We commence our discourse with a certain understanding as to the limits of its subject, *i.e.* as to the limits of its Universe. Every name, every term of description that we employ, directs him whom we address to the performance of a certain mental operation upon that subject. And thus is thought communicated. But as each name or descriptive term is in this view but the representative of an intellectual operation, that operation being also prior in the

order of nature, it is clear that the laws of the name or symbol must be of a derivative character,—must, in fact, originate in those of the operation which they represent. That the laws of the symbol and of the mental process are identical in expression will now be shown.

8. Let us then suppose that the universe of our discourse is the actual universe, so that words are to be used in the full extent of their meaning, and let us consider the two mental operations implied by the words "white" and "men." The word "men" implies the operation of selecting in thought from its subject, the universe, all men; and the resulting conception, *men*, becomes the subject of the next operation. The operation implied by the word "white" is that of selecting from its subject, "men," all of that class which are white. The final resulting conception is that of "white men." Now it is perfectly apparent that if the operations above described had been performed in a converse order, the result would have been the same. Whether we begin by forming the conception of "*men*," and then by a second intellectual act limit that conception to "white men," or whether we begin by forming the conception of "white objects," and then limit it to such of that class as are "men," is perfectly indifferent so far as the result is concerned. It is obvious that the order of the mental processes would be equally indifferent if for the words "white" and "men" we substituted any other descriptive or appellative terms whatever, provided only that their meaning was fixed and absolute. And thus the indifference of the order of two successive acts of the faculty of Conception, the one of which furnishes the subject upon which the other is supposed to operate, is a general condition of the exercise of that faculty. It is a law of the mind, and it is the real origin of that law of the literal symbols of Logic which constitutes its formal expression [(1) Chapter. II].

9. It is equally clear that the mental operation above described is of such a nature that its effect is not altered by repetition. Suppose that by a definite act of conception the attention has been fixed upon men, and that by another exercise of the same faculty we limit it to those of the race who are white. Then any further repetition of the latter mental act, by which the attention is limited to white objects, does not in any way modify the conception arrived at, viz., that of white men. This is also an example of a general law of the mind, and it has its formal expression in the law [(2) Chap. II.] of the literal symbols.

10. Again, it is manifest that from the conceptions of two distinct classes of things we can form the conception of that collection of things which the two classes taken together compose; and it is obviously indifferent in what order of position or of priority those classes are presented to the mental view. This is another general law of the mind, and its expression is found in (3) Chap. II.

11. It is not necessary to pursue this course of inquiry and comparison. Sufficient illustration has been given to render manifest the two following positions, viz.:

First, that the operations of the mind, by which, in the exercise of its power of imagination or conception, it combines and modifies the simple ideas of things or qualities, not less than those operations of the reason which are exercised upon truths and propositions, are subject to general laws.

Secondly, that those laws are mathematical in their form, and that they are actually developed in the essential laws of human language. Wherefore the laws of the symbols of Logic are deducible from a consideration of the operations of the mind in reasoning.

12. The remainder of this chapter will be occupied with questions relating to that law of thought whose expression is $x^2 = x$ (II. 9), a law which, as has been implied (II. 15), forms the characteristic distinction of the operations of the mind in its ordinary discourse and reasoning, as compared with its operations when occupied with the general algebra of quantity. An important part of the following inquiry will consist in proving that the symbols 0 and 1 occupy a place, and are susceptible of an interpretation, among the symbols of Logic; and it may first be necessary to show how particular symbols, such as the above, may with propriety and advantage be employed in the representation of distinct systems of thought.

The ground of this propriety cannot consist in any community of interpretation. For in systems of thought so truly distinct as those of Logic and Arithmetic (I use the latter term in its widest sense as the science of Number), there is, properly speaking, no community of subject. The one of them is conversant with the very conceptions of things, the other takes account solely of their numerical relations. But inasmuch as the forms and methods of any system of reasoning depend immediately upon the laws to which the symbols are subject, and only mediately, through the above link of connexion, upon their interpretation, there may be both propriety and advantage in employing the same symbols in different systems of thought, provided that such interpretations can be assigned to them as shall render their formal laws identical, and their use consistent. The ground of that employment will not then be community of interpretation, but the community of the formal laws, to which in their respective systems they are subject. Nor must that community of formal laws be established upon any other ground than that of a careful observation and comparison of those results which are seen to flow independently from the interpretations of the systems under consideration.

These observations will explain the process of inquiry adopted in the following Proposition. The literal symbols of Logic are universally subject to the law whose expression is $x^2 = x$. Of the symbols of Number there are two only, 0 and 1, which satisfy, this law. But each of these symbols is also subject to a law peculiar to itself in the system of numerical magnitude, and this suggests the inquiry, what interpretations must be given to the literal symbols of Logic, in order that the same peculiar and formal laws may be realized in the logical system also.

PROPOSITION II

13. *To determine the logical value and significance of the symbols* 0 *and* 1.

The symbol 0, as used in Algebra, satisfies the following formal law,

$$0 \times y = 0, \text{ or } 0y = 0, \tag{1}$$

whatever *number* y may represent. That this formal law may be obeyed in the system of Logic, we must assign to the symbol 0 such an interpretation that the *class* represented by 0y may be identical with the class represented by 0, whatever the class y may be. A little consideration will show that this condition is satisfied if the symbol 0 represents Nothing. In accordance with a previous definition, we may term Nothing a class. In fact, Nothing and Universe are the two limits of class extension, for they are the limits of the possible interpretations of general names, none of which can relate to fewer individuals than are comprised in Nothing, or to more than are comprised in the Universe. Now whatever the class y may be, the individuals which are common to it and to the class "Nothing" are identical with those comprised in the class "Nothing," for they are none. And thus by assigning to 0 the interpretation Nothing, the law (1) is satisfied; and it is not otherwise satisfied consistently with the perfectly general character of the class *y*.

Secondly, the symbol 1 satisfies in the system of Number the following law, viz.,

$$1 \times y = y, \text{ or } 1y = y,$$

whatever number *y* may represent. And this formal equation being assumed as equally valid in the system of this work, in which 1 and *y* represent classes, it appears that the symbol 1 must represent such a class that all the individuals which are found in *any* proposed class *y* are also all the individuals 1*y* that are common to that class *y* and the class represented by 1. A little consideration will here show that the class represented by 1 must be "the Universe," since this is the only class in which are found *all* the individuals that exist in *any* class. Hence the respective interpretations of the symbols 0 and 1 in the system of Logic are *Nothing* and *Universe*.

14. As with the idea of any class of objects as "men," there is suggested to the mind the idea of the contrary class of beings which are not men; and as the whole Universe is made up of these two classes together, since of every individual which it comprehends we may affirm either that it is a man, or that it is not a man, it becomes important to inquire how such contrary names are to be expressed. Such is the object of the following Proposition.

PROPOSITION III

If x represent any class of objects, then will $1 - x$ *represent the contrary or supplementary class of objects, i.e. the class including all objects which are not comprehended in the class x.*

For greater distinctness of conception let *x* represent the class *men*, and let us express, according to the last Proposition, the Universe by 1; now if from the conception of the Universe, as consisting of "men" and "not-men," we exclude the conception of "men," the resulting conception is that of the contrary class, "not-men." Hence the class "not-men" will be represented by $1 - x$. And, in general, whatever class of objects is represented by the symbol *x*, the contrary class will be expressed by $1 - x$.

15. Although the following Proposition belongs in strictness to a future chapter of this work, devoted to the subject

of *maxims* or *necessary truths*, yet, on account of the great importance of that law of thought to which it relates, it has been thought proper to introduce it here.

PROPOSITION IV

That axiom of metaphysicians which is termed the principle of contradiction, and which affirms that it is impossible for any being to possess a quality, and at the same time not to possess it, is a consequence of the fundamental law of thought, whose expression is $x^2 = x$.

Let us write this equation in the form
$$x - x^2 = 0,$$
whence we have
$$x(1 - x) = 0; \qquad (1)$$
both these transformations being justified by the axiomatic laws of combination and transposition (II. 13). Let us, for simplicity of conception, give to the symbol x the particular interpretation of *men*, then $1 - x$ will represent the class of "not-men" (Prop. III.). Now the formal product of the expressions of two classes represents that class of individuals which is common to them both (II. 6). Hence $x(1 - x)$ will represent the class whose members are at once "men," and "not men," and the equation (1) thus express the principle, *that a class whose members are at the same time men and not men does not exist.* In other words, that *it is impossible for the same individual to be at the same time a man and not a man.* Now let the meaning of the symbol x be extended from the representing of "men," to that of any class of beings characterized by the possession of any quality whatever; and the equation (1) will then express that it is impossible for a being to possess a quality and not to possess that quality at the same time. But this is identically that "principle of contradiction" which Aristotle has described as the fundamental axiom of all philosophy. "It is impossible that the same quality should both belong and not belong to the same thing. . . . This is the most certain of all principles. . . . Wherefore they who demonstrate refer to this as an ultimate opinion. For it is by nature the source of all the other axioms."

The above interpretation has been introduced not on account of its immediate value in the present system, but as an illustration of a significant fact in the philosophy of the intellectual powers, viz., that what has been commonly regarded

as the fundamental axiom of metaphysics is but the consequence of a law of thought, mathematical in its form. I desire
to direct attention also to the circumstances that the equation
(1) in which that fundamental law of thought is expressed is
an equation of second degree.* Without speculating at all in
this chapter upon the question, whether that circumstance is
necessary in its own nature, we may venture to assert that if
it had not existed, the whole procedure of the understanding
would have been different from what it is. Thus it is a consequence of the fact that the fundamental equation of thought
is of the second degree, that we perform the operation of
analysis and classification, by division into pairs of opposites,
or, as it is technically said, by *dichotomy*. Now if the equation
in question had been of the third degree, still admitting of interpretation as such, the mental division must have been three-
fold in character, and we must have proceeded by a species of
trichotomy, the real nature of which it is impossible for us,
with our existing faculties, adequately to conceive, but the laws
of which we might still investigate as an object of intellectual
speculation.

16. The law of thought expressed by the equation (1) will,
for reasons which are made apparent by the above discussion,
be occasionally referred to as the "law of duality."

*Should it here be said that the existence of the equation $x^2=x$ neces-
sitates also the existence of the equation $x^3=x$, which is of the third degree, and then inquired whether that equation does not indicate a process
of *trichotomy*; the answer is, that the equation $x^3=x$ is not interpretable in
the system of logic. For writing it in either of the forms

$$x(1-x)(1+x) \quad =0, \qquad (2)$$
$$x(1-x)(-1-x)=0, \qquad (3)$$

we see that its interpretation, if possible at all, must involve that of the
factor $1+x$, or of the factor $-1-x$. The former is not interpretable, because we cannot conceive of the addition of any class x to the universe
1; the later is not interpretable, because the symbol -1 is not subject to
the law $x(1-x)=0$, to which all class symbols are subject. Hence the
equation $x^3=x$ admits of no interpretation analogous to that of the equation $x^2=x$. Were the former equation, however, true independently of
the latter, *i.e.* were that act of the mind which is denoted by the symbol
x, such that its second repetition should reproduce the result of a single
operation, but not its first or mere repetition, it is presumable that we
should be able to interpret one of the forms (2), (3), which under the
actual conditions of thought we cannot do. There exist operations, known
to the mathematician, the law of which may be adequately expressed by
the equation $x^3=x$. But they are of a nature altogether foreign to the
province of general reasoning.

In saying that it is conceivable that the law of thought might have been
different from what it is, I mean only that we can frame such an hypothesis, and study its consequences. The possibility of doing this involves no such doctrine as that the actual law of human reason is the
product either of chance or of arbitrary will.

PART II

Why are geometry and arithmetic both considered to be parts of mathematics? What do they have in common? Or to put the question broadly, since there are many other parts to mathematics besides these two, what is the essential character of a mathematical science? One answer, of long standing, is that all branches of mathematics deal with quantity. Thus the ancient mathematicians pointed out that geometry deals with continuous quantities (such as lines), while arithmetic deals with discrete quantities (numbers).

But this answer is to a certain extent unsatisfactory. To say that mathematics "deals" with quantities does not reveal the essential character of the mathematical activity. Furthermore, it is even doubtful whether mathematics is necessarily concerned with quantities; for instance, when we look back on the bridge problem of Königsberg, or topological problems in general, it is not apparent that such problems deal with either continuous or discrete quantities. It seems more accurate to say these problems involve relations, such as "being inside or outside of" or "being to the right of" and similar ones.

There is, however, one characteristic that is common to all mathematical branches. This is the character of *deductiveness*. All mathematical propositions are demonstrated from certain definitions, axioms, or postulates. In different parts of mathematics the definitions and the postulates are different; what is not different is that conclusions are demonstrated, step by step, from certain things that are given.

It makes sense, therefore, to say that the basic characteristic of mathematics consists in demonstrating a conclusion from a hypothesis. And so the *purest* mathematics would be that which disregards completely *what* is being demonstrated and pays attention only to the process of demonstration or deduction. This means, of course, that the purest mathematics is the *theory of deduction*, or deductive logic.

This it is which George Boole attempts to do in the *Laws of Thought*. In the first chapter of this work, Boole describes his aim as follows:

The design of the following treatise is to investigate the fundamental laws of those operations of the mind by which reasoning is performed; to give expression to them in the symbolic language of a Calculus, and upon this foundation to establish the science of Logic and construct its method . . . .

Notice that by an opposite way of reasoning we have arrived at the same place where we were in Chapter 6. There we saw, with the help of Bertrand Russell's *Introduction to Mathematical Philosophy*, that mathematics can be reduced to logic. Here, we are now saying that logic can be seen as the heart of mathematics, if we abstract from the particularities of various branches of mathematics. (Russell was, of course, familiar with Boole's work.) In this chapter, following Boole, we will not try to reduce mathematics to logic; rather we shall use what knowledge of mathematics (especially arithmetic and algebra) we have to develop a simple and symbolic theory of logic.

George Boole was born in the year 1815 in the town of Lincoln in England. Because of the limited financial means of his family, Boole very largely had to educate himself. At the age of sixteen he began to teach in an elementary school for boys, and four years later he established his own school; his interest in mathematics dated from this time. As the result of some of his work, he gradually became acquainted with the leading mathematicians of England. In the year 1849, Boole was appointed professor of mathematics at Queen's College in Cork. His famous work, *The Laws of Thought*, of which we have two chapters here, was published in 1854. Boole died at the age of forty-nine, in the year 1864.

Boole's work marks the beginning of symbolic logic. Since his time, this science has been greatly developed and in some respects changed. One of the major changes is that of symbolism. If we were to reproduce a typical page here of Russell and Whitehead's *Principia Mathematica*, we would see symbol after unfamiliar symbol. The page would probably look as unfamiliar as though it were written in a strange language (as indeed it is). This proliferation of symbols has as its purpose clarity and unambiguity; unfortunately, though this purpose is worthy, there is the side-effect of frightening the ordinary reader.

One advantage of Boole's work is that he introduces a minimum of *new* symbolism. In fact, a major portion of his intent seems to be to reduce logical symbolism to algebraical symbolism, making only those changes which are absolutely required. But though the symbols are for the most part the same ones as those used in algebra, the meaning of those symbols is quite different.

This is what Boole tells us in Proposition I. There are just three classes of signs which he needs in order to symbolize logic. They are:

(1) Letters such as x, y, z, etc. These letters are used to represent things. The letters correspond to the things which are defined in Euclid's *Definitions*, for these letters are the elements on which we operate in order to prove certain propositions. This is exactly what we do in geometry with lines, triangles, circles, etc. We perform certain operations with them —as stated in the postulates—in order to prove geometrical propositions. There is one interesting difference: because logic deals with everything than can be thought about, the letters x, y, z, etc., may stand for anything. At the same time x, y, z, etc., need not be defined, because if we say, in a given problem, that x stands for "tree," we then mean by "tree" just what the word ordinarily signifies.

(2) Signs of operations. Boole mentions $+$, $-$, $\times$. This class of signs corresponds to Euclid's postulates. Later on Boole will tell us just what operations are signified by the various signs; they are similar to, but not the same as, the algebraic operations signified by the same signs.

(3) The third class of signs has only one member; this is the sign of identity, $=$.

Now let us see what we can say about these various kinds of symbols. First, we should note that the literal symbols such as x do not actually stand for things, but for classes of things. That is, as these symbols are here employed, they do not stand for individual things or persons (like "this tree," or "the man named Paul"), but rather classes of things that have a common characteristic such as "the class of all white things," or "the class of all attorneys," and so on. Further, we note that these literal symbols stand indifferently for things that in language are expressed by either nouns or adjectives. That is, x can as well stand for substantive things like "persons," "trees," "books," etc, or for qualities like "white," "dog-eared," "beautiful," and so on. Though this may seem surprising at first sight, it really is not. Either kind of word stands for a class. When we say x stands for "white," we mean more accurately that x stands for the class of all white things. And when we say that y stands for "tree," we mean more accurately that y stands for "the class of all trees." In addition, the members of the class "trees,"—that is, the individual trees—are known to belong to the class because they all share in one or more class-defining characteristics. But each characteristic would be expressed by an adjective, although it might be a very long compound word, standing for a very complicated characteristic, such as "possessing roots and leaves, and a hard trunk that grows by annual layers, etc." Both "white" and "tree," therefore, really signify a class with a certain characteristic. In the first case the characteristic just happens to be very simple, while in the second case it is complex.

Now if we want to signify things which belong to both classes x and y, we do so by forming the expression xy (analogous to the algebraic product). However, xy in logic will not stand for multiplication, but rather for the operation of forming a set out of all those members which are common to two sets. In the language of sets this is called forming the intersection of two sets. Multiplication of algebraic quantities is, therefore, the analog of forming the intersection of sets.

Multiplication has the property of being commutative; that is, the product of a times b equals the product of b times a. Is the operation of forming the intersection of two sets also commutative? We can easily see that it is. The individuals in set x which also belong to set y are the same as the individuals in set y which also belong to set x. This is easily seen if we represent the two sets x and y by circles. It is this way of rep-

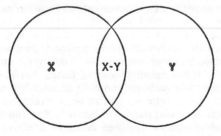

Figure 8–1

resenting sets that gave rise to the expression "intersection." The same thing can be seen if we express xy and yx in terms of the defining characteristics of x and y. If x is "white" and y is "tree," then xy stands for all those white things which are also trees. And yx stands for all those trees which are white. It is apparent that $xy = yx$. Intersection of sets is commutative, therefore, just as multiplication is. However, this does not follow simply from the symbolism employed; rather, it had to be proved. But because the commutative law holds for the intersection of sets, xy is a good way of symbolizing the intersection of x and y.

Next let us consider how to symbolize the set z that is formed from all those individuals which belong either to set x or to set y or to both x and y. Such a set is now called the union of x and y. If, as before, x and y stand for all white things and all trees, respectively, then the union of x and y consists of all those things which are either white, or trees, or both. The only things excluded from the union of x and y are those which are neither x nor y. Here we have made an arbitrary decision about the use of the word "or": if a is either b or c, this shall include the possibility that a is both b and c. This is usually called the weak usage of "or." If, on the other hand, "or" is used in its strong sense, then "a is either b or c" excludes the possibility of a being both b and c. Unless it is stated differently, the "or" employed in these pages and in logic in general is the weak "or."

Boole actually uses the strong "or." He uses the symbol "+" for it. In what follows, we shall assume, nevertheless, that Boole used the weak "or" and that "+" symbolizes the operation of forming the union, in its ordinary sense.

Is the operation symbolized by "+" commutative? Yes, it is, and incidentally this is true whether "or" is used in its weak or strong sense. The things which are either white, or trees (or both) are clearly the same as the things which are either trees, or white (or both). That is why "+" is a good symbol to use for the union of sets, since "+" in algebra is commutative.

Boole notes that the operation of forming the intersection is distributive with respect to forming the union. If x stands for "men," y for "women," and z for "European," then

$$z(x + y) = zx + zy$$

For the left-hand expression means: "All those European things which are also either men or women." The right-hand expression means: "All things which are either European men or European women." Once more we see how appropriate is the symbolism which Boole has chosen, since the symbols have the same properties whether they are interpreted algebraically or logically.

We should note, although Boole does *not* say it, that we

have now arrived at a point where the analogy between algebra and logic breaks down. For although, in algebra, multiplication is distributive with respect to addition, the reverse is not true: addition is not distributive with respect to multiplication. Let us gve an example:

$$5(3 + 4) = 5 \cdot 3 + 5 \cdot 4 = 15 + 20$$

But suppose I have

$$5 + (3 \cdot 4) = 17$$

If addition were distributed over multiplication, we should be able to say that

$$(5 + 3)(5 + 4)$$

is also equal to 17. But of course it is not; it is 72.

But matters are otherwise with sets. Here not only is intersection distributive with respect to union, but union is also distributive with respect to intersection. Let us give an example. Let z stand again for "European," let x stand for "Asiatic," and let y stand for "all women." Consider the union of z and xy—that is,

$$z + (xy)$$

From our definition of union and intersection we know that this means "all those things which are European or are Asiatic women." Now let us distribute the union and see what happens:

$$(z + x)(z + y)$$

What does this mean? The first parenthesis means "all things that are either European or Asiatic." The second parenthesis means "All European things or all women." What is the intersection of these two sets? That is, what sorts of individuals are common to both sets? They are "All European things or all Asiatic women"; but this of course is exactly the same as $z + (xy)$.

Should we be shocked that algebra and logic diverge here? Not at all. Boole does not claim that algebra and logic are the same; he merely maintains that logic can be symbolized in a fashion similar to that employed in algebra. As much as possible, Boole uses the same symbolism for logic as for algebra, but there is no absolute need to. In fact, the symbols for "intersection" and "union" usually employed in modern notation are different from Boole's. (The intersection a and b is written $a \cup b$, and the union of a and b is $a \cup b$.)

Now let us turn to the most important sign in Boole's system, namely, "$=$." We have already used it here and there, but now we must investigate more closely what its meanings and properties are. This sign stands for the equality of equivalence of two sets. If, for example, the class "man" (x) is defined by the properties "featherless biped" (yz), then we have

$$x = yz$$

It is actually more accurate to say that Boole's sign "$=$" stands for identity; for it can be employed only when the set on the left side of the equation is identical with the set on the right side. This is the case with "man" and "featherless biped"; it is also the case with the example which Boole gives, where the set of stars is identical with the set of the suns and planets. Identity is usually denoted in modern notation by the sign "$\equiv$." It is important to remember that Boole's sign $=$ means identity. This will prevent us from making mistakes. For example, how do we signify the statement "All men are animals"? Let x stand for man, and y for animals. Do we say then that

$$x = y ?$$

No, for this would mean that the set of men and the set of animals are identical. Obviously, however, the set of animals is much more extensive, since it includes other animals besides men. The set of men is identical with a *subset* of the set of animals. Boole is well aware of this; later in the book, he uses the symbol v to express this situation:

$$x = vy.$$

All men are *some* of the animals, or the set of men is a subset of the set of animals. The symbol "v" signifies either the word "some" or else that we are considering not the entire set y, but a subset of it.

But let us return to the sign of identity. Obviously, for any x,

$$x = x.$$

The set of x's is equivalent (identical) to the set of x's. If x stands for the set of trees, then the set of trees is identical with the set of trees. Now consider the expression $x \cdot x$, or x^2 if we follow algebraic usage. This means the class of all those trees which are also trees. It is obvious that

$$x = x^2.$$

Here is another departure from ordinary algebra, for this equation is not true in algebra. As before, however, we need not be shocked. On the contrary, it is these places where algebra and logic diverge that give us the most information about the character of both. This is true here; the law $x = x^2$ provides Boole with an important insight into the symbolism of logic.

While the relation $x = x^2$ is not generally true in algebra, there are two values of x for which it *is* true. For if we solve the quadratic equation, we find

$$x^2 - x = 0,$$

or
$$x(x - 1) = 0.$$
The two roots of this equation—that is, the two values of x which satisfy this equation—are 0 and 1. If $x = 1$, then it is true that $x = x^2$; similarly, if $x = 0$, then it is also true that $x = x^2$.

This suggests to Boole that the two numbers 0 and 1 might be introduced into the logical system, since they follow the same rules. He then asks the question, If these two numerical symbols are introduced into logic, what is their logical meaning?

It is an algebraic property of 0 that for any y,
$$0y = 0.$$
Logically interpreted, this means that the intersection of the set 0 and the set y is identical with the set 0. But this is true for only one set, namely the set of no members, the so-called null set. Hence 0 must represent the null set.

It is an algebraic property of 1, that for any y,
$$1 \cdot y = y.$$
Logically interpreted, this means that the intersection of the set 1 and the set y is identical with the set y. But this is true for only one set also, namely the set of all members, which Boole calls "the Universe."

Boole has already told us earlier that he interprets the sign "$-$" to be the opposite of "$+$" and that it means "except." Hence, he now says, the expression $1 - x$ means "everything except x."

What is the meaning of the basic logical equation,
$$x(1 - x) = 0?$$
The left side stands for the intersection of everything that is x with everything except x. What do these two sets have in common? Nothing, of course, and this is what the right side of the equation also states.

This, Boole says, is the symbolic expression of the Law of Contradiction. For the equation states that no class exists whose members at the same time possess the attribute x and the attribute of not having x. The equation expresses

that it is impossible for a being to possess a quality and not to possess that quality at the same time (p. 265).

This is where Boole stops, in the two chapters under consideration. His symbolism is now complete, or nearly so for operations with classes. What remains to be done? At least two major steps: First, Boole must go from statements about classes to propositions. That is, instead of merely expressing identities that state class-defining properties (like "The stars are all the suns and all the planets"), he must go to assertions like "All men are mortal." Secondly, he must develop a calculus for these propositions; that is, he must tell us what to do with these propositions in order to derive other propositions from them. Thus, he must develop what is called a "propositional calculus" (sometimes called a sentential calculus, since propositions are expressed by sentences).

In order to derive "All men are mortal" from two propositions like "All animals are mortal" and "All men are animals," a theory of deduction has to be developed. That is, rules must be stated, according to which certain operations are performed, leading to the desired results. Aristotle, in the Fourth century B.C., had already stated some rules for the theory of deduction, but his logic employed no mathematical symbolism. What is needed now is quasi-mathematical rules to accomplish the same thing.

All these things which we say *need* to be done have been accomplished by Boole and by later symbolic logicians. There is a completely developed propositional calculus and a theory of deduction. In fact, of course, symbolic logic goes far beyond this, into areas Boole never dreamed of. As is almost the case when a science becomes highly developed, the foundations of it are closely investigated (as in Russell and Whitehead's *Principia Mathematica*). As the result of such close and painstaking investigations, difficulties, problems, and even paradoxes have been discovered in logic. But this in no way lessens George Boole's accomplishment, who almost single-handedly founded the science of symbolic logic.

SUGGESTIONS FOR FURTHER READING

Those readers who would like to pursue some of the topic taken up in the preceding pages may wish to consult some of the following books. All of them are readily available in inexpensive paperback form.

Adler, Irving. *The New Mathematics*. New York: New American Library, 1960.

Bell, Eric Temple. *Mathematics: Queen and Servant of Science*. New York: McGraw-Hill, 1951.

————. *Men of Mathematics*. New York: Simon & Schuster, 1961.

Bowers, Henry and Joan. *Arithmetical Excursions: An Enrichment of Elementary Mathematics*. New York: Dover, 1961.

Dudeney, Henry Ernest. *Amusements in Mathematics*. New York: Dover, 1959.

Frege, Gottlob. *The Foundations of Arithmetic*. New York: Harper & Row, 1960.

Hilbert, David. *The Foundations of Geometry*. La Salle, Ill.: Open Court, 1960.

Hofmann, Joseph E. *Classical Mathematics*. New York: Philosophical Library, 1960.

Hooper, Alfred. *Makers of Mathematics*. New York: Random House (Vintage Books), 1948.

Kasner, Edward, and Newman, James. *Mathematics and the Imagination*. New York: Simon & Schuster, 1940.

Kenna, L.A. *Understanding Mathematics with Visual Aids*. Paterson, N.J.: Littlefield, Adams, & Co., 1962.

Klein, Felix. *Famous Problems of Elementary Geometry*. New York: Dover.

Körner, S. *The Philosophy of Mathematics: An Introduction.* New York: Harper & Row, 1962.

Langer, Suzanne K. *Introduction to Symbolic Logic.* New York: Dover, 1953.

Lewis, C.I., and Langford, C. H. *Symbolic Logic.* New York: Dover, 1959.

Newman, James (ed.). *The World of Mathematics.* 4 vols. New York: Simon & Schuster, 1960.

Russell, Bertrand. *Essay on the Foundations of Geometry* (1897). New York: Dover, 1956.

Singh, Jagjit. *Great Ideas of Modern Mathematics.* New York: Dover, 1959.

Smith, David Eugene. *History of Mathematics.* 2 vols. New York: Dover, 1958.

————. *A Source Book in Mathematics.* 2 vols. New York: Dover, 1959.

Sominskii, I.S. *The Method of Mathematical Induction.* New York: Blaisdell Publishing Co., 1962.

Sommerville, D.M.Y. *The Elements of non-Euclidean Geometry.* New York: Dover, 1958.

Struik, Dirk J. *Concise History of Mathematics.* New York: Dover, 1948.

Turnbull, H.W. *The Great Mathematicians.* New York: Simon & Schuster, 1962.

Weyl, Hermann. *Philosophy of Mathematics and Natural Science.* Princeton, N.J.: Princeton University Press, 1959.

INDEX

Other SIGNET SCIENCE LIBRARY Books

(60¢ each except where noted)

THE ABC OF RELATIVITY *by Bertrand Russell*

A clear, penetrating explanation of Einstein's
theories and their effect on the world.　　(#P2177)

ELECTRONICS FOR EVERYONE (revised and expanded)
by Monroe Upton

This easy-to-read, authoritative book helps you
to understand today's wonders in the field of
electricity, and forecasts the exciting future
of science. Illustrated.　　(#T2164—75¢)

FRONTIERS OF ASTRONOMY *by Fred Hoyle*

An assessment of the remarkable increase
in our knowledge of the universe.　　(#T2309—75¢)

MODERN THEORIES OF THE UNIVERSE *by James A Coleman*

A concise, impartial explanation of the two
leading contemporary theories concerning
the origin of the universe.　　(#P2270)

MEDICINE AND MAN *by Ritchie Calder*

A comprehensive and authoritative survey
of important medical events and discoveries
from earliest times to the present.　　(#P2168)

THE NATURE OF THE UNIVERSE *by Fred Hoyle*

A noted astronomer explains the latest facts
and theories about the universe with clarity
and liveliness. Illustrated.　　(#P2331)

SATELLITES, ROCKETS AND OUTER SPACE *by Willy Ley*

A newly revised and up-dated report on the
science of rocket development, including an
evaluation of the satellite, Telstar.　　(#P2218)

SEEING THE EARTH FROM SPACE *by Irving Adler*

A timely, up-to-date report on Russian and
American satellites, and what we are learning
from them about our earth. Illustrated.　　(#P2050)

THE CRUST OF THE EARTH, *Samuel Rapport and Helen Wright, eds.*
Selections from the writings of the best geologists of today, telling the fascinating story of billions of years in the life of the earth. (#P2083)

THE EDGE OF THE SEA *by Rachel Carson*
A guide to the fascinating creatures who inhabit the mysterious world where sea and shore meet—from Maine's rocky coast to the coral reefs beyond the Florida Keys. Illustrated. By the author of *Silent Spring*. (#P2360)

THE SEA AROUND US *by Rachel Carson*
An outstanding best-seller and National Book Award winner, an enthralling account of the ocean, its geography, and its inhabitants. (#P2361)

UNDER THE SEA WIND *by Rachel Carson*
The story of life among the birds and fish on the shore, open sea, and on the sea bottom. Illustrated. (#P2239)

NEW HANDBOOK OF THE HEAVENS *by Hubert J. Bernhard, Dorothy A. Bennett and Hugh S. Rice*
A guide to the understanding and enjoyment of astronomy for beginners as well as the more advanced, with star charts and data, descriptions of the heavenly bodies, and astronomical facts and lore. (#P2023)

THE SUN AND ITS FAMILY *by Irving Adler*
A popular book on astronomy which traces scientific discoveries about the solar system from earliest times to the present. Illustrated. (#P2037)

THE STARS *by Irving Adler*
A clear introduction to the nature, motion, and structure of the stars. (#P2093)